WITHDRAWN

*Mathematical
Thinking
in the Social Sciences*

T. W. ANDERSON

NICOLAS RASHEVSKY

JAMES S. COLEMAN

JACOB MARSCHAK

LOUIS GUTTMAN

PAUL F. LAZARSFELD

HERBERT A. SIMON

Mathematical
Thinking
in the Social Sciences

edited by **PAUL F. LAZARSFELD,** COLUMBIA UNIVERSITY

NEW YORK / RUSSELL & RUSSELL

Contents

181516

ACKNOWLEDGEMENTS

The editor wishes to thank the Columbia University Bureau of Applied Social Research, under whose sponsorship the volume was prepared.

The following organizations provided financial support for the completion of various papers included in this volume:

The Social Science Research Council
The Human Resources Research Institute of the Air University, Maxwell Air Force Base
Office of Naval Research
The Columbia University Planning Project for Advanced Training in Social Research
The Rand Corporation, which also holds a separate copyright for the seventh paper in the volume.

Introduction:
Mathematical Thinking in the
Social Sciences

The role of mathematical thinking in the social sciences has
become the topic of many discussions, controversies, and hopeful
efforts. The source of this increased interest is at least a twofold
one. The success of mathematics in the natural sciences is a lure
for the younger social sciences, and the prestige and charm of
mathematical work a temptation for many of its practitioners. In
addition, sociologists and social psychologists have increasingly
felt the need for a more rigid and precise language. This is true
for both traditions, which are often tagged as the "microscopic"
and the "macroscopic" approach to human affairs.

The man who carries out experiments or makes concrete
observations on a phenomenon of social interaction finds himself
confronted with so many factors that he can no longer cope with
them adequately in an intuitive and discursive way. But the great
system builders also, who do not concern themselves with these
innumerable details, now work in a different intellectual climate.
A hundred years ago the task seemed to be to make sweeping
guesses as to the future development of society. Fifty years ago
the interest focussed on basic concepts which would properly classify the crucial social phenomena. Today the trend is toward
singling out the basic variables from which all specific concepts
and interrelationships can be derived. Even those who do not believe in any early use of mathematics try to utilize some rudiments of formalization, in order to clarify their underlying
assumptions, and to derive specific findings from more general
models.

No one can foretell future intellectual developments. Even
the most ardent optimist would not claim that mathematics has yet
led to important discoveries in the behavioral sciences.[1] Their
best argument would be that it contributes to clarity of thinking

3

and, by permitting better organization of available knowledge, facilitates decisions as to needed further work. In turn, it can be safely said that the pessimists who claim an intrinsic incompatibility between the problems of the social scientist and the structure of mathematical work have at no point been able to set up a valid argument; there is no idea or proposition in this field which cannot be put into mathematical language, although the utility of doing so can very well be doubted. How the role of mathematical thinking in the social sciences will evolve is more difficult to predict, because neither mathematics nor social science is unchangeably fixed. There are many historical examples in the natural sciences where the subject matter itself forced new developments in the mathematical field. And inversely, it could very well be that the application of mathematics affects the way in which the behavioral sciences formulate their problems.

Nevertheless there is no reason to sit back and wait passively to see what will happen. The development of a creative and useful science of human behavior and social relations is a critically important task for our times. No one can tell how quickly this will come about. But the application of mathematical thinking is one of the tools which might help; therefore, it must be tried in the most rational and vigorous way possible. To this end, at least three roads seem promising. We need people who are trained both in mathematics and in some sector of the social sciences. The Social Science Research Council, with the help of the Ford Foundation, has inaugurated a series of training seminars, with the double purpose of giving mathematical instruction to social scientists and of injecting social science materials into college courses in mathematics. Under the able direction of Dr. William Madow, this effort is likely to increase the needed personnel for the intellectual experiment to be made on the borderline of the two spheres of work. At the same time, actual investigations have to be carried on. Indeed a variety of recent publications give evidence of increased activities in various mathematical-social science fields. The early efforts of Thurstone to put psychological measurement on a rational basis have led to many developments in the field of measurement generally, in the theory of tests and in factor analysis. The learning psychologists, who are further along than virtually any other group in the direction of precise theory construction, have recently teamed up with mathematicians in a variety of ways. Mathematical biology has been extended into the area of social relations. Techniques of mathematical economics, like time series analysis or theory of games, are beginning to find applications to sociological topics.[2]

In addition to training and creative work there is a third road. We need investigations which clarify in a more general way the possible relations between mathematics and the social sciences. We should take specific problems and look at them with the end in mind of understanding better how the structure of behavioral science thinking and the structure of various mathematical methods fit each other. It is along this line that the present volume intends to make its main contribution.

The general idea was to represent a number of "cases" as examples for situations as they might typically develop between the social sciences and mathematics. The most obvious case is one in which the behavioral scientist's problem is fairly explicit and where he looks for an appropriate mathematical formalization. In other cases the elements of the original problem need to be more carefully analyzed before the whole can be cast into a more precise form. Sometimes the contribution comes from the other direction. An existing mathematical tool is studied to see for what kinds of social science problems it might or might not provide an adequate language. Then there is the flowering of axiomatics which put the formulation of mathematics on a much firmer basis. Is it not possible that a similar type of analysis would help to explicate concepts of the social scientist and throw some light on what alternatives he might have overlooked? "Cases" of formalization and rational reconstruction of some social science writing would belong here. Another "case" should provide a feeling for the continuity in the relation between mathematics and social science: a relatively simple formalization will help to highlight the essential features of a substantive problem, lead to a more adequate formalization, and so on. Certainly there is also a need for "cases" in which the specific nature of behavioral data forced the mathematician to develop new ideas in his own field.

The remainder of this introduction aims to develop the idea of case studies in collaboration, by describing briefly the contributions included in this symposium. They were all solicited by the editor but they cannot in any way give a complete picture of all the possible interrelationships between social scientist and mathematician. Even their schematic enumeration would be difficult and probably not too useful at the present stage. The volume tries to give a fair sampling of the intellectual situations in which social scientists meet with mathematicians and what happens when they do.

The paper by Anderson grew out of a specific request addressed to him by an empirical research worker. Sociologists and social psychologists are much concerned with problems of short-term changes. Their material is sometimes similar to the time series of the economists. A number of people would be interviewed, or otherwise observed repeatedly over a period of time. They might be voters who, during a presidential campaign, are repeatedly asked for whom they intend to vote, what they have read, how they feel about various issues, with whom they have talked, etc. Or students might, in the course of a year, be asked repeatedly such questions as, how they think they are getting along in their lectures, what they are interested in, what actual work they have done, etc. In all these cases a relatively large number of variables is recorded through time, and the problem is to study their mutual interaction. How can such data be economically summarized? How can they be placed into a more general theoretical context? Anderson realized that the recent developments in the analysis of stochastic processes would be an appropriate mathematical tool. In a "Markov chain" we have a simple model, where the transition probabilities tell what an individual, found in one class at one time, is likely to do at the next observation. The idea is illustrated by data from a study in which a sample of people reported repeatedly, during an election campaign, how they felt about various issues and for whom they intended to vote. This paper can be read from at least two points of view. It gives the social scientist some basic ideas of stochastic analysis which undoubtedly will play an ever-larger role in the studies of social processes, changes in attitudes, etc.; the algebra in this case is fortunately fairly simple, so that with a modicum of mathematical effort the social scientist can see how much can be gained through the use of more formal procedures. Inversely, the mathematical statistician will find in Anderson's paper at least an intimation of some new theorems which have not been known before.[3]

The study of interrelated variables through time is so crucial for the behavioral scientist that it would have been most instructive to add one or two more papers dealing with this matter in different ways. Space did not permit this, but reference, at least, to other alternatives should give the reader leads for further readings. W. G. Baumol wrote an introduction to "economic dynamics";[4] he is very much interested in the relation between what he calls the "magnificent" approach of the great system builders in economics, and the more modest idea of "process analysis." This process analysis is identical with the problem which was the origin of

Anderson's paper. Baumol's mathematical tools, however, are differential equations for which he gives an introduction which should be understandable to any social scientist with a modest amount of college mathematics. Obviously, the economist, as other behavioral scientists, feels a strong need for a tie-up between the discursive and the mathematical traditions of their fields; and they look for a logical penetration of the various mathematical tools which help in the study of change, over a larger number of periods. A very similar situation is represented by the mathematization of learning theory, which has been carried out in recent years by Bush and Mosteller. They will explore in a forthcoming publication the implications of the "linear operators" for their theory; some initial exposition is available now.[5]

The classical way of analyzing change in interrelated variables is, of course, differential equations. Some time ago the Department of Sociology at Columbia University sponsored a series of lectures on "Mathematical Thinking in the Social Sciences". One of the speakers was Rashevsky, who was asked to present a bird's eye view of the work he has done on the mathematics of human relations. Of his three lectures, two are published in this volume. Both of these deal with the basic problem of the effect of contacts between human beings and use as their main tool differential equations. In the first lecture the effect of contact is analyzed in terms of imitation -- one person doing what he sees others do. In the second lecture it is analyzed in broader terms. Each person in a group has a certain trait and a probability of contact with every other person in the group. As a result of their mutual contacts, the traits of individuals are affected. Given an initial distribution of traits, what new distributions can be expected as a result of repeated contacts?

Imitation and other mutual influences are classical problems for the social scientist. He should therefore be very interested to see what the mathematician can contribute. But Rashevsky's mathematical equipment is not simple. The editor therefore felt that an expository analysis was needed to make his contribution fit into the framework of the present volume. Coleman undertook the task, and his discussion, together with Rashevsky's own presentation, represents our second case. It is a good example of how the anatomy of the mathematical model should be presented to a modestly trained audience, which is especially interested in its bearing on social science subject matters. Coleman begins with a verbal description of four models (adding two from Rashevsky's other publication), and then stresses two points. He analyzes the

kinds of variables appearing in the models, with special emphasis
on the relation between the logical nature of the concepts and what
might be called the mathematical structure of the indices by which
they are represented. Secondly, he classifies the various equations in order to show in what way the processes in which the behavioral scientist is interested are represented by various mathematical tools. This leads to the possibility of characterizing the
four Rashevsky models once more in a system which combines
both the mathematical anatomy of the concepts and the mathematical anatomy of the processes involved. Finally Coleman does
what might in the long run prove most helpful in such efforts. He
leaves the mathematical machinery as it is but transfers it to
other subject matters, thereby achieving two ends. He shows that
Rashevsky's procedures are applicable to material in which the
experimental sociologist and social psychologist can really provide
data without too much difficulty; and he brings out once more the
specific relations between the mathematical elements of the models
and the elements of the concrete social situations.[7]

Just as Markov chains aid in clarifying what the behavioral
scientist usually calls social processes and psychological processes, so do interaction models help greatly to clarify the topic of
the relation between individual and group. There is a great deal
of unclarity in such statements as, for example, the individual is
affected by his primary group, or individuals acquire opinions as a
result of their environment. After all, the group and the environment consist of individuals who are likely to be influenced as much
by us as we are influenced by them. Therefore, a logically clear
construction of the notion of group depends upon finding a formalism which would give similar positions to all elements of the group.
It should at the same time be able to show that, as a result, certain
group characteristics emerge which in turn affect all constituent
elements. A great deal of heated debate in this field turns out to
evaporate once the problem is formulated in correct mathematical
terms. It is, of course, necessary to really understand what is the
essence of the mathematical formulation, and the Rashevsky-
Coleman case in our symposium attempts to add to this understanding. Again, some comparative literature should be of help, although
in this field no other efforts of similar extent are available. For
the notion of singling out the elements of a mathematical analysis,
we might refer to a recent book, *The Anatomy of Mathematics*, by
Kirschner and Wilcox.[8] The classical examples of such an effort
are, of course, the famous lectures of Felix Klein on elementary
mathematics from an advanced point of view, which are now

available in English translation.[9] On the mathematics of small
groups there is available a paper by Leeman, which deals with a
similar subject matter; that is, people meet at random, take likes
and dislikes to each other, meet again, and so forth. This paper,
incidentally, applies a stochastic process analysis to a group
problem.[10] A different direction is pursued in the formalization
which Herbert A. Simon gave to a number of ideas of Homans'
book *The Human Group;* here the group is the basic entity and the
relation with its constituent elements is not treated. It should,
however, be worthwhile to show exactly in which respect the present material differs from Simon's paper.[11] (The general idea of
Simon's work can be found in the final contribution to the present
symposium, which will be discussed presently from a somewhat
different point of view.)

  Turning now to Marschak's contribution (also part of the
Columbia lecture series), we find still another case of communication between mathematics and social science. There is general
awareness that probability ideas play a dominant role, explicitly
or implicitly, in the study of human behavior. No one believes
that behavioral laws can be as simple as the laws of the natural
sciences. It is necessary to consider many more variables, to
begin with; but even then we can only state that certain behavioral
combinations are more frequent than others. The predictions of
the social scientist will always be probabilistic ones. It is therefore indispensable for him to have a clear idea of the logic underlying probabilistic reasoning; and, inversely, the last decade has
shown that concern with human and social data will force new
developments on the mathematical theory of probability. Marschak
was asked to review the whole situation. In his first lecture he
traces the major changes undergone by the concept of probability
in the hands of the mathematicians themselves. The main emphasis is placed on the recently re-emerging idea of "subjective
probability", based on the individual's ability to make choices
under uncertainty. This idea is reconciled with the use of methods
of inference from objective samples and frequencies, such as the
methods discussed in Marschak's subsequent lectures. The reader
will note how close this notion of subjective probability is to the
social scientist's notion of attitude.

  Marschak's second lecture deals with the question of what
role probability concepts, generally speaking, play in the social
sciences. His main point is that they have to be introduced in what
he calls the pre-statistical phase of an investigation. It is not
possible to analyze statistical data except by matching them against

some theoretical expectations. In the mathematical treatment of
behavioral subject matters these assumptions are introduced by
models, that is, systems of equations between variables. Some of
these variables are random. They are represented by probability
distributions, or possibly by parameters of such distributions:
means, variances, correlations. Furthermore, unless the sample
is very large, it is not permitted to neglect the fact that the estimates of these parameters are themselves subject to random
fluctuations. The entire lecture deals with various aspects of one
basic theme: how do we weave back and forth from empirical observations to the parameters of the "underlying" model incorporating our theoretical assumptions, in terms which are always in
part probabilistic. In the third lecture Marschak then raises the
question of how probabilistic models of this kind are related to
problems of policy and action. Given a complex social structure,
we wish to assess the consequences of manipulating one variable
upon the other elements in the system. Marschak selects as his
example the effect of a government tax policy; he shows how difficult it would be, even in an oversimplified case, to estimate all
possible consequences without the aid of mathematical formalisms.

It is no coincidence that for this entire unit an economist was
judged to be the most desirable expositor. As former director of
the Cowles Commission for Research in Economics, Marschak
has been for years in charge of a large series of studies, all of
which explored the role of mathematics in the study of economic
behavior. It is the merit of his contribution for this symposium
that Marschak lifts his experience out of its specific economics
context and shows its bearing on social science problems in
general.[12]

The unit on probabilities forms a good transition between the
two preceding and the two following cases in our collection. It has
become habitual to distinguish two major ways in which mathematical thinking can bear on the social sciences. We have dynamic
models representing processes and interactions which come about
through time; and we have measurement models which clarify concept formation and the relation between concepts and empirical
observations. The first two units in our present volume come
within the first category above. Marschak's lectures provide a
transition: they deal with the conceptual role of probability notions
as well as their applications to the analysis of activities and processes. The remaining two contributions in our volume deal essentially with measurement problems, and each of these again
stands for a very characteristic case exemplifying further

interconnections between mathematics and the behavioral sciences. We now turn to the papers by Louis Guttman, which are elaborations on two of the three lectures he gave in the Columbia series. Since these lectures represent two different situations, they should be considered separately.

The early efforts of social and psychological measurement took very much for granted that there would be no logical differences between the variables to be used in the social sciences and those which the natural sciences dealt with. The population expert was interested in age or number of children; the economist dealt with quantity of goods or amount of dollars; the psychologist interested in intelligence tests seemed to deal with the number of questions accurately answered. Guttman was one of the first writers who saw how much of the social scientist's work deals with what has come to be called qualitative characteristics or attributes. Such distinctions as male or female, white or Negro, owning or not owning a house, agreeing or disagreeing with a certain position -- are the kinds of raw data from which we build up behavioral indexes and scales. A clear analysis of the operations of combining these basic elements into the more complex measures had been badly neglected by previous workers. A first systematic approach was offered in Guttman's scalogram analysis and in the cumulative scale, which has since become well known under Guttman's name. In the volume on *Measurement and Prediction*,[13] Guttman and his associates gave an elementary presentation of his ideas and a precise mathematical formulation. Each measuring instrument, test or scale consists of a number of "items", i.e., responses or properties which individuals might or might not have. The "items" included in a scale are assigned weights derived from the axiom that people who have a certain property should be of maximum score similarity among themselves, and most dissimilar in their general test score from those who do not have the item property.

Guttman showed that the equation embodying this axiom had many solutions; to each series of weights there corresponded a different ordering of people according to a different attitude "component": intensity, closure, etc. Guttman's first publication was quite tantalizing to the research fraternity. He had given the mathematics of his higher components but had not yet had an opportunity to explore their psychological implications. In the first of his lectures included in this volume he now carries out his promise in great detail and reports empirical findings as well as very far-reaching speculations. From our point of view, this

paper represents a rather unique case. To begin with, here is
what is essentially a mathematical equation. It has a number of
interesting mathematical properties. Guttman then turns around
and gives these properties very plausible substantive interpretations. Many social scientists have proposed dimensions along
which attitudes can be characterized; by necessity, however, their
dimensions were arbitrary, on however much psychological insight
they were based. Guttman now proposes a classification which is
derived from a unitary mathematical basis. Whether his derivations will be corroborated by empirical data, and what role they
will play in a future theory of attitudes is, of course, not yet possible to predict. The exterprise itself, however, is certainly a
rather unique application of mathematics to a behavioral problem.[14]

Guttman's second contribution harks back to a very different
tradition. Following early efforts of Spearman, Thurstone has
developed his work on factor analysis, which has so deeply influenced psychological work. The idea, now so well known, is that the
scores of a large number of tests can derive from a small number
of factors. The factors are related to the test scores by a system
of linear equations. The coefficients of these equations -- the
factor loadings of the tests -- can be computed from the correlations between the tests as they are actually observed. For about
twenty years the main efforts of the factor analysts were directed
toward improving the methods for this difficult computation, and
for coping with certain indeterminacies which were necessarily
imbedded in the whole idea. Only within the last few years has it
become obvious that factor analysis was really a special case of
model building; the computation of factor loadings was a special
case of identification of model parameters, as discussed in
Marschak's second lecture. For a long time one very specific type
of equation linking test scores and factors was the only one investi-
gated in detail. It is true that one can find in the literature occasional
regretful references to this situation, but it seems to have been assumed that more complex mathematics would be too difficult to
handle. Guttman has now shown that one can develop, without such
difficulties, a large number of other factor patterns which will open
up entirely new avenues of empirical investigation. On the one hand,
as Guttman himself shows, new interpretations of older data will be
possible. On the other hand, we can speculate on new types of factor
structures which will guide us to the collection and analysis of new
kinds of empirical material. Even a variety of neurological ideas
can now be translated into this generalized form of factor analysis.

In addition to the intrinsic importance of this paper, it illustrates very well the long-term interaction between mathematics and the problems of the social sciences. It was Spearman's merit that he gave the first formalization to the old notion of basic faculties. By an algebraic generalization, Thurstone was led to the idea of multiple factors, which permitted taking into account what might be called the basic organization of such faculties. Then followed a period of active collection and analysis of data, reaching its broadest scope, perhaps, in Cattell's compendium of the factor structure of personalities.[15] Slowly it became obvious that the idea of simple additivity of factors -- even if the notion of various "levels" of factors were included -- cannot cope with the empirical evidence. Now Guttman has once more increased the complexity of the basic model so that new ideas about personality organization can be transformed into research operations and made subject to empirical tests. Such continuities have recently appeared in other contexts and will certainly increase in frequency. A good example is furnished by sociometric procedures. They are based on the idea that the mutual attractions between members of a group can be used to characterize the position of individuals, as well as the general social structure of the group. After a while mathematicians noted that the raw material of such choices can be presented in matrix form. Festinger then saw that the formalism of matrix multiplication permitted him to reproduce and to bring order into many of the indices which sociometrists had developed intuitively.[16] In a next step Katz developed mathematically the notion of indirect choices which will certainly affect, in turn, the discussion of leadership notions.[17]

A similar continuity can be established between the first Guttman scale and Lazarsfeld's latent structure analysis. Guttman's original idea was to provide an intrinsic criterion by which qualitative elements could be put together into a score which is quantitative, or at least permits a systematic ordering of people (and sometimes other objects). However, his criterion was a rather restricted one. It was, for example, not applicable to projective tests where each response had only a certain probability of expressing an underlying attitude. Now it is possible to develop more flexible procedures by mathematicizing the operation of the scale construction itself. In latent structure analysis a model is set up, relating the parameters of an intended classification to manifest qualitative observations; the relationship is probabilistic. Since no prescription is made about the general form of this relationship, the idea does not lead to one specific scale, but rather to a system through which any number of scales can be related to each other. It will be noted that latent structure analysis is a combination of certain basic ideas of Thurstone on factor spaces, and Guttman's awareness that different types of mathematics are needed for qualitative and quantitative raw materials; the link between the two is a basic axiom on the nature of explanations, which is derived from the practice of survey analysis.

The mathematics of latent structure analysis was presented in *Measurement and Prediction*.[18] The purpose of the present contribution is to show as precisely as possible which elements in the logic of social research procedures were meant to correspond to the algegraic elements in the basic equations. It had been pointed out often that disposition concepts play a basic role in the social sciences.[19] Lazarsfeld's paper is a case which exemplifies how a mathematical formulation can translate such a general idea into a specific research operation.

At this point the list of cases included in this symposium is exhausted. The editor felt, however, that a general discussion of model building in the social sciences should be included in this volume. For this contribution he turned to a political scientist whose early writings were on a discursive level and who, through the dynamics of this work, has become one of the leaders in the application of mathematics to social science problems. Simon was asked to attempt a guess as to the direction in which the field as a whole is likely to develop in the foreseeable future. The editor agrees with Simon's canons of strategy. The only reason we did not use this paper as a programmatic statement at the beginning of the volume was the feeling that the reader would appreciate it more after studying the cases presented in our collection. In illustrating his point of view, incidentally, Simon makes a valuable contribution. He selected the notion of rational behavior, and traces how, over a period of almost a century, the interaction between conceptual analysis and mathematical formulation has led to ever more flexible tools for studying a large range of human behavior.

A few comments might be in order to help a variety of readers to use our symposium most fruitfully. The mathematically trained student will, of course, be chiefly interested in the way familiar tools are applied in a new subject area; he might also, by this devious route, get acquainted and interested in one or another concrete problem of the social sciences. Only in the paper by Anderson and in the second lecture of Guttman will new mathematical developments be found. The social scientist who has no mathematical training will find rough going through many of these pages.

However, even in papers like Coleman's, Anderson's, and in the third lecture of Marschak, he should be able to get the general idea of the argument fairly easily. The first lecture of Guttman's, the contributions of Lazarsfeld and a great part of Simon's paper were written for the reader not specialized in mathematics. The audience for which the volume was mainly intended is the social scientist with a modicum of training in mathematics, who should find that these efforts of his earlier education were not in vain, after all. It is only fair to add that the editor also hopes that our symposium will have a certain propagandistic effect among mathematicians, as now is the time for them to come to the aid of the behavioral scientist.

A special word of thanks should be given to the authors who have been so cooperative in adjusting their contributions to the general purpose of this volume. Anderson's analysis was originally done for a project on "panel analysis", sponsored by the Social Science Research Council, and his ideas were developed on a higher mathematical level. Anderson patiently supervised the work of cutting down and partially rewriting the paper to make it understandable to a broader audience.[20] Rashevsky read patiently several editions of Coleman's analysis and gave him much valuable advice. The editor understands that Rashevsky approves of Coleman's exposition of his work in its present form. When Marschak had rewritten his lectures for publication, the editor pointed out a few sections which were likely to create difficulties for the less trained reader. Marschak was good enough to rewrite and extend these sections. Guttman's magnanimity is obvious. He spent many months in extending what had been two brief lectures into fundamental papers, one of which is really a complete monograph.[21] Simon interrupted urgent work in order to write the contribution which the editor felt was needed to round out the picture he is trying to present in the volume as a whole.

Finally, the reader should be made aware of the many cross-references which can be made between the various papers. Only a few of these can be mentioned here. Take, for example, the problem of combining elementary information into broader complexes. The problem appears in the form of group characteristics in Coleman's paper (see page 122); it reappears in Marschak's second lecture as the problem of aggregates in economics (page 194); it is basic to the whole problem of building scales from qualitative data, as discussed in Guttman's first lecture and in Lazarsfeld's paper. The problem of translating social processes into mathematical form is also taken up at least three times: in Anderson's Markov chains; in Rashevsky's differential equations; and in Marschak's discussion of the relation between mathematical models and policy.[22] A third useful cross-reference can be suggested: Marschak's presentation of subjective probabilities has great affinity to the notion of latent probabilities, as they appear in Lazarsfeld's latent structure analysis; both of them can be fruitfully compared with the role probabilities play in stochastic models, as exemplified by Anderson's presentation.

The editor is well aware that this symposium neither covers all essential subject matters nor does it represent all possible ways in which mathematics and social scientists might cooperate. For example, it would have fitted closely into the framework of this volume to have taken two concepts such as "utility" and "attitude", which are treated quite separately by economists and social psychologists, respectively; a mathematical comparison could have clarified the extent to which the two are the same under different names, and to what extent they serve different purposes. There is little doubt that a trend toward formalization will profitably bring together a variety of pursuits in the behavioral sciences which, at the moment, have little contact. As to subject matters, two areas are deliberately omitted. One is distribution phenomena as they are handled by ecologists or the group of social physicists;[23] there is, however, a fairly accessible literature available along these lines. Inversely, the recent efforts to apply the theory of games and decision making to problems of social organization is so new that no contributor could be found who would be willing to commit himself on probable future developments. Altogether, this symposium makes no claim to having covered in any exhaustive way the role of mathematical thinking in the social sciences. It will have served its purpose if its readers get a feeling for the present state of affairs, and if some of them become stimulated to contribute their own efforts toward a further development.

Paul F. Lazarsfeld

1. Probability Models for Analyzing Time Changes in Attitudes[1]

By *T. W. ANDERSON*
Columbia University

Section I. INTRODUCTION

In this paper we propose a simple probability model to serve as a basis for analyzing changes in attitudes over time. This model is supposed to describe in a certain sense how individuals modify their opinions as time passes. The formal description of the process of attitude change leads to predictions of future attitudes based on opinions held at present and in the past. Elaboration of simple models makes the description more accurate and correspondingly raises more questions about the nature of the process. A number of the problems raised require answers of a statistical nature; that is, observed numerical data are used to decide problems of the models. The probability nature of the models provides the natural basis for developing suitable statistical methods.

It goes without saying that the study of attitude changes is of considerable interest and importance. Observation and measurement of attitudes is fundamental to much of the social sciences; they are of no less interest in many non-academic fields. Obviously, many attitudes are not held constantly; individuals change their opinions from time to time. Therefore, an investigator often will not be satisfied to know what opinions are held presently. He will want to know how and why attitudes change and how they can be predicted. What we present here is a mathematical model to aid in the study of such questions.

An attitude here is considered to be simply a choice of a specified set of responses to a question. For example, a person's answer to the question "Do you favor continuation of a Democratic administration?" defines an attitude in the sense of this paper. This notion can be broadened to include any situation to which an individual responds in one of a finite number of ways; the time

17

series analysis we consider relates to such situations which are repeated after certain time intervals.

The kind of questions asked in public opinion polls, sociological studies, market research investigations, and some government surveys may exemplify the area considered here. However, we are interested in such opinions or answers not at just one time but at a number of successive times. Some surveys and polls repeat the same questions on successive interviews. The data we treat are the successive responses of the same individuals to a given question. We are interested not only in the total change of attitudes, but also in the frequencies of different kinds of changes. Some surveys are specifically designed to gather such data. In these so-called "panel surveys" a set (i.e., panel) of respondents are interviewed on repeated occasions. Records are kept of successive responses of the respondents. Thus not only does the investigator know how much the percentage of responses in different categories have changed but he also knows the percentages of people who made one response and then another.

It is evident that the field of attitude change is a complicated and profound one. The attitude of any given person on any given topic is subject to many influences. These influences and the psychology of the person vary with the passage of time. A simple mathematical model can hardly be hoped to "explain" in complete detail this process. With increasing complexity of the model we could hope to approach an accurate description.

In the models proposed here we do not attempt to take account explicitly of a large number of these influences. We do take account of attitudes that have been held previously. Moreover, it is shown how the model can be complicated in order to handle other factors influencing attitude change. In effect we present here a whole family of models that differ not only in the numerical values of the parameters, but also differ in the degree of complexity. In some areas and for some purposes the simple models will give adequate descriptions of the time series. In many areas more analysis will be needed to find models within this class which are useful. We present statistical methods which will enable the investigator to select the most suitable model in the class.

Use of these models implies certain assumptions with regard to individual behavior or opinion change. For instance, it is assumed that for all persons in a certain class, the probability of a certain change is the same. It is also assumed that only a certain amount of past history affects present attitudes. A more restrictive and less realistic assumption is that persons change independently. That is, the possible change of a given individual is not affected by the changes of other individuals occurring at the same time. (This is statistical independence in the sense that when coins are tossed they come up heads and tails independently.) Other assumptions are also implied. These are necessary in a formalization. Application of the models will show to what extent the assumptions are fulfilled and to what extent unrealistic assumptions are misleading.

In any field it is desirable to construct mathematical models based on well-developed theory which in turn is based on observation of large numbers of cases. In the field of attitude change, however, there is not this well-developed theory that is desired. In lieu of this theory and instead of developing it extensively, we have considered general models which may reasonably be expected to describe many processes. To the extent that the models fit the data they will be useful in prediction; they explain the process in the sense that they embody the laws of change.

However, because these models have not been based on an underlying theory, they do not directly relate to any concepts or variables outside of the kind considered explicitly. We obtain certain parameters describing change of responses to questions, but we cannot directly interpret them in terms of basic sociological or psychological terms. For instance, when an econometrician uses time series analysis to find that national income and total national consumption are related in a certain way, he may interpret one of his parameters as the "propensity to consume." This parameter not only describes a relationship between two time series, but it also is a variable of a highly developed theory (Keynesian) and it is taken to describe, in a sense, behavior of individuals (appearing in the time series only aggregately). Obviously models based on theories are desirable because they can be expected to be more accurate representations. Furthermore, they are related to a larger body of material; in one direction this gives the model greater usefulness; in the other direction the related material suggests more hypotheses and pertinent questions about the model. Another advantage of the model in which parameters have more basic theoretical interpretations is that the model based on one set of data can be modified for situations where some characteristics, but not all, are different.[2]

In this field of attitude change we can point up the difference between an *ad hoc* model and one based on a more or less sophisticated theory. A theory of attitude formation, which is not fully developed, states that there are leaders of opinion and followers;

that the followers take their opinions from the leaders. We could set up a model based on this theory that would give predictions under unchanged conditions and indicated changes in the environment and would in addition predict the changes of opinion if the leaders were affected in certain ways. Here the causes of opinion change in the followers can be analyzed in terms of the leaders.

In any science there will be a discrepancy between the collection of generalizations forming the body of the theory and the observed phenomena. In many cases in the physical sciences the discrepancies between the stated relations and the observed facts are slight; usually in the social sciences they are large.

It is convenient to classify these discrepancies into two categories. One category consists of the *errors of observations*. Generally speaking, one does not measure exactly the quantities that the theory is constructed to explain. In the case of using survey results in studying attitudes, we find that the data concern a sample of people while we wish to generalize about a population. In these cases the errors of observation are the usual errors of sampling. In some cases the errors are systematic; for instance the *Literary Digest* sample contained too few people of the lower economic levels, and any sample drawn in a similar way would have the same kind of error. In other cases the errors may be considered as random; that is, one can set up a probability law for describing the sample results in terms of the underlying population. The use of this probability model for describing the errors of observation is well known. The difference between what the poller thinks a question means and what the respondent thinks it means might also be included as an error of observation.

The other kind of discrepancy is due to the theory being incomplete or, in some respects, incorrect. Here again there may be a systematic error. In this case the theory is wrong to some extent. On the other hand the discrepancies may be due to the fact that people are to some extent "unpredictable". It is possible that by taking enough factors into account one could predict as accurately as one would wish the aggregate behavior of a group of people. Actually, one is limited with regard to the number of factors included in a study. If the neglected factors have a certain kind of irregularity, we could say that the net effect of these "irrelevant" factors is a random effect. These effects we shall call *disturbances in relations*. A distinguishing feature between the random errors of observation and the random disturbances in relations is that the former are outside of the actual phenomena one is interested in and do not effect them while the latter are part of the phenomena studied and their effects are incorporated into the ensuing phenomena.

The use of probabilities models in the social sciences is probably furthest developed in economics. A theory might say that two economic quantities for a given market and a given time, say the price p and the quantity q of a good sold (defined by the economist), are related in a supply function f(p,q) = 0. We may observe a price P and a quantity Q and see if it satisfies the relation

$$\alpha \ P \ + \ \beta \ Q \ + \ \gamma \ = \ 0$$

for some numerical values of α, β and γ. In general the relationship is not satisfied exactly. There may be systematic discrepancies of either kind. The observed price P may be an average for the period of time different from the economist's definition of p or the constants α, β and γ may be incorrect (or the relation may not be linear). There may be irregular errors that can be treated as random. The observed price P may differ from the price p defined by the theorist because of bookkeeping errors or the suppliers may be influenced by factors not taken into account, such as weather or political events. The systematic errors are questions of data gathering, definitions, and construction of the mathematical theory. We are more interested in the random disturbances, in particular, disturbances in relations.[3]

We can give an example of these types of errors from our area of attitude studies from the prediction of the recent election results. The errors of Gallup, Roper, and Crossley in some elections were due partly to the defects of their sampling procedures as well as the "random" error; these are errors of observation. Secondly, the errors are due to people changing their minds. The change of attitudes may be inherent fluctuations in the minds of some individuals or it may be due to some outside influences. It can be observed from the data that opinions changed from summer to fall. To some extent these are random changes.

Public opinion investigators have given great consideration to the first kind of error, namely, error of observation (including "sampling errors"). However, the second type seems more important. Indeed, by drawing large enough samples the first type of error can be made negligible — at least that part of observational error due to sampling. The second type of error — that of disturbances in relations — may be reduced by increasing the scope of the study but the inherent vagaries of human nature may still leave this error large. Most of the statements about attitudes and their

relations in time sequences can be phrased as predictions. The
accuracy of these predictions is limited mainly by the second type
of error.

In this paper we shall consider some simple probability
models for describing this second type of discrepancy. The use
of a model for the combination of the two types of error shall not
be treated now. Thus we assume that the questions and attitudes
of the people about whom the generalizations are made are the
people interviewed.

Before discussing further the nature of the probability model
we note that in this case as in many other cases a deterministic
(i.e., nonprobabalistic) model can be obtained from the probability
model. As will be seen in Section 2 we let $n_i(t)$ be the number of
people holding the i -th opinion at time t and n ($= \Sigma_i\, n_i(t)$) be
the number of people studied. The model gives a probability distribution for $n_1(t), \ldots, n_m(t)$. If the number of people studied is
large, then the proportion $r_i(t) = n_i(t)/n$ is roughly like the probability average $\rho_i(t) = E\, r_i(t)$. In a simple model we obtain

$$\sum_{i=1}^{m} p_{ij}\; \rho_i(t-1) = \rho_j(t), \quad j = 1, \ldots, m \qquad (1.1)$$

in terms of these averages. This yields a kind of "flow" model.
The equations say that of the people holding opinion i at the time
$t-1$, a proportion p_{ij} of these will shift to opinion j at time t;
the total number holding opinion j at time t is the sum of the
people changing from each opinion i (including $i=j$). The more
elaborated probability models also yield deterministic models in
the same way.

What are the advantages of using a probability model? In
the first place it states precisely the hypothesized relationships
between the data (including the properties of the random disturbances). In a mathematical model all of the factors taken into consideration are stated, and the way in which they are combined is
indicated exactly. By explicitly putting into the model probability
distributions of some of the quantities one has in the model an "explanation" of some of the discrepancies between a non random
theory and observed facts. The random quantities can be given
substantive meaning.

A concise formulation is not the primary objective of a
mathematical model. A more important advantage of the probability model is that it permits us to draw the logical conclusions
of the theory if we know the model precisely. By using mathematical methods we are assured that the consequences obtained are

those implied by the theory. These two aspects of model building not only clarify the ideas one has about the phenomena studied, but suggest further problems. One is led to questions that are meaningful in this model.

It is essential that the mathematical model be related to observations of the real world. The elements of the theory should be operationally defined.

How does one use one's data to evaluate how well the theory describes the facts? One wishes to test hypotheses in the theory and to specify the parts of the theory that are still unknown. For example, one may wish to estimate a constant in the model. The third advantage of the probability model is that using the theory of statistical inference one can deduce the best statistical methods for using the data from the properties of the model. More than that, the kind of data to be collected are implied by these considerations.

The models suggested in this paper may be too simple to explain the process of changes of opinion in many cases. However, only by considering these simple models can we see how to formulate more sophisticated theory.

First, we shall consider a very simple case of attitude change, namely, an attitude depends only on the attitude at the next previous time point. This example will illustrate how we draw conclusions from the model, how we decide what are meaningful questions (i.e., questions in operational terms) and how we devise statistical methods for estimating certain parameters.

Then we shall consider other models for situations which present more complicated problems. In these examples it will be clear that setting up these models permits us to make inferences that would not be evident from other approaches.

In the direction of indicating when causes of changes in opinions operate we develop a technique for determining when the change is too great to be considered as due to the irregularities that are treated as random. Secondly, we show how to determine the lag in attitude; that is, how far in the past opinions held affect the present. In two respects we go beyond the "primitive model" in which only the effect of one attitude on itself is considered. We consider the mutual interaction between two attitudes, and indicate that latent structure analysis can be used with these models.

Unfortunately, there is a paucity of time series data in this field. It is hoped that development of methods of analysis will stimulate the collecting of more data. Most of the illustrations in this text are based on the Sandusky study of the election campaign of 1940 made by the Bureau of Applied Social Research. In this case we have seven successive interviews with each respondent.

Section II. A SIMPLE MODEL FOR CHANGES IN ATTITUDE

DEFINITION OF THE MODEL FOR CHANGES
IN THE ATTITUDE OF ONE PERSON

We shall suggest a probability model here to represent the changes in attitude of one person. Later it will be shown how this model is applied to a group of people. The model suggested here has been studied considerably by mathematicians and physicists. Most of the conclusions given in the following sections are well known in mathematical terms. Here we shall give interpretations in psychological terms.

This model is simple in several respects. For one thing we shall set up a model which explains changes in a given attitude only in terms of the previous history of changes in this one attitude; other factors will be neglected. Moreover, we shall not take into account explicitly how strongly this attitude is held. While the model may seem almost trivial, we shall study it in some detail because models which are more complicated in terms of psychological interpretations have the same mathematical properties. Later we shall show how more realistic models can be based on this simple one.

We shall assume that at any particular time a person holds one of many different opinions; these will be conveniently numbered as opinions 1,2, . . . , m. For example, if the attitude concerns the intention of voting there are two opinions, either "I do not intend to vote" (denoted by 1, say) or "I do intend to vote" (denoted by 2). If the attitude concerns the nominee to be voted for, the opinion is "I intend to vote for Dewey" (denoted by 1), "I intend to vote for Truman" (denoted by 2), or "I do not know for whom I shall vote" (denoted by 3).

At the outset we shall suppose that a person's attitude is ascertained at regular time intervals. We may interview this person the first day of every month, or we may question him each June thirtieth. We shall denote successive time points by t = 0,1,2, . . . Later this model can be generalized to hold for irregular time intervals.

At any given time t the individual under consideration holds one of the m opinions, say the i-th one. We shall assume that the probability that this individual holds the opinion j at the next time point, i.e., $t + 1$, is p_{ij}. Since the number p_{ij} is a probability, it must be non negative, and since one of the m opinions must be held at the time $t + 1$, the sum of these probabilities over all j must be 1; that is,

$$\sum_{j=1}^{m} p_{ij} = 1 \qquad (i = 1, \ldots, m). \tag{2.1}$$

By knowing the opinion held by an individual at the origin of our time, we can predict in a probability sense how his attitude will change from one opinion to another as time goes on.

It will be observed that the opinion taken by the individual at $t + 1$ depends only on his attitude at time t. No other determinants are taken into account explicitly. In a sense other factors are taken into account implicitly. The statement made about a person's attitude at the next time is a probability statement. It is assumed that the effects of other influences on his attitude are of such a nature that their total effect can be considered random. Those inner forces that affect one's attitude are also assumed to be of an irregular sort whose effect can be described as random. The net effect of these factors is such that we can assign a probability that he will change his mind from one opinion to another.

We assume that these "transition probabilities" p_{ij} are the same during the period of time under consideration. This implies that the factors affecting the attitude act in much the same random way in the period of observation.

We can give a frequency interpretation to the probabilities defined here even though the probability model is specified for just one given individual. The numbers p_{ij} depend on the psychological make-up of the individual and upon his environment. We can imagine this individual or one similar to him as being placed in a large number of similar environments. Suppose in each of these circumstances he holds opinion i. Then count the number of situations in which he changes to opinion j. The relative frequency of this change will be approximately p_{ij}. Our frequency interpretation is similar to that the econometrician uses when he sets up a probabilistic econometric model; if his model relates aggregate time series of the national economy, for example, he interprets probabilities of events as the relative frequency of events happening in a large number of identical national economies.

Now let us give an example of our probability model. Suppose we ask our respondent each month "Do you think Russia wants peace?". Let "No" be denoted by 1 and "Yes" by 2. The matrix of transition probabilities might be

$$\begin{pmatrix} .9 & .1 \\ .2 & .8 \end{pmatrix}. \tag{2.2}$$

If an individual holds the opinion in January that Russia does not want peace, the probability is .9 that he will hold the same opinion in February, and it is .1 that he will change his mind; if an individual answers "Yes" to our question in January, the probability is .2 that he will answer "No" in February and .8 that he will answer "Yes." The probabilities .9 and .1 indicate that while an individual will hold the opinion 1 with some tenacity there is a 1/10 chance that something will occur to make him change his opinion. It may be that Russia will make some peace move, that the person will read a magazine article favorable to Russia, or that some emotional experience will make him more tolerant to a foreign country. On the other hand a person thinking in January that Russia wants peace has a chance of 2/10 of being affected by some occurrence that changes his mind.

The remainder of this section will be devoted to obtaining the consequences of this model. These results are theorems in probability with interpretations in the study of attitude changes. They are based on the m opinions and the matrix of transition probabilities.

$$P = \begin{pmatrix} p_{11} & p_{12} & \cdots\cdots & p_{1m} \\ p_{21} & p_{22} & \cdots\cdots & p_{2m} \\ \cdot & \cdot & & \cdot \\ \cdot & \cdot & & \cdot \\ \cdot & \cdot & & \cdot \\ p_{m1} & p_{m2} & \cdots\cdots & p_{mm} \end{pmatrix} \tag{2.3}$$

First we shall see that knowing P and the individual's opinion at the beginning of the period we can assign a probability to every sequence of opinions held; that is, we can make probability statements concerning any question of the individual's attitude. In particular, we can find the probability that over a particular time span he changes his mind from one specified opinion to another. A very interesting property of the model is that under certain conditions there is a tendency as time passes for the probability of a given opinion held to be independent of the initial opinion. We can also find the proportion of time that an individual with a given initial opinion holds some specified opinion.

THE STOCHASTIC PROCESS

If we know the initial opinion of the individual at time 0 and the matrix P, we can calculate the probability of any sequence of opinion held. If the initial opinion is i, the probability of holding opinion j at time 1 is p_{ij}. The probability of holding opinion j at time 1 and k at time 2 is simply $p_{ij} \cdot p_{jk}$, for p_{jk} is the probability of going from j at time 1 to k at time 2, as we have assumed the "transition probabilities" constant through time. In general, the probability of the sequence of opinion $i_0, i_1, i_2, \ldots, i_n$ (for n + 1 time points) is

$$p_{i_0 i_1} \cdot p_{i_1 i_2} \cdot p_{i_2 i_3} \cdot \ldots \cdot p_{i_{n-1} i_n} \qquad (2.4)$$

if the initial opinion is i_0. In the above example we see that if a person says No at the opening interview the probability of No at the next and Yes at the following is .9 x .1 = .09. Given the initial opinion No, the following table gives the probabilities of the possible sequences of opinion over two time points:

	t = 0	1	2	Probability
Sequence	No	No	No	.81
	No	No	Yes	.09
	No	Yes	No	.02
	No	Yes	Yes	.08

The frequency interpretation is that if we placed our individual in many similar circumstances and if he started with the opinion No, the relative frequency of the cases in which he would hold to that opinion for two periods without changing would be approximately .81.

This set of 4 different sequences and the associated probabilities is called a *stochastic process* (in this case conditional on No as the initial opinion). In general a stochastic process is a sequence of events (a set of events ordered in time) together with probabilities of these sequences. In our study, an event is the holding of an opinion. Given the initial opinion, we can find the probability of any sequence of opinions; all of these time series of opinions and the related probabilities constitute a stochastic process for this initial opinion. Given another initial opinion or given another set of p_{ij}, we obtain a different process. If we assigned probabilities to the initial opinions, the set of all possible sequences of opinion together with the probability of each sequence would constitute a *stochastic process*. In simple terms a stochastic process is a probability model for time series.

These processes we study are called *Markov processes* or more specifically *Markov chains*. The term *"Markov"* implies that the process is such that the probability of an opinion at time t + 1 depends only on the opinion held at time t.

One process of a trivial sort is given by the probabilities $p_{ii} = 1$, $p_{ij} = 0$ for i ≠ j. In this case it is certain that a person holds his opinion forever. Only the sequences (0,0,...,0), (1,1,...,1), etc., have probabilities different from zero. Another trivial case is that of $p_{ij} = 1/m$. In this case whatever the opinion at time t, every opinion is equally likely at t + 1. The probability of every sequence of opinions is the same.

PROBABILITIES OF CHANGES
OVER VARIOUS TIME PERIODS

Since a probability can be assigned to each sequence, we can obtain a probability for any change in opinion we may consider. In our example, we wish to determine the probability that a person holding opinion 1 in January will have the same opinion in March. This may occur in 2 exclusive ways. He can hold opinion 1 for the 3 months, or change to opinion 2 in February and back to 1 in March. The probability of the first sequence is .9 x .9 = .81, and that of the second is .1 x .2 = .02. Thus by the theorem of total probabilities, the probability sought for is .81 + .02 = .83 which is the probability of a person saying "No" in January also saying "No" in March.

In a similar manner the probabilities of the other sequences may be computed i.e., "Yes" in January, "No" in March, etc. We obtain the matrix

$$P(2) = \begin{pmatrix} .83 & .17 \\ .34 & .66 \end{pmatrix}. \tag{2.5}$$

P(2) is also a matrix of transition probabilities, and would represent the probabilities of change if we interviewed the individual every 2 months.

For the m opinion case we suppose that the individual holds the opinion i at time t; consider the probability that he holds opinion k at time t + 2. At time t + 1 he may hold any opinion. Hence, the probablity of k at time t + 2 is the sum of the probability of opinion 1 at t + 1 and opinion k at t + 2, the probability of 2 at t + 1 and k at t + 2, etc.; that is,

$$p_{i1}p_{1k} + p_{i2}p_{2k} + \cdots + p_{i,m}p_{m,k} = \sum_{j=1}^{m} p_{ij}p_{jk} . \tag{2.6}$$

Call this number $p_{ik}^{(2)}$.

Equation (2.6) bears a striking resemblence to the i,k-th element of the matrix which is defined as the product of two other matrices. More exactly, if A is an r x s matrix with elements a_{ij}, and B is an s x t matrix with elements b_{jk}, then the matrix C = A x B = AB is one with elements

$$c_{ik} = \sum_{i=1}^{s} a_{ij}b_{jk}$$

and is an r x t matrix. We notice that the number of columns in A must equal the number of rows of B for the product to be defined.

In our particular case both a_{ij} and $b_{ij} = p_{ij}$, and $c_{ij} = p_{ij}^{(2)}$, therefore P(2) = P · P = P² . For the example

$$P(2) = \begin{pmatrix} .9 & .1 \\ .2 & .8 \end{pmatrix} \times \begin{pmatrix} .9 & .1 \\ .2 & .8 \end{pmatrix} = \begin{pmatrix} .83 & .17 \\ .34 & .66 \end{pmatrix} \tag{2.5'}$$

which is equal to (2.5).

In a similar manner we can compute the probability of a person with opinion i at time t holding opinion k at time t + s. Let p(s) = $p_{ij}^{(s)}$ be the matrix of probabilities of going from one opinion to another in s time periods. In this case we sum over all possible opinions at t + 1, t + 2,..., t + s - 1.

Thus, given P, we can easily obtain the probability of a particular transition in s steps. The matrix P(s) is again a matrix of transition probabilities since each entry is non negative and each row sum is unity. In the, case of our example, we have

$$P = P^1 = \begin{pmatrix} .9 & .1 \\ .2 & .8 \end{pmatrix} , \tag{2.2}$$

$$P(2) = P^2 = \begin{pmatrix} .83 & .17 \\ .34 & .66 \end{pmatrix}, \qquad (2.5)$$

$$P(3) = P^3 = \begin{pmatrix} .781 & .219 \\ .438 & .562 \end{pmatrix}. \qquad (2.7)$$

It will be noticed that in this case the greater the time interval is, the greater is the probability of the individual changing his mind.

LIMITING PROBABILITIES OF HOLDING A GIVEN OPINION.

We can calculate P(s) for any s. What can we say about P(s) for very large s? We are interested in knowing what kind of probability statements we can make now for some time far in the future. For the example previously considered, it can be shown that

$$P(s) = \begin{pmatrix} \dfrac{2}{3} + \dfrac{(.7)^s}{3} & \dfrac{1}{3} - \dfrac{(.7)^s}{3} \\ \dfrac{2}{3} - \dfrac{2(.7)^s}{3} & \dfrac{1}{3} + \dfrac{2(.7)^s}{3} \end{pmatrix} \qquad (2.8)$$

We see that as s increases each element of P(s) gets close to the corresponding element of the matrix:

$$\begin{pmatrix} \dfrac{2}{3} & \dfrac{1}{3} \\ \dfrac{2}{3} & \dfrac{1}{3} \end{pmatrix}. \qquad (2.9)$$

This matrix shows that for a time point sufficiently far in the future, the probability is about 2/3 that the opinion is 1 (No) regardless of the present opinion, for $p_{i1} = 2/3$ for any i. Thus, knowledge of the present opinion of the person is of less and less use in prediction as the time span increases. This confirms our intuition that our ability to predict a person's opinion decreases as the time interval increases.

This result is a particular example of the following general theorem.

Theorem. There exist m *uniquely defined non negative numbers* p_j *with* $\sum_{j=1}^{m} p_j = 1$ *such that*

$$\lim_{s \to \infty} p_{ij}^{(s)} = p_j \qquad (i = 1,\ldots, m) \qquad (2.10)$$

if (a) *for some* j *and some* s *all* $p_{ij}^{(s)}$, *are positive or* (b) *there is only one characteristic root of* P *that is one in absolute value.* The significance of this theorem is that under conditions (a) or (b) the probability of opinion j at time t + s approaches p_j as s increases irrespective of the opinion held at time t.[4]

Condition (a) means that at some particular time s there is a non zero probability of opinion j no matter what opinion is held at time t = 0. In our example, this condition is immediately verified for s = 1 and j = 1 or 2.

Condition (b) is not only sufficient but is necessary as well, and there always exists at least one root of absolute value unity.

It can also be shown that the p_j in (2.10) are those which are components of the characteristic vector associated with the root of absolute value equal to one. That is to say the vector

$$p = \begin{pmatrix} p_1 \\ \cdot \\ \cdot \\ \cdot \\ p_m \end{pmatrix} \qquad (2.11)$$

as given by the equation

$$\sum_{i=1}^{m} p_i p_{ij} = p_j \qquad (j = 1,2,\ldots, m) \qquad (2.12)$$

is the vector of the limiting probabilities. Since P is unique except for a constant multiplier, we impose the condition $\sum p_j = 1$.

Let us illustrate this theory by

$$P = \begin{pmatrix} .9 & .1 \\ .2 & .8 \end{pmatrix} \qquad (2.13)$$

From (2.12)

$$.9p_1 + .2p_2 = p_1 \qquad\qquad (2.14)$$
$$.1p_1 + .8p_2 = p_2$$

we obtain

$$.9p_1 + .2p_2 = p_1.$$

Imposing the condition $p_1 + p_2 = 1$ we get

$$p_1 = 2/3, \qquad p_2 = 1/3 \qquad\qquad (2.15)$$

which agrees with our previous result.

It should be noticed that the approach of $P(s)$ to the limiting matrix depends on $\lambda_i^s (i = 1,...,m)$ approaching 0. The smaller these roots, the faster is the convergence.

It may be objected that this model (with only one root of absolute value one) is not realistic for sociological phenomena because as time goes on the probability of a given individual taking on a given opinion does not become independent of his initial opinion. The unreality may be modified, however, by two considerations. One is that our time of study may be so short that the limit is not approached and the model may be adequate in our range of study; the other consideration is that if the process holds only for each of a restricted class of individuals it may be a good approximation. At any rate this feature of the process is one to bear in mind when we come to use it to explain the behavior of specified individuals.

LIMITING PROPORTION OF TIME
WITH ONE OPINION

In general we can say that over a period of time a person tends to spend a certain portion of time holding a given opinion. If the conditions given above are satisfied, then the proportion of time does not depend on the initial opinion.

Suppose that our individual holds opinion i at time 0 and we ask what is the proportion of time that he holds opinion j. Suppose we treat the successive time points $t = 1,2,...,T$. Let

X(t) be a random variable that is 1 if opinion j is held at time t and 0 if a different opinion is held at time t. Then

$$\Pr \{ X = 1 \} = p_{ij}(t),$$
$$\Pr \{ X = 0 \} = 1 - p_{ij}(t) .$$
(2.16)

The total number of time points at which opinion j is held is $X(1) + ... + X(T)$, and the proportion of time is

$$X_T = \frac{1}{T} \sum_{t=1}^{T} X(t) .$$
(2.17)

It can be shown that if T is large enough X_T is very probably near a certain number (depending on P), that is, that there is a number a such that

$$p \lim_{T \to \infty} X_T = a.$$
(2.18)

This means that if we take a long enough time range we can be pretty sure that the proportion of time opinion j is held is about a.

Let us see what this number a must be. The expected value of X_T is

$$EX_T = \frac{1}{T} \sum_{t=1}^{T} EX(t)$$
(2.19)

$$= \frac{1}{T} \sum_{t=1}^{T} p_{ij}(t)$$

It can be shown that as $T \to \infty$, (2.19) $\to a$. The variance of X_T approaches 0 as T approaches infinity, hence by Tchebychev's Theorem we find that (2.18) is true.

FREEDOM IN SPECIFYING STATIONARY
STATE AND TURNOVER

Let us see how much flexibility there is in specifying a model for some particular time series. We shall see that in the case of a dichotomous attitude we can specify the stationary state and the turnover.

The model is specified by the matrix P. The number of free parameters in P is $m(m - 1)$

$$(\text{since } \sum_j p_{ij} = 1).$$

The number of free parameters in p (the characteristic vector of P corresponding to the root of unity) is $m - 1$. Thus we can assign p and still have the choice of $(m - 1)^2$ parameters in P.

Let us see how this works in the case of $m = 2$. Then

$$P = \begin{pmatrix} p_{11} & p_{12} \\ p_{21} & p_{22} \end{pmatrix}. \qquad (2.20)$$

Suppose p (the stationary state) is given by $p' = (p_1 \ p_2)$. From (2.1) we have

$$\begin{aligned} p_{11} &= 1 - p_{12}, \\ p_{21} &= 1 - p_{22}. \end{aligned} \qquad (2.21)$$

That p indicates the stationary state is shown by,

$$p'p = p'. \qquad (2.22)$$

The second component equation of (2.22) is

$$p_1 \, p_{12} + p_2 \, p_{22} = p_2. \qquad (2.23)$$

Thus

$$p_{22} = 1 - \frac{p_1}{p_2} \, p_{12}, \qquad (2.24)$$

and using (2.21) we obtain

$$p_{21} = \frac{p_1}{p_2} \, p_{12}. \qquad (2.25)$$

Using (2.21) in (2.23) we obtain

$$p_1 (1 - p_{11}) + p_2 (1 - p_{21}) = 1 - p_1 \qquad (2.26)$$

or

$$p_1 p_{11} + p_2 p_{21} = p_1 \ ,$$

which is the first component equation of (2.22). Thus (2.22) is satisfied if p_{11}, p_{21} and p_{22} are expressed in terms of p_{12} given by (2.21), (2.25) and (2.24), respectively. Thus we can assign the stationary state and the turnover.

DEFINITION OF THE MODEL FOR CHANGES IN ATTITUDE OF MANY PERSONS

Until now, we have considered a probability model to explain the sequence of opinions held by a given individual. Our frequency interpretation of probability here is that if we took this individual and an increasing number of identical individuals and set them in roughly similar environments,[5] the proportion of these identical individuals holding a given sequence of opinions approaches the probability of the sequence as defined by the model.[6] The probability model above was thought of as applying to one particular individual. Now we are going to assume that we have a number of different individuals who are similar enough so that we can use the same probability model for each. That is, the same matrix P applies to all. The initial opinions need not be the same. Out of these n individuals we are interested in the *number* holding a given opinion at a given time, (not which person holds what opinion) or in the number holding a given pair of opinions at given pairs of time, or in the number of people holding a given sequence of opinions over all times studied. Since each individual's sequence of opinions is a random variable (i.e., there is a probability attached to each possible sequence), the total number of individuals holding a given sequence is a random variable. The interpretation of this in terms of limiting frequency of occurrence is for repeating many times the entire environment for the n individuals, or we may interpret probability as the expected proportion of people having the property. We shall now build up a theory for the aggregate of opinions held by a set of individuals.

Let us first make a slight digression here to consider the derivation and interpretation of the multinomial probability distribution.

Suppose we have a random variable which can take one of the three values 1, 2, or 3, with probabilities p_1, p_2, and p_3, respectively. Suppose we take n independent observations on this variable and we ask the question "What is the probability of observing n_1 1's, n_2 2's and n_3 3's, where $n_1 + n_2 + n_3 = n$?". The answer is given by the multinomial formula

$$\frac{n!}{n_1!\, n_2!\, n_3!}\; p_1^{n_1}\, p_2^{n_2}\, p_3^{n_3}\; , \tag{2.27}$$

where

$$p_1^{n_1}\, p_2^{n_2}\, p_3^{n_3}$$

is the probability of getting the required result in any given order and $n!/n_1!\, n_2!\, n_3!$ is the number of different orders. (2.27) is seen to immediately generalize to m states and the formula is

$$\frac{n!}{n_1!\, n_2!\, \ldots\, n_m!}\; p_1^{n_1}\, p_2^{n_2}\, \ldots\, p_m^{n_m}. \tag{2.28}$$

Returning to our problem, let us suppose that at time $t - 1$ there are $n_1(t - 1)$ persons holding opinion 1. For each such person, there is a probability p_{1j} ($j = 1,2$) that he will hold opinion j at time t. What is the probability that of *these* $n_1(t - 1)$ persons, there will be, at time t, $n_{11}(t)$ holding opinion 1, and $n_{12}(t)$ holding opinion 2? As each person's change is assumed independent of any other's, a correspondence can be made with the problem treated in the digression above. Thus:

$$
\begin{aligned}
n_1(t-1) &\longrightarrow n \\
p_{11} &\longrightarrow p_1 \\
p_{12} &\longrightarrow p_2 \\
n_{11}(t) &\longrightarrow n_1 \\
n_{12}(t) &\longrightarrow n_2
\end{aligned}
$$

and the answer is:

$$\frac{[n_1(t-1)]!}{[n_{11}(t)]!\, [n_{12}(t)]!}\; p_{11}^{n_{11}(t)}\, p_{12}^{n_{12}(t)} \tag{2.30}$$

The reader should be careful to notice that this is *not* the probability that a certain number of people hold opinion 1 (Russia wants peace) and a certain number hold opinion 2, at time t. This *is* the probability that of the group who held opinion 1, at t - 1, a certain number will retain this opinion while the rest of this group will change. It should also be observed that use of the multinomial law implies that individuals change independently. An alternative to this assumption is that "leaders" change on their own and the other people follow their leaders; this could not be described by the multinomial law.

In our example, if an individual holds that Russia does not want peace in January, the probability is .9 that in February he has the same belief and is .1 that he changes his mind. Suppose we have 20 people who hold in January that Russia does not want peace. Then the probability that 17 have the same opinion in February and 3 change is

$$\frac{20!}{17!\ 3!}\ (.9)^{17}\ (.1)^3\ . \tag{2.31}$$

If 30 hold in January that Russia does want peace, the probability that 6 of these 30 change their minds and 24 continue to hold the same opinion is

$$\frac{30!}{6!\ 24!}\ (.2)^6\ (.8)^{24}. \tag{2.32}$$

For the m opinion case the formula is given by

$$\frac{n_i(t-1)!}{n_{i1}(t)!\ n_{i2}(t)!\ \ldots\ n_{im}(t)!}\ p_{i1}^{n_{i1}(t)}\ p_{i2}^{n_{i2}(t)}\ \ldots\ p_{im}^{n_{im}(t)} \tag{2.33}$$

Returning to our example, suppose we wish to find the probability that $n_1(t)$ people hold opinion 1 at time t_0. Now a person holding 1 at time t, arrived at this state in one of two exclusive ways: by holding 1 at t - 1 and maintaining it (prob. $= p_{11}$) or by having 2 and changing his mind (prob. $= p_{21}$). Therefore

$$n_1(t)\ =\ n_{11}(t)\ +\ n_{21}(t) \tag{2.34}$$

From (2.34) we see that for a given $n_1(t)$ the distribution of $n_{11}(t)$ and $n_{21}(t)$ are not independent, thus it will be necessary to obtain the joint distribution of the quantities and make the appropriate transformation. Now the distribution of $n_{11}(t)$ is given by (2.33) and that of $n_{21}(t)$ is given by the formula obtained by changing the first subscript of the n's and p's in (2.33) from 1 to 2. It should be noticed that these are distributions conditioned on $n_1(t-1)$, $n_2(t-1)$, and that $n_{11}(t) + n_{12}(t) = n_1(t-1)$ and $n_{21}(t) + n_{22}(t) = n_2(t-1)$. If we do not impose the condition on $n_1(t)$ (and at the same time $n_2(t)$ for $n_1(t) + n_2(t) = n_1(t-1) + n_2(t-1)$; i.e., we do not lose any people), then the pair $n_{11}(t)$, $n_{12}(t)$ are independent of the pair $n_{21}(t)$, $n_{22}(t)$, and the joint distribution is given by their product, i.e.,

$$\frac{n_1(t-1)!\, n_2(t-1)!}{n_{11}(t)!\, n_{12}(t)!\, n_{21}(t)!\, n_{22}(t)!}\, p_{11}^{n_{11}(t)}\, p_{12}^{n_{12}(t)}\, p_{21}^{n_{21}(t)}\, p_{22}^{n_{22}(t)} \qquad (2.35)$$

In our example if

$$\begin{pmatrix} n_1(t-1) \\ \\ n_2(t-1) \end{pmatrix} = \begin{pmatrix} 20 \\ \\ 30 \end{pmatrix}, \qquad (2.36)$$

the probability that

$$\begin{pmatrix} n_{11}(t) & n_{12}(t) \\ \\ n_{21}(t) & n_{22}(t) \end{pmatrix} = \begin{pmatrix} 17 & 3 \\ \\ 6 & 24 \end{pmatrix} \qquad (2.37)$$

is (2.35).

In this case there are 23 holding opinion 1 and 27 holding opinion 2 at time t. The probability of $n_1(t)$ and $n_2(t)$ given $n_1(t-1)$ and $n_2(t-1)$ is the sum of (2.35) over all $n_{ij}(t)$ $(i, j = 1, 2)$ such that $n_{i1}(t) + n_{i2}(t) = n_i(t-1)$ $(i = 1, 2)$, $n_{1i} + n_{2i} = n_i(t)$ $(i = 1, 2)$. In our example we can obtain 23 with opinion 0 and 27 with opinion 1 from the matrices.

$$
\begin{pmatrix} 20 & 0 \\ 3 & 27 \end{pmatrix}, \quad \begin{pmatrix} 19 & 1 \\ 4 & 26 \end{pmatrix}, \ldots, \quad \begin{pmatrix} 0 & 20 \\ 23 & 7 \end{pmatrix} \tag{2.38}
$$

The probability is

$$
\sum_{\nu=0}^{20} \frac{20!}{(20-\nu)!\,\nu!} \frac{30!}{(3+\nu)!\,(27-\nu)!} (.9)^{20-\nu}(.1)^{\nu}(.2)^{3+\nu}(.8)^{27-\nu}
$$

$$
= \left[\sum_{\nu=0}^{20} \frac{20!}{(20-\nu)!\,\nu!} \frac{30!}{(3+\nu)!\,(27-\nu)!} \left(\frac{(.1)\ (.2)}{(.9)\ (.8)} \right)^{\nu} \right] (.9)^{20}(.2)^{3}(.8)^{27} \tag{2.39}
$$

For the general m opinion case we may define a vector $n(t-1)$ as in (2.36) and an "m by m" matrix $N(t)$ as in (2.37). The distribution of $N(t)$ is

$$
L[n(t-1); N(t)\,|\,P] = \prod_{i=1}^{m} \left\{ \frac{n_i(t-1)}{\prod\limits_{j=1}^{m} n_{ij}(t)} \prod_{j=1}^{m} p_{ij}^{n_{ij}(t)} \right\} \tag{2.40}
$$

when the symbol on the left hand side of (2.40) is to be understood as the distribution of $N(t)$ conditioned on $n(t-1)$ for the transition probability matrix P.

Finally, to get the joint distribution of $N(1)$, $N(2)$, . . . , $N(T)$ we take the product of (2.40) over all t, i.e.

$$
f[n(0); N(1), \ldots, N(T)\,|\,P] = \prod_{t=1}^{T} f[n(t-1); N(t)\,|\,P] \tag{2.41}
$$

where the conditions

$$
\sum_{k} n_{ik}(t) = n_i(t-1), \quad \sum_{k} n_{kj}(t) = n_j(t) \tag{2.43}
$$

hold. (2.41) is the distribution of all the random quantities involved. Any other distribution will be a marginal obtained from
(2.41).

As in the model for one individual, we may determine the distribution of all possible elementary sequences of opinions for a group
of n_0 persons holding opinion i_0 at $t = 0$. As a special case let us
use the previous example (page 30). Here there are two opinions,
Yes, and No, and for three time periods gives $(3 - 1)^2$ different sequences with the probabilities as given there. Hence the probability
that n_1 person will hold opinion sequence 1 (No, No, No), n_2 sequence 2 (No, No, Yes) etc. is

$$\frac{n_0!}{n_1!\, n_2!\, n_3!\, n_4!} \; (.81)^{n_1} (.09)^{n_2} (.02)^{n_3} (.08)^{n_4} \qquad (2.44)$$

where $n_1 + n_2 + n_3 + n_4 = n_0$

In the general m opinion case for $t = 0, 1, \ldots T$, the distribution
is given by

$$\frac{n_0!}{n_1!\, n_2!\, \ldots n_s!} \; p_1*^{n_1} p_2*^{n_2} \ldots p_s*^{n_s} \qquad (2.45)$$

Where s is the number of sequences $= T^m$ and p_i^* is the probability of the i-th sequence as given in (2.4), and $\Sigma n_i = n_0$.

From the point of view of these elementary probabilities of
sequences of opinions we could give a quite different interpretation
of the probability. We could conceive of our population having as
elements sequences of opinions such that the proportion of the population having a given sequence is (2.4). Then if we draw a sequence
at random, the probability it is a given sequence is (2.4). If this
population is sufficiently large, we are led to (2.45) when we draw
n sequences from this population if all start with i_0.

This second interpretation (in terms of random sampling of
individuals with sequences of opinions) can be combined with the
former interpretation to give a composite interpretation (which is
probably more realistic). In this paper, however, we shall use the
first interpretation. It is more convenient, in particular for
prediction.

It may be argued that a large group of individuals may not be homogeneous enough for their opinions and potential opinions to be explained by one process. The answer to this argument is that a non-homogeneous group may be split into smaller groups. Then for each smaller, more homogeneous group we use a probability model of the sort described.[7]

PROPERTIES OF THE MODEL DERIVED
FROM THE MODEL FOR ONE PERSON

We shall now see the implications of this model. The properties described for the one-person model will carry over to this model in certain senses.

(1) *The Stochastic Process*. The distribution (2.43) gives the probability of a sequence

$$n(1), n(2), \ldots, n(T) \tag{2.46}$$

if $n(0)$ is given. This is a stochastic process [depending on $n(0)$] because the sequence of vectors is a sequence of random vectors (i.e., to each possible sequence there is a probability attached). The process in the one-person model is a special case where the vector $n(0)$ has one component equal to 1 and the others equal to 0.

We can also define the probability of a sequence of matrices.

$$N(1), N(2), \ldots, N(T). \tag{2.47}$$

This is also a stochastic process.

Indeed, we can define the probability of a set of the numbers of people having different sequences of opinions. For example, we could obtain the probability that of 11 people holding 0 as initial opinion, 3 have the sequence $1, 1, 0, 0$, over a period of 4 time intervals. In fact, as indicated before, another way of setting up the probability (2.43) is to consider each sequence of opinion i_1, i_2, $\ldots$, i_T, and add the probabilities of those sequences such that we obtain $n_i(t)$ people with opinion i at t (for all i and t).

We have assumed that $n(0)$ is given. If we assign a distribution to $n(0)$ we get a stochastic process that is independent of the numbers of people in the initial state.

(2) *Probabilities of Changes over Various Time Periods.* On page 27 we saw that if a person holds opinion i at time t, the probability is $p_{ij}^{(s)}$ that he holds opinion j at time t+s. The same reasoning carries over for the model in this part. All we need to do is replace the matrix **P** by **P**(s), and consider vectors of the form n(t), n(t+s) etc.

Consider the example we have used before. In this case

$$\mathbf{P}(2) = \begin{pmatrix} .83 & .17 \\ .34 & .66 \end{pmatrix}. \tag{2.6}$$

Thus if

$$n(0) = \begin{pmatrix} 20 \\ 30 \end{pmatrix}, \tag{2.48}$$

the probability of

$$n(2) = \begin{pmatrix} 23 \\ 27 \end{pmatrix} \tag{2.49}$$

is

$$\sum_{\nu=0}^{20} \frac{20!\ \ 30!}{(20-\nu)!\,\nu!\,(3+\nu)!\,(27-\nu)!}\ (.83)^{20-\nu}(.17)^{\nu}(.34)^{3+\nu}(.66)^{27-\nu}. \tag{2.50}$$

This formula is obtained in the way as (2.39).

(3) *Limiting Probabilities of Holding a Given Opinion.* If the matrix **P** of transition probabilities has one characteristic root unity and the others less in absolute value, we know that **P**(s) approaches a limiting matrix with all the elements in a column the same; that is, sufficiently far in the future the probability is about p_i that a person holds opinion i irrespective of the opinion held now. Let n be the sum of the components of n(0), namely, the number of people studied. Then the probability of

$$\nu = \begin{pmatrix} \nu_1 \\ \cdot \\ \cdot \\ \cdot \\ \nu_m \end{pmatrix} \tag{2.51}$$

occuring at a time point far in the future is approximately the multinomial expression

$$\frac{n!}{\nu_1! \dots \nu_{..}!} \; p_1^{\nu_1} \dots p_m^{\nu_m} . \tag{2.52}$$

In our example

$$(p_1 \; p_2) = (2/3 \; 1/3) . \tag{2.53}$$

If there are 50 people, the limiting probability of 23 no's and 27 yes's is

$$\frac{50!}{23! \; 27!} \; (2/3)^{23} \; (1/3)^{27} . \tag{2.54}$$

(4) *Limiting Proportion of Time with One Opinion.* The average frequency any person with initial opinion i has opinion j over a period of time tends toward p_{ij} defined by (2.12). Thus if there are $n_i(0)$ people with opinion i at time 0, on the average the proportion p_{ij} of these will hold opinion j. The average number of people holding opinion j over a long period of time is

$$\sum_{i=1}^{m} n_i(0) p_{ij} .$$

By average here, we mean adding the number of people with opinion j at time 1, 2, . . . , T and dividing by T.

(5) *Asymptotic Normality.* Suppose $n_i(t-1)$ is given. If $n_i(t-1)$ is large enough it follows from a general theorem of the multinomial distribution that $n_{i1}(t), \dots, n_{i,m}(t)$ are approximately normally distributed with expected values

$$E\left\{ n_{ij}(t) \,|\, n_i(t-1) \right\} = n_i(t-1)\, p_{ij} \tag{2.55}$$

and covariances

$$E\left\{ [n_{ij}(t) - En_{ij}(t)]\,[n_{ik}(t) - En_{ik}(t)]\,|n_i(t-1)] \right\} \tag{2.56}$$

$$= n_i(t-1)[\delta_{jk} - p_{ij}]\,p_{ik}$$

where $\delta_{jk} = 1$ if $j = k$ and is 0 otherwise. Equations (2.55) and (2.54) follow from the general theory of the multinomial distribution[8] and are true regardless of the size of $n_i(t-1)$, though the approximate normality depends on $n_i(t-1)$ being large.

As the conditional distribution of $n_{ij}(t)$ depends only on P, it follows that $n_{ij}(t)$ is independent of $n_{hk}(t)$ for given $n_i(t)$ and $n_k(t)$ for $i \neq h$. The asymptotic distribution of $n_j(t)$ ($j = 1, 2, \ldots, m$) can be derived from the above and is normal (if all $n_i(t-1)$ are large) with mean

$$E\left\{ n_j(t)\,|n(t-1) \right\} = E\left\{ \sum_{i=1}^{m} n_{ij}(t)\,|n(t-1) \right\} \tag{2.57}$$

$$= \sum_{i=1}^{m} E\left\{ n_{ij}(t)\,|n_i(t-1) \right\} = \sum_{i=1}^{m} n_i(t-1)\,p_{ij} .$$

The covariances are

$$E\left\{ [n_j(t) - E\,n_j(t)]\,[n_k(t) - En_k(t)]\,|n(t-1) \right\} \tag{2.58}$$

$$= \sum_{i=1}^{m} n_i(t-1)\,(\delta_{jk} - p_{ij})\,p_{ik} .$$

In general, if n is large any of the distributions given in this chapter can be approximated by a multivariate normal distribution.

Section III. AN EXAMPLE

In this chapter we give an application of the model which we have developed in section 2, to a situation in which the required type of data has been collected.

THE DATA

The Bureau of Applied Social Research[9] conducted a panel study of potential voters in Erie County, Ohio, during 1940. This is one of the few studies which has several interviews with the same people.

A group of about 600 people were interviewed in May, June, July, August, September, and October. (A seventh interview in November had different questions.) One of the questions asked at each interview was for which party (candidate) the respondent intended to vote. We have grouped the replies as Republican (R), Democrat (D), and "Don't Know" (DK). The last group includes, besides the specific answers "Don't Know", the replies "Other Candidates" and refusals to reply.

In the following tables the data are given according to pairs of successive interviews. Let May be time 0, June time 1, etc. Then the tables below are the 5 matrices $N(1), \ldots, N(5)$. There were 445 people who responded to all six interviews.

It will be observed that after July the number of Don't Knows decreased in each period. These last three interviews were after both conventions had been held. The fact that the number of Republican voters was greater than the number of Democratic voters at each time is a characteristic of the area. However, we are primarily interested in the changes in attitude, rather than the opinions themselves.

It is of the nature of a probabilistic theory, that there is never exact agreement between any quantity observed, and the corresponding quantity given by the theory. In fact, the theory makes statements about *random variables* – and thus gives only the probabilities that they will take on a given set of values.

Thus two problems arise which do not exist in the application of deterministic schemes. They are: 1) If there are any undetermined parameters in the scheme, there will, in general, exist a

JUNE

	R	D	DK	Total
R	125	5	16	146
MAY D	7	106	15	128
DK	11	18	142	171
	143	129	179	445

JULY

	R	D	DK	Total
R	124	3	16	143
JUNE D	6	109	14	129
DK	22	9	142	173
	152	121	172	445

AUGUST

	R	D	DK	Total
R	146	2	4	152
JULY D	6	111	4	121
DK	40	36	96	172
	192	149	104	445

SEPTEMBER

	R	D	DK	Total
	184	1	7	192
AUGUST D	4	140	5	149
DK	10	12	82	104
	198	153	94	445

OCTOBER

	R	D	DK	Total
R	192	1	5	198
SEPTEMBER D	2	146	5	153
DK	11	12	71	94
	205	159	81	445

large number (possibly infinite) of functions of the observations which can be used to estimate them. We must then set up criteria for "goodness" and seek functions which possess these properties. 2) Some *formal* method of deciding whether the observations are in agreement with the data is needed.

In other terms, the application of a probabilistic theory requires the use of a set of statistical methods which have been developed for the theory.

For the models described thus far such a set of methods exist[10]. However we shall only present here the results which are needed. We might say in passing that all our estimating procedures are maximum likelihood, and the likelihood ratio criterion is that one which is used for testing[11].

The maximum likelihood estimate $\hat{p}_{ij}$ of the transition probabilities p_{ij} are

$$\hat{p}_{ij} \quad \frac{\sum\limits_{t=1}^{T} n_{ij}(t)}{\sum\limits_{t=1}^{T} n_i(t-1)} = \frac{\sum\limits_{t=1}^{T} n_{ij}(t)}{\sum\limits_{t=0}^{T} \sum\limits_{j=1}^{m} n_{ij}(t)} \tag{3.1}$$

However each table also provides estimates of p_{ij} and are given by

$$\hat{p}_{ij;t} = \frac{n_{ij}(t)}{n_i(t-1)} \tag{3.2}$$

This gives some indication of the changes in the transition probabilities. The $(\hat{p}_{ij;t})$ matrices are:

	JUNE		
	R	D	DK
R	.856	.034	.110
MAY D	.055	.828	.117
DK	.064	.105	.831

	JULY		
	R	D	DK
R	.867	.021	.112
JUNE D	.047	.845	.108
DK	.127	.052	.821

	AUGUST		
	R	D	DK
R	.961	.013	.026
JULY D	.050	.917	.033
DK	.233	.209	.558

	SEPTEMBER		
	R	D	DK
R	.958	.005	.037
AUGUST D	.027	.940	.033
DK	.096	.115	.789

	OCTOBER		
	R	D	DK
R	.970	.005	.025
SEPTEMBER D	.013	.954	.033
DK	.117	.128	.755

The five matrices appear to be quite similar. The first two matrices are very much alike. The last three are quite similar except that the third row of the third matrix is different from the third row of the last two matrices. It should be noted that the Republican Convention occurred between the June and July interviews and the Democratic Convention was held between the July and August interviews.

COMPUTATION OF $\hat{P}$ (= $\hat{P}_{ij}$)

If we assume that there is one matrix of transition probabilities for the entire period, the estimate $\hat{P}$ is obtained by using (3.1). Thus

$$\hat{P} = \begin{pmatrix} .928 & .014 & .058 \\ .037 & .900 & .063 \\ .132 & .122 & .746 \end{pmatrix} \qquad (3.3)$$

For example, .928 is our estimate of the probability that a man intending to vote Republican one month has the same intention one month later. The probability that a Democrat retains his vote intention is .900. On the other hand, a person holding a "Don't Know" opinion has a probability of .132 of making up his mind within a month to vote Republican and a probability of .122 of making up his mind to vote Democratic.

If we assume that the matrix of transition probabilities remains constant, there is a stationary state defined by the charactertistic vector of P corresponding to the root one. Our estimate is the characteristic vector of our matrix estimate. It is

$$\hat{p} = \begin{pmatrix} .506 \\ .303 \\ .191 \end{pmatrix} \qquad (3.4)$$

This gives us the expected proportion of vote intention if the campaign had gone on for a much longer time.

TESTING THE HYPOTHESIS THAT P IS CONSTANT

We may question the assumption that the matrix of transition probabilities is constant as it may be expected that the probabilities of one changing his mind are different before the conventions and after the conventions. This is observed casually in the tables above. We see that before the conventions the probability is about .85 of retaining one's opinion for a month. However, after the conventions the probability is about .95 of retaining vote intention for one of the major parties and about .75 of retaining a "Don't Know" opinion.

We can use the likelihood ratio criterion λ for testing this hypothesis:

$$\lambda = \prod_t \prod_i \prod_j \left(\frac{\hat{p}_{ij}}{\hat{p}_{ij;t}} \right)^{n_{ij}(t)} \qquad (3.5)$$

where p_{ij} is given by (3.1) and $p_{ij;t}$ by (3.2), small values of λ are considered significant. It is known that $-2 \log \lambda$ is distributed as x^2 with $(T-1)[m(m-1)]$ degrees of freedom for large n.

Our test criterion has $4 \cdot 3 \cdot 2 = 24$ degrees of freedom. The 5% significance point of the x^2 distribution with 24 degrees of freedom is 36.415. The criterion computed from our data, however, is 101.512. Therefore, we reject the hypothesis. That is, we decide that our simple model does not hold good for the entire campaign period.

The question then arises as to whether a model will be an adequate description for the changes during a part of the period of study. We shall see what successive time points may be considered as involving the same matrix. In the following table we give the statistical analysis. The null hypothesis in each case is that the changes over the period indicated in the first column are explained by one matrix P.

The first two tables above (May-June and June-July) can be explained by one matrix; that is, we accept the hypothesis that the same matrix P is involved from May to July. However, the hypothesis that the next table, July-August, is also explained by the same matrix P cannot be accepted. We further decide that August-September and September-October changes fit one pattern, but that July-August changes do not fit that pattern either. The result of this analysis is that the changes in the first two periods are explained by one model, the changes in the third period are explained

Time Changes	χ^2	Degrees of Freedom	Decision
May-June, June-July	7.64	6	Accept
May-June, June-July, July-August	27.96	12	Reject at 1% or 5% levels of significance
July-August, August-September, September-October	21.86	12	Reject at 5% level of significance
August-September, September-October	1.50	6	Accept

by a second model, and the changes in the fourth and fifth periods are explained by a third model.[12]

These results are very interesting from the point of view of interpretation. The first matrix represents the changes in opinion from May to June. We notice that about 85% of people with a specific party intention in May hold the same intention in June, and about 10% of them have no intention in June. Of the people who have no intention in May about 85% have still not made up their minds in June. The second matrix, representing changes from June to July is about the same. This is surprising because the Republican Convention was held between these two interviews. Apparently, the process does not become different until both conventions are held. Then we obtain a new process. Our statistical analysis tells us that the changes are different from July to August, and the Democratic Convention was held between these two interviews. The July-August matrix is different from the preceding in that the probability of holding to a specific party intention is much higher and the probability of reserving judgment is lower. In other words people are making up their minds more and are sticking to their party choices more.

The last two matrices are alike, and we believe the same process is at work from August to October. People with Republican intention have a high probability of retaining this intention; those with Democratic intention have a higher probability of retaining it than before, and the DK people are not making up their minds as fast as before. It is interesting to note that the difference between the third matrix and the fourth and fifth is essentially a matter of time scale; that is, the July-August matrix represents changes at twice the speed as the August-September and September-October matrices. If we square the last matrix, we get approximately the July-August matrix:

$$\begin{pmatrix} .970 & .005 & .025 \\ .013 & .954 & .033 \\ .117 & .128 & .755 \end{pmatrix}^2 = \begin{pmatrix} .944 & .013 & .043 \\ .029 & .914 & .057 \\ .204 & .219 & .577 \end{pmatrix} \quad (3.6)$$

In other words, the second convetion sets into operation a new process which slows down as the campaign progresses. From July to August the making of party intentions occurs rapidly, then less rapidly.

PREDICTION

It is of interest to project our series ahead in time. Let us see how we forecast vote intention in November on the basis of our knowledge of the process and the vote intention in October. We shall assume that the process operating from August to October continues to operate. On the basis of the August-September and September-October data we estimate the matrix P as:[13]

$$\hat{P} = \begin{pmatrix} .964 & .005 & .031 \\ .020 & .947 & .033 \\ .106 & .121 & .773 \end{pmatrix} \quad (3.7)$$

Now let us see how we predict the vote using this matrix $\hat{P}$. Of the 205 people with Republican intentions in October we would predict that .964 x 205 = 197.6 would actually vote that way; of the 159 with Democratic intentions .020 x 159 = 3.2 would vote Republican and of the 81 with DK intentions, .106 x 81 = 8.6 would vote Republican. This makes a total of 209.4 vote for Republican. The summary of the prediction is

Predicted Vote

		R	D	DK	Total
October Intention	R	197.6	1.0	6.4	205
	D	3.2	150.5	5.3	159
	DK	8.6	9.8	62.6	81
	Total	209.4	161.3	74.3	445

We predict that 5 more people will have Republican intention, 2 more people will have Democratic intention and 7 less will have no intention.

It should be emphasized that we are predicting what people would say if asked in November for whom they will vote. Now we shall compare this prediction with the actual vote. The tabulation of October vote intention and the vote in November is given below. "DK" represents not voting.

Actual Vote in November

		R	D	DK	Total
October Intention	R	192	3	10	205
	D	4	132	23	159
	DK	8	11	62	81
	Total	204	146	95	445

We notice there are discrepancies between the predicted vote intention and the actual vote. We predict 6 more Republicans, 15 more Democrats and 21 less "DK's". The most reasonable explanation of this discrepancy is the difference between verbalizing a vote intention and action. It is well known that in general not everyone who intends to vote actually does so. Furthermore, other studies show that Democrats are more vote-delinquent. Our analysis bears this out.

The various predictions may be summarized as:

	R	D	DK
October intention	205	159	81
Prediction using $\hat{P}$	209.4	161.3	74.3
Prediction using $\hat{p}$	241.7	148.6	54.7
Actual Vote	204	146	95

Section IV. SOME MORE GENERAL MODELS

In this chapter we set forth certain more general models for one attitude as well as some for several attitudes and heterogeneous populations. In the latter case we relate some of these models to latent structure analysis.

MORE GENERAL MODELS FOR ONE ATTITUDE

The models presented in sections 2 and 3 seem rather specialized because the probability of an individual holding a particular opinion depends only on what opinion he held the time previously and not on opinions held earlier in time.

It is possible to consider certain more general models for which the mathematics is the same. We may suppose that at any time t an individual may hold one of m opinions. The probability of his holding a specified opinion, say the k-th, is a number that depends on his opinions at times $t-1, t-2, \ldots, t-q$. Here q is called the order of the process. In the case of a second order process, for example, we can denote by π_{ijk} the probability that an individual holding opinion i at t-2 and j at t-1 will hold k at t. For a set $\{\pi_{ijk}\}$ to form a set of probabilities the following hold:

$$\pi_{ijk} \geq 0, \tag{4.1}$$

$$\sum_{k=1}^{m} \pi_{ijk} = 1. \tag{4.2}$$

The first order model considered in the earlier sections is a degenerate case of the second order model obtained when π_{ijk} does not depend on i; that is, when $\pi_{ijk} = p_{jk}$.

As an example, take the dichotomous attitude considered in section 2. Suppose the probabilities of opinions are given as below:

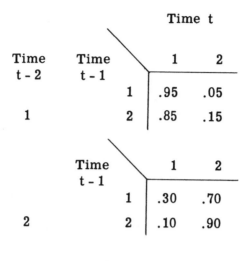

Thus if a person believes that Russia wants peace (denoted by 2), for two successive periods, the probability is .90 that he has this opinion in the next period. This is the number in the second row and second column of the second matrix.

In this type of model we specify an individual's opinion at time -1 and time 0 and not try to "explain" his opinions at these times. Then we study his opinion changes over T time periods. If a person holds opinion i_{-1} at $t = -1$ and i_0 at $t = 0$ then the probability that he holds a sequence of opinions $i_1, i_2, \ldots, i_T$ in the T periods is the product

$$\pi_{i_{-1}i_0i_1} \ \pi_{i_0i_1i_2} \cdot \cdots \cdot \pi_{i_{T-2}i_{T-1}i_T} = \prod_{t=1}^{T} \pi_{i_{t-2}i_{t-1}i_t} . \tag{4.3}$$

For instance, in the above example, if a person holds opinion 2 for two successive periods the probability of holding opinion 2 in the next two periods is $\pi_{222} \cdot \pi_{222}$, bit of he held opinion 1 for two successive periods, the probability of holding 2 in the next two periods is $\pi_{112} \cdot \pi_{122}$.

In a manner similar to that in section 2 we may consider the situation of a number of individuals. Let $n_{ijk}(t)$ be the number of people holding opinion i at t - 2, j at t - 1 and k at t; let

$$n_{ij}(t - 1) = \sum_{k=1}^{m} n_{ijk}(t) . \tag{4.4}$$

The conditional distribution of the $n_{ijk}(t)$ $(k = 1, \ldots, m)$ given $n_{ij}(t-1)$ is given by the multinomial expression

$$\frac{n_{ij}(t-1)!}{\prod\limits_{k} n_{ijk}(t)!} \prod\limits_{k} \pi_{ijk}^{n_{ijk}(t)} \qquad (4.5)$$

The joint distribution of $n_{ijk}(t)$ for $i, j, k, = 1, \ldots, m$ and $t = 1, \ldots T$ is the product of (4.4) over i, j and t with (4.5) holding. We assume $n_{ij}(0)$ given.

REDUCTION TO THE FIRST ORDER CASE

It is possible to apply the results obtained for the first order case to problems involving higher order processes by reformulating the above model. This is done by the device of defining a certain *state* as the situation of holding certain sequences of opinions over q successive time intervals.

We shall focus our attention on the second order model but the ideas are general. The idea is given most easily by considering the simplest case, namely, m = 2 and q = 2 (second order, dichotomous model). Let the *state i* at time t be defined in terms of opinions held at times t - 1 and t, respectively, as follows:

State	Opinion at t - 1	Opinion at t
1	1	1
2	1	2
3	2	1
4	2	2

For instance, state 1 is the situation of holding opinion 1 for two successive periods.

The probability of going from state i to state j is one of the set $\{ \pi_{\alpha\beta\gamma} \}$. For instance, the probability of going from state 1 at t - 1 (opinion 1 at t - 2 and 1 at t - 1) to state 2 at t(opinion 1 at t - 1 and 2 at t) is π_{112}.

In general the probability of going from state i to j is given by

$$P = (p_{ij}) = \begin{pmatrix} \pi_{111} & \pi_{112} & 0 & 0 \\ 0 & 0 & \pi_{121} & \pi_{122} \\ \pi_{211} & \pi_{212} & 0 & 0 \\ 0 & 0 & \pi_{221} & \pi_{222} \end{pmatrix} \tag{4.6}$$

It will be noticed that many entries in **P** are 0. For instance, it is impossible to go from 1 to 3 because that would imply holding both opinions 1 and 2 at time t - 1. The matrix **P** for our example in section 4.1 is

$$\begin{pmatrix} .95 & .05 & 0 & 0 \\ 0 & 0 & .85 & .15 \\ 30 & .70 & 0 & 0 \\ 0 & 0 & .10 & .90 \end{pmatrix} \tag{4.7}$$

Many of the properties of the models of sections 2 and 3 hold for **P** defined here. Given **P** and $n_i(0)$ (remembering that i refers now to the *state* - a sequence of opinions) we can define the entire process. Given $n_i(t)$ we can compute the probability of $n_{ij}(t + s)$. Here we would make use of the matrix $P(s) = P^s$, which is defined as in Section 2.

We may also investigate whether for some time far enough in the future, there is a distribution of states which does not depend on the present state. If such is the case, then we make the statement that, regardless of the present state, for some time in the distant future say T units, the probability is π_{ij} that a person will hold opinion j at T and i at T - 1. The π_{ij} are calculated in the same manner as for the first order case. For i $\neq$ j, π_{ij} is the proportion of people who are still changing their opinion. There may be changes in parts of the system, but as a whole it is in equilibrium.

AN EXAMPLE USING THE SECOND ORDER MODEL

Let us return to the example used in Section 3, of the voting intention of respondents. The maximum likelihood $\hat{\pi}_{ijk}$ estimates of the transition probabilities π_{ijk}, of the second order model are

Time t

Time t - 2	Time t - 1	R	D	DK
	R	.962	.010	.028
R	D	.273	.727	.000
	DK	.395	.116	.489

		R	D	DK
	R	.783	.000	.217
D	D	.019	.934	.047
	DK	.105	.263	.632

		R	D	DK
	R	.855	.012	.133
DK	D	.080	.840	.080
	DK	.134	.117	.749

In general the q-th order formula is

$$\hat{\pi}_{\alpha_0, \alpha_2, \cdots \alpha_q} = \frac{\sum_{t=1}^{T} n_{\alpha_0, \alpha_2, \cdots \alpha_q}(t)}{\sum_{t=1}^{T} n_{\alpha_0, \alpha_2, \cdots, \alpha_{q-1}}(t-1)} \tag{4.8}$$

We notice that the three tables above are similar in that the diagonal elements are large. However, there are differences between the tables in that the probability of holding an opinion from t - 1 to t depends on whether the opinion was also held at t - 2. For example, the probability of holding to Republican intention from t - 1 to t is .962 if Republican intention was held at t - 2, is .783 if Democratic intention was held at t - 2, and is .855 if DK was held at t - 2. Thus we see that we gain by taking account of opinion two time points back.

Now let us compute the stable state for the matrix of estimates. It is

$$
\begin{pmatrix}
.594 & .006 & .021 \\
.008 & .251 & .013 \\
.019 & .014 & .074
\end{pmatrix}
$$

Thus we estimate that the probability that a person has Republican intention two successive time points far in the future is .594; the probability that he have a DK opinion followed by Democratic intention is .014, etc. The above matrix is not a matrix of transition probabilities (the row sums are not one); it is a matrix of probabilities of joint occurrences at two successive times far in the future. It should be noticed that these probabilities do not depend on the initial opinions.

The column sums are (.621, .271, .108) which are the probabilities of Republican intention, Democratic intention, and DK opinion, respectively, at time t; the row sums are the same respective probabilities at time t - 1. Since the process is stationary, these sets of three are identical (except for errors of rounding off numbers). If we compare this vector with that obtained in Section 2 (page 29), under the assumption of a first order process (.543, .334, .123) we see that the difference in assumptions leads to a difference in the estimated steady state.

In passing we mention that it is possible to test whether the model is first order against alternative that it is second order. The likelihood ratio criterion λ for the second order case is

$$
\lambda = \frac{\left[\displaystyle\prod_{t=1}^{T} \prod_{j=1}^{m} n_j(t-1)! \right] \left[\displaystyle\prod_{t-1}^{T} \prod_{i,j,k=1}^{m} n_{ijk}(t)! \right] \left[\displaystyle\prod_{j,k=1}^{m} \hat{\pi}_{jk}^* \sum_t n_{jk}(t) \right]}{\displaystyle\prod_{j,k=1}^{m} \left[n_{jk}(0)! \left\{ \displaystyle\prod_{t=1}^{T-1} n_{jk}(t)! \right\}^2 n_{jk}(T)! \right] \left[\displaystyle\prod_{i,j,k=1}^{m} \hat{\pi}_{ijk}^* \sum_t n_{ijk}(t) \right]} \tag{4.10}
$$

where $\hat{\pi}_{ijk}^{*}$ is the maximum likelihood estimate (4.9) and $\hat{\pi}_{jk}^{*}$ is that derived on page 45 where a first order model is assumed. Under the null hypothesis (i.e. $\pi_{1jk} = \pi_{2jk} = \ldots = \pi_{mjk} = \pi_{jk}^{*}$), $-2 \log \lambda$ has an asymptotic χ^2 distribution with $m(m-1)^2$ degrees of freedom.

A MODEL FOR SEVERAL ATTITUDES

The theory presented above may be easily generalized to the case of R attitudes. It is only necessary to define the state in a proper manner. We shall assume that the R attitudes of a person at t given his attitudes at t - 1 does not depend on those held previous to t - 1. As in the case of one attitude this restriction is easily removed.

As an example, consider the case of R = 2 and m = 2. Two questions, A and B, are asked; each can be answered "no" or "yes." We shall define four states based on the opinions on A and on B as follows:

$$1 = (1.1) = \text{"no" on A, "no" on B,}$$

$$2 = (1.2) = \text{"no" on A, "yes" on B,}$$

$$3 = (2.1) = \text{"yes" on A, "no" on B,}$$

$$4 = (2.2) = \text{"yes" on A, "yes" on B.}$$

We shall assume that the probability of an individual's state at time t depends only on his state at time t - 1. Thus we shall consider the matrix of transition probabilities,

$$P = \begin{pmatrix} p_{11,11} & p_{11,12} & p_{11,21} & p_{11,22} \\ p_{12,11} & p_{12,12} & p_{12,21} & p_{12,22} \\ p_{21,11} & p_{21,12} & p_{21,21} & p_{21,22} \\ p_{22,11} & p_{22,12} & p_{22,21} & p_{22,22} \end{pmatrix} \tag{4.10a}$$

where $p_{ij,kl}$ indicates the probability that if one holds opinion i on A and j on B one will hold k on A and l on B at the next time point.

Let $n_{ij,kl}(t)$ be the number of people holding opinion i on **A** and j on **B** at time $t - 1$ and k on **A** and l on **B** at **T**. Then it is clear how we can use the model of Section 2 to define the probability of a sequence $\{n_{ij,kl}(t)\}$ given $n_{ij}(0)$. This model is easily generalized to the case of **R** attitudes.

In dealing with models of changes of more than one attitude one of the questions we might like to ask is whether the changes are independent, that is, whether the probability of going from i on **A** and j on **B** to h on **A** and k on **B** equals the probability of going from i to h on **A** times the probability of going from j to k on **B**. Symbolically this is

$$p_{ij,hk} = \pi_{ih}^{A} \; \pi_{jk}^{B} \; . \tag{4.11}$$

As an example we consider a panel study of two interviews.[14] On each interview the respondent was asked whether he had seen an advertisement of a particular product and whether he had bought that product. The question we are interested in is whether we can assume that the changes in number of people seeing the advertisement are independent of the changes in the number buying the product. Let 1 on the first action be to see and 2 not to see the advertisement; let 1 on the second action be to buy and 2 not to buy the product. The observations are tabulated below

SEE - BUY MATRIX

Second Interview

		11	12	21	22	Total
	11	83	8	35	7	133
First	12	22	68	11	28	129
Interview	21	25	10	95	15	145
	22	8	32	6	493	539
	Total	138	118	147	543	946

The estimated matrix of transition probabilities is

$$
\{ p_{ij,hk} \} = \begin{pmatrix}
.624 & .060 & .263 & .053 \\
.171 & .527 & .085 & .217 \\
.174 & .069 & .655 & .104 \\
.015 & .059 & .011 & .915
\end{pmatrix}
\qquad (4.12)
$$

We observe that if a person has seen the advertisement at the first interview but not bought the product the (estimated) probability that he sees the advertisement and buys the product later is .171 and that he does not see the advertisement but buys the product is .085. On the other hand if he has neither seen the advertisement nor bought the product at the time of the first interview, the probability that he see the advertisement and buy the product is .015 and that he not see the advertisement but buy the product is .011. There seems to be a difference in the change with regard to buying depending on observing the advertisement.

Now let us make the statistical test. First we compute

$$
\hat{\pi}^A = \begin{pmatrix}
.691 & .309 \\
.110 & .890
\end{pmatrix}
\qquad (4.13)
$$

$$
\hat{\pi}^B = \begin{pmatrix}
.856 & .144 \\
.070 & .930
\end{pmatrix}
\qquad (4.14)
$$

$\hat{\pi}^A$ is the estimate of the transition probabilities of changes on seeing and $\hat{\pi}^B$ of the changes on buying. For example, if a person saw the ad originally, we would say the probability is .691 that he would see the ad the next time. If the changes were independent we would expect that the transition probability matrix for seeing and buying together would be

$$\begin{pmatrix} .591 & .100 & .264 & .045 \\ .048 & .642 & .022 & .287 \\ .094 & .016 & .762 & .128 \\ .008 & .102 & .062 & .823 \end{pmatrix} \qquad (4.15)$$

The χ^2 criterion turns out to be 37.84. This is significant at the 1% level using the χ^2-table with 8 degrees of freedom. This implies that the changes in seeing are not independent of the changes in buying.

The general formulas for testing independence of changes of 2 attitudes is

$$-2 \log \lambda = \sum_{t=1}^{T} \sum_{i,k=1}^{m^A} \sum_{j,k=1}^{m^B} \left[n_{ij,hk}(t) \log \hat{p}_{ij,hk} - \log \hat{\pi}_{ik}^A - \log \hat{\pi}_{jk}^B \right] \quad (4.16)$$

where

$$p_{ij,hk} = \frac{\sum_{t=1}^{T} n_{ij,hk}(t)}{\sum_{t=1}^{T} n_{ij}(t-1)} \qquad (4.17)$$

and

$$\hat{\pi}_{ik}^A \text{ and } \hat{\pi}_{jk}^B$$

are the maximum likelihood estimates of

$$\pi_{ik}^A \text{ and } \pi_{jh}^B$$

if we consider the two attitudes as separate - as in Section 2.

It should be remarked that even though the *changes* are independent, this does not imply that the attitudes themselves are independent at any given time. However, if the changes are independent the attitudes themselves will show a tendency toward independence as time goes on.

MODELS FOR HETEROGENEOUS POPULATIONS

One of the most severe assumptions made in the previous models is that the same transition probability matrix P holds for each individual in the group under observation. We have assumed that the only determining factors of a person's attitude at t are the attitude held at t - 1, t - 2, etc., all the other factors being assumed to operate in a random fashion. Actually, we may know that the other factors operate systematically, and we may even know how they operate.

In many situations where continuous variables are involved, one accounts for exogenous influences by "correcting" for these influences by using "regression" on functions of the external variables. It is customary to assume that the effects are linear; one fits by least squares linear functions of the exogenous variables. (i.e., factors which influence the system but are not influences by it). Then one studies the residuals of the observations from these linear effects. The analogue for discrete variables is stratification. One stratifies his population on the basis of the exogenous discrete variables. Then each stratum he treats as homogeneous. Now let us see how this technique is applied to our problem.

We think that certain factors operate so that some people behave in one way and certain other people behave in another way. Thus, we assume that we should use more information than just a person's initial attitude to determine the probability of his opinion in the future. For example, a man in state i may have a probability of p_{ij}^m of going to state j, but a woman may have a different probability of moving from i to j, say p_{ij}^w. Thus the state of men are determined by one process and that of women by another. Since we can observe whether an individual is a man or woman, we can set up one process for men and one for women. In general, then, we can stratify our set of individuals on observed characteristics and set up a process for each stratum.

As an example of stratification we consider the vote intention of August, September and October and stratify on the basis of interest in the compaign. Each respondent is classified into one of the three groups "High Interest", "Moderate Interest", and "Low Interest". For each group we have a table of the numbers of respondents with the various combinations of intentions in August and September and a table for September and October. For each group we estimate the matrix of transition probabilities. They are given below. There were 141 respondents in the first group, 135 in the second, and 162 in the third.

High Interest	R	D	DK
R	.976	.000	.024
D	.011	.978	.011
DK	.125	.333	.542

Moderate Interest	R	D	DK
R	.968	.016	.016
D	.019	.953	.028
DK	.182	.151	.667

Low Interest	R	D	DK
R	.932	.000	.068
D	.030	.910	.060
DK	.081	.074	.845

It will be noticed that the greater the interest the greater the probability that a person with Republican intention one month will have this same intention the next month and similarly for persons with Democratic intention. On the other hand the greater the interest the less the probability that a person responding DK one month respond the same way next month.

After we have made a stratification we may wish to test whether it is necessary for the study of a given attitude; i.e., we wish to know whether $p^{(1)} = p^{(2)} = \ldots = p^{(q)}$ where $p^{(i)}$ is the transition probability matrix for the i-th stratum. If $q = 2$ the test criterion is:

$$\sum_{i=1}^{m} \hat{C}_i \sum_{j=1}^{m} \frac{(\hat{p}_{ij}^{(1)} - \hat{p}_{ij}^{(2)})^2}{p_{ij}^*} \geq \chi^L_{m(m-1)} \tag{4.18}$$

where

$$\frac{1}{\hat{C}} = \frac{1}{\sum\limits_{t=1}^{T} n_i^{(1)} (t-1)} + \frac{1}{\sum\limits_{t=1}^{T} n_i^{(2)} (t-1)}$$

and p_{ij}^* is the estimate of p_{ij} obtained by ignoring the stratification.

In many sociological situations the "best" stratification is not always made on an observable attribute, but rather on one that must be inferred from the manifest data. These have been termed *latent attributes*.

We can apply the idea of latent attribute analysis to our problem. The essential feature is that here we have strata which cannot be distinguished by any outside data but must be inferred only from the data on the attitude we are studying. Thus, we assume that there are q states (or classes) of the latent attribute; there are q strata, but we do not know in which stratum an individual is.

For example, in the study of political campaigns we might say that some people are fundamentally Republicans and some are fundamentally Democrats but that their observed behavior (other than their answers to the questions we give) does not indicate it. As another example, consider asking people about attitudes toward capitalism, freedom, etc. There may be some underlying philosophy that divides people into two groups that have different probabilities of answering the question.

In the previous example, degree of interest could be considered a latent variable if we did not have information about each respondent's interest. In any case the mathematics of composing the entire population from the subpopulations or strata is the same for stratification on manifest or latent variables.

2. Two Models: Imitative Behavior and Distribution of Status

By NICOLAS RASHEVSKY

University of Chicago

Section I. IMITATIVE BEHAVIOR

The developments of mathematical biology in the last two decades have greatly contributed toward a better understanding of many biological phenomena, ranging from cell growth and division to various manifestations of the functions of the brain. In particular, the development of the mathematical biology of the central nervous system has resulted in the derivation of numerous mathematical expressions which represent very well different psychophysiological phenomena such as reaction times, discrimination, learning, and some emotional reactions. Thus it becomes possible to some extent to describe mathematically the behavior of an individual under the influence of given environmental conditions. A large part of the environment of every individual is, however, composed of other individuals. The behavior, the reactions of those other individuals are stimuli or stimulus patterns which effect the behavior of the given individual. Thus by a natural generalization we pass from mathematical biology to the study of the behavior of an individual as a member of society, that is, into the domain of social science. In our three lectures we shall discuss the applications of this extension of mathemathical biology to some aspects of social behavior.

Though the modern sociologist not infrequently uses statistical methods, which require a high degree of mathematical training, the methods of theoretical research, as exemplified by celestial mechanics, theoretical physics, or mathematical biology, are not too familiar to sociologists. It may, therefore, be useful to emphasize some important characteristics of theoretical research.

The theoretical scientist studies propositions of the form "If . . . . , then . . . . ." When he finds that his "then" corresponds to observable phenomena, he concludes that his "if" may hold. In this way he is led to an understanding of possible hidden mechanisms which lie behind directly observable phenomena but which themselves are not amenable to direct experimentation or observation.

When the phenomenon studied is relatively simple, the "If . . . . , then . . . ." reasoning may be made with the help of ordinary logic. If, however, the phenomenon is complex, ordinary logic fails and recourse must be taken to mathematical analysis. Hence the practical synonymity of the expressions "Theoretical Science" and "Mathematical Science."

The following example may serve as an illustration. Simple logic leads us to the proposition: "If a stone is attracted by the earth, then, when left free, it will fall." But no amount of logic could lead us to the following, more complex, statement: "If a stone is attracted by the earth, and if the force of attraction is uniform, then, when free, that stone will fall in such a way that the distance traveled, when plotted against time, will be a parabola." Only mathematical analysis enables us to reach such a conclusion. When we pass to even more complex cases of planetary motions, the need for mathematical analysis becomes even greater.

Propositions formulated mathematically are quantitative in nature. This gives them an advantage over non-mathematical, qualitative propositions. We may reach a qualitative conclusion that under such and such circumstances a certain phenomenon must be observed. If we make an experiment to verify our conclusion and fail to observe the expected phenomenon, then the experiment neither proves nor disproves anything. For either our proposition is wrong or the expected phenomenon may be too small or too weak to be detected with our available experimental equipment. If, however, we state that under such and such quantitative conditions a phenomenon of such and such magnitude must be observed, and if the experiment fails to verify this conclusion, then we know that our conclusion is wrong. But the elimination of a wrong conclusion represents a step toward positive knowledge. Moreover, the mathematical analysis does in many cases enable us to determine *how* our "if" should be modified in order to give the quantitatively correct "then."

In studying any phenomenon the theoretical scientist never attempts to deal with the whole phenomenon in all its complexity. This would be an impossible task. The scientist creates a conceptual model of the actual phenomenon, which embodies only a few salient features of the actual phenomenon. In other words, the scientist abstracts: he studies one possible aspect at a time. When confronted with the need to find an explanation of a given phenomenon, he studies *in abstracto* all, or as many as possible, conceivable explanations. Then, by comparing the results of his studies with actual observation, he decides which of the possible explanations apply best.

This procedure is best illustrated with the example of celestial mechanics. First Newton formulated his general laws of motion, which describe the motion of bodies under the influence of any kind of force. Next he studied the motion under different kinds of central forces. It was then found that the actual motion of planets is such as should occur under the influence of a central force, which varies as the inverse square of the distance. The conclusion was thus reached that the force of gravitation varies with distance in this manner.

It will now be useful to give a very brief and, therefore, inadequate presentation of some essentials of the mathematical biology of the central nervous system. For details the reader must be referred to other publications.[1]

The human brain is composed of a very large number, about 10^{10}, of nerve cells or neurons. These neurons are interconnected into very complex structures. The fundamental property of the neurons is that a neuron is thrown into a certain physiological state, called excitation, either through stimuli that come from the environment or through the process of transmission of excitation from one neuron to another. The neurons which become exited directly by environmental stimuli are connected to various receptor organs, and are called peripheral. Peripheral neurons transmit their excitation to higher order neurons. Not all neurons, however, transmit their excitation to others. Some neurons, when excited, actually inhibit the excitation of other neurons with which they are in contact. Such neurons are called *inhibitory*, as distinguished from the *excitatory* ones mentioned above.

A very important characteristic of the excitation of neurons is its discontinuous nature. The state of excitation follows the so-called "all-or-none law." A neuron is either excited to the fullest extent, or it is not excited at all. No gradations exist. The duration of a single excitation is very short: of the order of a millisecond. Several such short excitations may, however, follow each other.

The proper mathematical description of the discontinuous process of excitation and of its transmission requires a rather specialized brand of mathematics, and presents appreciable difficulties. It is, however, possible to simplify the problem by making use of the fact that in all actual cases of behavioral reaction a tremendously large number of neurons is involved. Here is where the first "if" of our theoretical study enters. It is possible to prove mathematically the following statement.

A. "If each neuron acts discontinuously, as described above, but if a very large number of neurons is involved, and if certain plausible arrangements of some neurons are assumed, then the statistical result of the very large number of discontinuous actions will be an apparently continuous process which can be described by simple equations. Those equations refer now not to individual neurons, but to large groups of neurons. Those groups we shall call neuroelements."

The equations just mentioned are as follows:

a) A stimulus of physical intensity S produces in a peripheral neuroelement an intensity of excitation E equal to

$$E = \alpha(S - h),\qquad\qquad(1)$$

where α and h are constants. Equation (1) holds only for $E \geq 0$, that is, for $S \geq h$. The quantity h is called the threshold. If the intensity S of the stimulus, as is frequently the case, is rather large, so that $S \gg h$, then, as a good approximation to (1), we find

$$E = \alpha S.\qquad\qquad(2)$$

b) If the peripheral neuroelement is an excitatory one, that is, if it is composed of excitatory neurons, then, at its central end, where it connects with a higher order neuroelement, it produces a physiological state ϵ, according to the equation

$$\frac{d\epsilon}{dt} = AE - a\epsilon, \tag{3}$$

where A and a are constants which may vary from neuroelement to neuroelement. For the explanation of the nature of ϵ, we must again refer to the above-mentioned publications.[1]

   c) If the peripheral neuroelement is an inhibitory one, that is, if it is composed of inhibitory neurons, then, at its central end, it produces a state j, according to

$$\frac{dj}{dt} = BE - bj, \tag{4}$$

where B and b are constants. Regarding the nature of j we must also refer the reader elsewhere.

   d) The intensity of excitation E_1 of any higher order neuro-element is given by

$$E_1 = \alpha_1 (\epsilon - j - h_1) \tag{5}$$

where α_1 and h_1 are again constants, and where ϵ and j are the states produced by the neuroelement of lower order, which acts on the particular neuroelement. Thus $\epsilon - j$ plays the role of the stimulus S in equation (1). As we see from (5) the excitation E_1 increases with ϵ and decreases with j. We therefore refer to ϵ as the excitatory factor, to j as the inhibitory factor.

   If, for a given value of $\epsilon > h_1$ the factor j increases suf-ficiently, so that $j > \epsilon - h_1$, then the originally present intensity of excitation E_1 vanishes as soon as $j = \epsilon - h_1$.

   If we now could verify equations (1) - (5), we could conclude that the "if" part of statement A, which relates to certain plausible arrangements of neurons, may hold. Unfortunately equations (1) - (5) cannot be directly verified experimentally. Therefore, we in-troduce a second stage of the "If . . . . , then . . . ." method. We shall derive statements containing equations (1) - (5) in the "if" part. That "if" part must, however, also contain something else.

Given a particular arrangement of neuroelements, some of which are subject to external stimuli, we can, barring mathematical difficulties, compute at any given time the intensities of excitation E in each neuroelement, and thus describe the properties of such an arrangement. Those properties will be different for different arrangements. The second stage of our "If . . . . , then . . . ." reasoning is, therefore, of this form: "If equations (1) - (5) hold, and if the neuroelements are arranged in such and such a way, then the arrangement will have such and such properties."

For example, we have: "If equations (1) - (5) hold, and if we have a structure composed of two neuroelements, one stimulated peripherally and the other exciting an end organ, then the total time t between the application of a constant simulus of intensity S and the initiation of the end reaction is given by such and such an equation." It so happens that this equation very well describes the actual relations between reaction times and the intensities of constant stimuli, as illustrated in Figure 1.

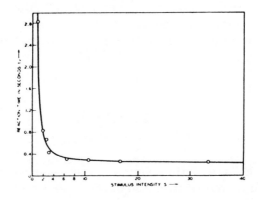

Figure 1.

Such agreements between mathematical conclusions and observation are quite numerous, and hold for a variety of different phenomena. They warrant the acceptance of equations (1) - (5) and of the assumed structural arrangements.

The following structure is of special interest for our purposes. It consists of two parallel chains of neuroelements, as shown in Figure 2. Let the first chain, consisting of neuroelements I, III, and V, be excited by a stimulus of intensity S_1 when no other stimuli act on any other parts of the structure. As a result of this situation, an intensity of excitation E_1 develops in neuroelement I, according to equation (1) or (2). This results in the

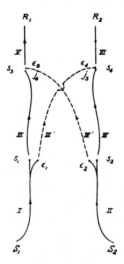

Figure 2.

formation of an amount ϵ_1 of excitatory factor at the connection s_1. If the stimulus S_1 is constant and lasts a sufficient time, then E_1 is also constant, as seen from (1) or (2). In that case equation (3) is readily integrated. That equation now refers to ϵ_1 at s_1, and we must, therefore, put in it $E = E_1$. The integration gives

$$\epsilon_1 = \epsilon_{01} e^{-at} + \frac{AE_1}{a}(1 - e^{-at}), \tag{6}$$

where ϵ_{01} is the value of ϵ_1 which existed at the moment of application of S_1; in other words, at the moment of establishment of E_1. The time t is counted from that moment. As t increases ϵ_1 tends asymptotically to the constant value

$$\epsilon_1 = \frac{AE_1}{a}. \tag{7}$$

If S_1 is sufficiently strong so that we can use expression (2), then it follows from (2) and (7) that

$$\epsilon_1 = \frac{A\alpha}{a}S_1 . \tag{8}$$

If, as we said above, the stimulus S_1 lasts long enough, then the value given by expression (7) will be practically reached and remain such as long as S_1 remains constant.

This constant amount ϵ_1 of ϵ at the connection s_1 acts, according to equation (5), as a constant stimulus on the neuroelement III, producing a constant intensity of excitation E_1'. The latter results in the production of an amount ϵ_3 of ϵ at s_3. Finally, this excites the neuroelement V, and that excitation results in some reaction R_1.

In a similar way a stimulus S_2 applied to the peripheral end of the other chain, which consists of neuroelements II, IV, and VI, will result in a reaction R_2, different from R_1, when no other stimuli are applied to any parts of the structure. If, however, the stimuli S_1 and S_2 are applied and both kept simultaneously, then the situation becomes more complicated. The amount ϵ_1 at s_1 acts as a stimulus on the *inhibitory* neuroelement III', and this results in the appearance of an amount j_3 of the factor j at the connection s_4 of the second chain. Since ϵ_1 increases with S_1 according to equation (8), j_3 also increases with S_1. But, according to equation (5), j_3 decreases the intensity of excitation of neuroelement IV, which is caused by ϵ_4. Hence the stimulus S_1, while producing reaction R_1, inhibits reaction R_2. Similarly, the stimulus S_2, via the inhibitory neuroelement IV', inhibits R_1 while producing R_2. With a proper choice of constants involved when $S_1 = S_2$ the inhibitory effects will *just* cancel the excitatory, and neither reaction R_1 or R_2 will be produced. Suppose, however, that S_1 becomes greater than S_2. In that case, while ϵ_4 remains the same j_3 increases, so that reaction R_2 still cannot be produced. But while j_4 remains the same ϵ_3 increases. If, as we said, for $S_1 = S_2$ the effect of inhibition just canceled that of excitation at both the connections s_3 and s_4, then with $S_1 > S_2$, with increased excitation at s_3, the reaction R_1 will be produced. Similarly, if $S_2 > S_1$ the reaction R_2 will be produced, but not R_1.

Such would be the situation if everything were constant in the system. But the state of every biological system is subject to random fluctuations around some average values. Thus while for a constant S_1 the average value of ϵ_1 will be given by expression (8), ϵ_1 will actually fluctuate around that value in a random fashion. Fluctuations of small magnitude will be more frequent than fluctuations of larger magnitude. A similar thing holds about the amount ϵ_2. The latter is given by an equation similar to (8), and is, therefore, equal to $(A\alpha/a)S_2$. Thus, if S_1 is greater than S_2, and, therefore, *on the average* $\epsilon_1 > \epsilon_2$, it is possible that an accidental fluctuation of either ϵ_1 or ϵ_2 will, for a while, make $\epsilon_2 > \epsilon_1$. But this will have the same effect as if $S_2 > S_1$; in other words, it will result in the reaction R_2. Hence, if we take into account the presence of fluctuations, we find that when $S_1 > S_2$ on the average reaction R_1, but not R_2, will be produced, but *occasionally* R_2, but not R_1, will occur. And vice versa: when $S_2 > S_1$ occasionally R_1 will be produced.

How frequent are these occasions? We have said above that small fluctuations occur more frequently than large ones. When S_1 is only slightly greater than S_2, and hence when ϵ_1 is only slightly greater than ϵ_2, a relatively small, and, therefore, relatively frequent, random fluctuation of ϵ_1 or ϵ_2 may make $\epsilon_2 > \epsilon_1$, and result in producing reaction R_2. But if $S_1 \gg S_2$, and, therefore, $\epsilon_1 \gg \epsilon_2$, it will require a much stronger and, therefore, less frequent, fluctuation to make $\epsilon_2 > \epsilon_1$ and to produce reaction R_2.

Hence, if $S_1 > S_2$, occasionally reaction R_2 will be produced, but the frequency of these occasions decreases as $S_1 - S_2$ increases. A similar conclusion holds for $S_2 > S_1$: occasional reactions R_1 are produced, but their frequency decreases with increasing $S_2 - S_1$.

If the distribution function of the random fluctuations is given — for example, if it is known to be a normal distribution — then expressions relating the probability P_1 and P_2 of occurrence of R_1 or R_2 to the difference $S_1 - S_2$ can be derived. Those expressions vary somewhat with the distribution function of the fluctuations. However, for symmetric distributions they all are rather similar. Their graphs look like the one represented on Figure 3. For $S_1 = S_2$ we have $P_1 = P_2 = 1/2$. Both R_1 and R_2 are equally probable. As $S_1 - S_2$ increases, P_1 tends to 1, P_2 tends to zero. As $S_2 - S_1 = -(S_1 - S_2)$ increases, P_1 tends to zero, P_2 to 1.

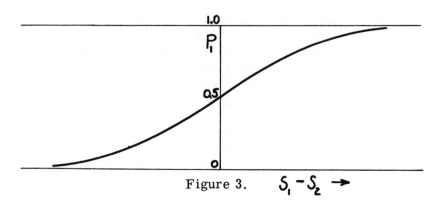

Figure 3. $S_1 - S_2$ →

As we said above, reactions R_1 and R_2 may be of any kind.
Let us now consider the particular case in which R_1 stands for the
verbal reaction: "S_1 is greater than S_2," while R_2 stands for the
verbal reaction: "S_2 is greater than S_1." In that case we shall
justly call R_1 the "correct" reaction, if $S_1 > S_2$; while R_2 will
be, in this case, the "wrong" reaction. If $S_2 > S_1$, than R_1 is the
wrong reaction and R_2 is the correct one.

Now we may translate the properties of the system considered
into the following anthropopsychic statement: "*If* an individual is to
make a statement as to which of two stimuli presented to him is the
greater one, and if the neural process of this action is mediated
through a structure such as shown on Figure 2, and governed by
equations (1) - (5), *then* he will make the correct judgment the
more frequently, the greater the difference between the stimuli,
and the relation between the incidence of correct statements and
difference of the stimuli will be given by expressions such as those
graphically represented on Figure 3."

The "then" part of the above statement is amenable to experimental verification. A comparison of the theoretically predicted values to those found experimentally is shown in Figure 4
for the case in which the stimuli are two different weights. The
agreement between theory and experiment is strikingly good, and
gives us further confidence in the usefulness of the "if" part of
our statement.

In Figure 4, P_c = proportion of correct judgments, P_w = proportion of wrong judgments, and P_e = proportion of times subject
was not able to make judgment. The existence of this inability to
decide is accounted for in the theory by the threshold quantity, h,
in equation 5.

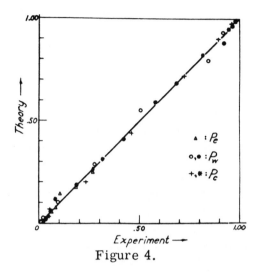

Figure 4.

We now shall point to a consequence of the above which is of particular interest to social scientists. As we have seen, if the difference between two stimuli S_1 and S_2 is given, we can compute the relative frequency with which the greater stimulus will be judged as being greater. We now may reverse the process, and, from the known relative frequencies of judging one stimulus of a pair as being the greater or the lesser one, compute *with the same certainty* the difference between the two stimuli. In this way we may establish a scale and measure intensities of stimuli which are not measurable directly. As an example of such stimuli we may cite the aesthetic feeling induced by different patterns or sound sequences. All we can say in these cases is that one stimulus of a pair is more or less pleasant ("greater" or "lesser"). But from the relative incidence of such "greater" or "lesser" judgments in regard to any pair of stimuli in a given set, we can compute the actual values of those stimuli.

Psychophysicists long ago developed formal methods of es-tablishing in this way a scale for directly non-measurable stimuli. On the part of some psychological purists, the objection was raised that the psychophysicist does not know what he measures. A com-parison of the psychophysical methods with the method of calculat-ing the stimuli from frequencies of "greater than" or "less than" judgments, as outlined above and as developed originally by H. D. Landahl[2], shows that the two are identical. Hence, as Landahl points out[3], the psychophysical methods actually measure the in-tensities of the central excitations, ϵ_1 and ϵ_2, which correspond to external stimuli S_1 and S_2. But the S's are linear functions of the ϵ's.

In sociology the measurements of such quantities as attitudes, drives, social status, etc. can be performed by psychophysical methods, which now have a neurophysiological justification.

In the foregoing discussion we assumed the reactions R_1 and R_2 to be produced by external stimuli. We may, however, apply the same reasoning to the case in which these reactions are produced by some internal stimuli, which are not directly accessible to observation. Such internal stimuli may properly be called "drives" or "desires," and be interpreted in our neurological picture, shown in Figure 2, as the excitations at s_1 and s_2, caused not by peripheral stimuli S_1 and S_2, but by some inner physiological processes. In this case ϵ_1 measures the drive for reaction R_1, while ϵ_2 measures the drive for reaction R_2. These reactions may be of any kind, as long as they are mutually exclusive. Thus R_1 may designate walking, R_2 sitting; or R_1 may stand for voting republican, R_2 for voting Democratic, etc. Though we cannot measure the drives ϵ_1 and ϵ_2 directly, we can compute them from the relative frequency of R_1 and R_2. Thus an individual who equally frequently votes Republican and Democratic has equal drives for both behaviors, so that $\epsilon_1 = \epsilon_2$ or $\epsilon_1 - \epsilon_2 = 0$. Since it is the difference $\epsilon_1 - \epsilon_2$ that determines the relative frequencies of R_1 and R_2, therefore it is useful to introduce a new variable

$$\phi = \epsilon_1 - \epsilon_2 . \tag{9}$$

When $\phi = 0$, that is, $\epsilon_1 = \epsilon_2$, the individual has no preference toward either R_1 or R_2, and performs those two reactions equally frequently. If ϕ is positive, $\epsilon_1 > \epsilon_2$, and the reaction R_1 is performed more frequently than R_2. If $\phi < 0$, then $\epsilon_2 > \epsilon_1$, and R_2 is the more frequent reaction. The relation between P_1 (or $P_2 = 1 - P_1$) and ϕ is again given by a curve similar to the one shown in Figure 3.

Consider now a large social group composed of N_0 individuals, who have different values of ϕ with respect to some particular pair of mutually exclusive reactions R_1 and R_2; for example, voting Republican or Democratic. The quantity ϕ will be distributed according to some distribution function $N(\phi)$, so that the number of individuals whose ϕ lies in the interval ϕ, $\phi + d\phi$ is given by

$$N(\phi) d\phi . \tag{10}$$

Instead of saying, "the number of individuals whose ϕ lies in the interval ϕ, $\phi + d\,\phi$," we shall say more briefly, "the number of individuals with a given ϕ."

If the function $N(\phi)$ has a maximum at $\phi = 0$, and is symmetric with respect to $\phi = 0$, so that $N(\phi) = N(-\phi)$, then, if each individual acts only according to his own drive, it is readily seen that at any given moment one-half of the population will exhibit reaction or behavior R_1, the other half will exhibit R_2. Indeed, all individuals with a given ϕ have a probability $P_1(\phi)$ of exhibiting R_1, and a probability $P_2(\phi) = 1 - P_1(\phi)$ of exhibiting R_2. Therefore, of the $N(\phi)\,d\phi$ individuals with a given ϕ, a number $P_1(\phi)\,N(\phi)\,d\phi$ will exhibit reaction R_1, and $[1 - P_1(\phi)]N(\phi)\,d\phi$ will exhibit reaction R_2. As seen from Figure 3, $P_1(-\phi) = P_2(\phi)$ and $P_2(-\phi) = P_1(\phi)$. Of all the $N(-\phi)\,d\phi$ individuals with a given $-\phi$, a number $P_1(-\phi)\,N(-\phi)\,d\phi$ will exhibit R_1, while $[1 - P_1(-\phi)]$ $N(-\phi)\,d\phi$ will exhibit R_2. But, because of $N(-\phi) = N(\phi)$, and because of $P_1(-\phi) = P_2(\phi)$, these numbers are correspondingly equal to $P_2(\phi)\,N(\phi)\,d\phi$ and $P_1(\phi)\,N(\phi)\,d\phi$. Hence, taking the two groups, those with ϕ and with $-\phi$ together, we see that of the $2N(\phi)\,d\phi$ individuals

$$P_1(\phi)\,N(\phi)\,d\phi + P_2(\phi)\,N(\phi)\,d\phi = [P_1(\phi) + P_2(\phi)]N(\phi)\,d\phi = N(\phi)\,d\phi$$

individuals exhibit R_1 and $N(\phi)\,d\phi$ exhibit R_2. By subdividing the whole population into groups having a given ϕ and $-\phi$, we see that $1/2\ N_0$ individuals exhibit R_1, $1/2\ N_0$ exhibit R_2.

Thus if the population as a whole does not show any preference toward R_1 or R_2, that is, if the average value $\bar{\phi}$ of ϕ is zero, half the individuals will perform R_1, half R_2, provided everyone acts only in accordance with his drives toward R_1 or R_2. It must also be remarked that at *different times*, in general, different individuals will exhibit R_1 or R_2.

Of course, if $N(\phi)$ has a maximum for $\phi \gtrless 0$, and is not symmetric with respect to $\phi = 0$, this conclusion does not hold. If the group as a whole favors positive ϕ, R_1 will be exhibited by more individuals than R_2.

Now we come to the crucial point of our discussion. Though people usually act according to their inner drives and preferences when left alone, their behavior is frequently markedly affected by the behavior of other individuals in the social group. Amongst many individuals there is a tendency to act one way or another, not because those individuals have any particular preference, but "because others act that way," or "because everybody acts that way." In other words, there is a tendency to imitate other individuals.

How can we interpret such a tendency in terms of our neurological picture? Apparently the sight of another individual who exhibits R_1 acts upon the first individual as an external stimulus S_1 which adds a *variable amount* ϵ_1' to the constant amount ϵ_1 which is produced by inner physiological states and which determines the natural inner drive towards R_1. It is natural to assume that the sight of X individuals exhibiting R_1 will be X times as effective as the sight of one individual.

The variation of ϵ_1' is given by the fundamental equation (3), in which we put $\epsilon = \epsilon_1'$ and $E = E_1$. Using expression (2), we have $E_1 = \alpha\, S_1$. Thus equation (5) now becomes

$$\frac{d\epsilon_1'}{dt} = A\,\alpha\, S_1 - a\epsilon_1'. \tag{11}$$

But, as we have just mentioned, the stimulus S_1 is proportional to the total number X of individuals which exhibits R_1. Thus, denoting by c a constant of proportionality, we have

$$S_1 = cX, \tag{12}$$

and equation (11) now becomes

$$\frac{d\epsilon_1'}{dt} = A\,\alpha\, cX - a\epsilon_1'. \tag{13}$$

Absorbing αc into the constant A, we may also write

$$\frac{d\epsilon_1'}{dt} = AX - a\,\epsilon_1'. \tag{14}$$

Similarly we conclude that the sight of another individual performing reaction R_2 acts on the given individual as a stimulus S_2, which produces an additional amount of ϵ_2' at s_2. Denoting by Y the total number of individuals which exhibits reaction R_2, we find in a similar manner as before,

$$\frac{d\epsilon_2'}{dt} = A Y - a \epsilon_2' . \tag{15}$$

Putting

$$\epsilon_1' - \epsilon_2' = \psi, \tag{16}$$

and subtracting equation (15) from equation (14), we find:

$$\frac{d\psi}{dt} = A (X - Y) - a\psi . \tag{17}$$

In the absence of any imitation effects, the preference of an individual for R_1 or R_2 is measured by the quantity $\phi = \epsilon_1 - \epsilon_2$. Now that an amount ϵ_1' has been added to ϵ_1, and an amount ϵ_2' to ϵ_2, that preference is measured by

$$(\epsilon_1 + \epsilon_1') - (\epsilon_2 + \epsilon_2') = \phi + \psi . \tag{18}$$

In deriving equation (17) we have assumed that the constants A and a are the same for all individuals. This is certainly a restrictive assumption, but for a first approximation it is justified. Under these conditions the amount ψ added to ϕ is the same for all individuals. An individual who had any given value of ϕ is now characterized by the value $\phi + \psi$. But whereas ϕ is a constant for every individual, and is due to internal physiological states, ψ varies according to equation (17). When ψ is positive, the whole distribution curve $N(\phi)$ is simply shifted by the amount ψ in the direction of positive ϕ's, without change of shape. When ψ is negative, this shift is in the opposite direction.

We shall now investigate how this shift of the distribution of the preference affects the behavior of the social group. To this end we must study the properties of the solutions of equation (17). If $\psi = 0$, then, as we have seen, $X = Y = 1/2 N_0$. If, however, ψ is positive, then the distribution curve is shifted toward positive values. While the average initial ϕ was zero, the average $\phi + \psi$ is not zero, but equal to $\psi > 0$. Hence there will now be more individuals with higher values of P_1 than with lower values. In other words, there will be more individuals who exhibit R_1 than individuals who exhibit R_2. Hence, when $\psi > 0$, we have $X > Y$, or X - Y > 0. As ψ increases, so does X - Y. However, X - Y cannot exceed the value N_0, which is reached when X = N_0, Y = 0; that is, when all N_0 individuals exhibit behavior R_1. This happens only when P_1 = 1, P_2 = 0 for all individuals, and that happens only for $\psi = \infty$. Hence, as ψ increases from 0 to + ∞, the first term, A(X - Y), of the right side of equation (14) increases from zero to an asymptotic value equal to AN_0, as shown by the curve OO' of Figure 5. Similarly, as ψ decreases from 0 to - ∞, and X becomes smaller than Y, the term A(X - Y) tends to - AN_0, as shown by the branch OO'' of the curve in Figure 5.

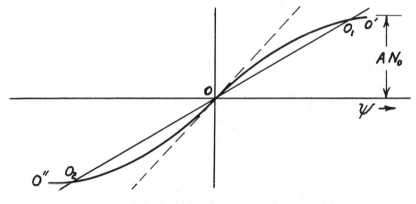

Figure 5.

The term aψ in equation (17) is represented by a straight line passing through the origin. This line may intersect the line O''OO' either only at O (figure 5, broken line), or at three points O_1, O, and O_2 (Figure 5, full line). In the first case for every positive value of ψ the absolute value of the positive term A(X - Y) of equation (17) is less than the absolute value of the negative term - aψ. Hence for any positive ψ we have dψ/dt > 0, and ψ decreases.

In a similar manner we see that for any negative ψ we have dψ/dt > 0, and ψ increases. Thus in that case ψ always tends to zero. We see from equation (17) that for ψ = 0 we have dψ/dt = 0, and the above discussion shows that the point ψ = 0, X = Y is in this case a point of stable equilibrium.

Hence if the constants in equation (17) are such that the straight line aψ intersects the curve O''OO' of Figure 5 only at the point O, then, in spite of the presence of imitative tendencies, half of the social group will exhibit reaction R_1, and the other half will exhibit reaction R_2. The tendency to imitate does not have any effect in this case.

The situation, however, is quite different if the straight line $a\psi$ intersects the curve O''OO' at three points. At any of these three points we have $A(X - Y) = a\psi$, hence $d\psi/dt = 0$. Therefore, they are all points of equilibrium. It is, however, readily seen that the point $\psi = 0$, $X = Y$ is a point of unstable equilibrium. Any slight shift of ψ toward positive values makes the absolute value of $A(X - Y)$ exceed the absolute value of $a\psi$, and, therefore, makes $d\psi/dt > 0$. Hence any slight increase of ψ will cause it to increase further, until ψ reaches the value of the abscissa of the point O_1. Any further increase of ψ makes $|a\psi| > |A(X - Y)|$, so that beyond the point O_1 the quantity ψ decreases. Hence O_1 is a point of stable equilibrium. By a similar argument we see that a slight decrease of ψ from the value $\psi = 0$ will make $d\psi/dt < 0$ and will result in a further decrease of ψ until the point O_2 is reached, which is also a point of stable equilibrium.

But in the configuration O_1 the majority of the social group exhibits behavior R_1, because $X - Y$ here is very near to N_0. Similarly in configuration O_2 the majority exhibits behavior R_2. Hence, in this case, as a result of imitation, the majority of the social group will exhibit either behavior R_1 (or behavior R_2), in spite of the fact that, because of the symmetry of $N(\phi)$, half of the group shows preference for the opposite behavior.

Which of the two behaviors the group as a whole will actually choose is determined by pure chance, just as pure chance deter-mines whether a symmetric wedge placed with its edge on a hori-zontal surface will topple over to the right or left.

The mechanism of the instability at the point O can be readily visualized. When $X = Y$ each individual is subject to equal and opposite imitation stimuli toward R_1 and R_2 which cancel each other. Each individual, therefore, behaves according to his own preference ϕ. If, however, due to an accidental fluctuation, a slight excess of X over Y is even temporarily formed, this results in a slight shift toward positive ψ's due to imitation, and this shift in its turn enhances the excess of X - Y. The process goes on ava-lanche-like until the stable configuration, in which most individuals exhibit R_1, is reached.

For this process to happen it is necessary, as we have seen, that the straight line $a\psi$ intersect the curve O''OO' of Figure 5 at three points. This requires that the slope a of the straight line should be less than the slope of the curve at $\psi = 0$. The exact ana-lytical expression of the curve O''OO' depends on the form of the distribution $N(\phi)$ and on the form of the function $P_1(\phi)$ (Figure 3), which in its turn depends on the form of the distribution of the

inner fluctuations discussed on page 73.   If both distributions are
normal, and if σ is the standard deviation of the former and k the
standard deviation of the latter, then, as has been shown by H. G.
Landau[5],

$$A(X - Y) = \frac{2\, AN_0}{\sqrt{2\pi(k^2 + \sigma^2)}} \int_0^{\psi} \exp\, -\frac{x^2}{k^2 + \sigma^2}\ dx. \qquad (19)$$

Hence the slope of the curve at $\psi = 0$ is equal to

$$\frac{2\, AN_0}{\sqrt{2\pi(k^2 + \sigma^2)}}, \qquad (20)$$

and the existence of three points of intersection requires

$$a < \frac{2\, AN_0}{\sqrt{2\pi(k^2 + \sigma^2)}}. \qquad (21)$$

Resolved with respect to N_0 this gives

$$N_0 > \frac{a\,\sqrt{2\pi(k^2 + \sigma^2)}}{2A}. \qquad (22)$$

If the constants a, A, k and σ are given, then N_0 must exceed a certain value in order that mutual imitation leads to a "crowd
behavior," that is, a behavior characterized by the choice by the majority of a reaction which does not correspond to actual preferences
of the group as a whole.
In a way it may be said that equation (22) answers the age old
question as to how many people form a crowd. We see that the necessary number of individuals is the larger the larger σ. But a
large σ means a society which is rather non-uniform with respect
to the preference ϕ. Thus the more homogeneous a society, the
more likely it is to exhibit crowd behavior. The number N_0 also
increases with a. But, as has been shown by H. D. Landahl[4], the
constant a measures the speed of reaction to a stimulus. Individuals with a large a have shorter reaction times. In our particular

case a measures the reaction time to the imitation stimulus. The number N_0 also increases with k. But the larger k, the more apt an individual is to make a wrong reaction to a stimulus (cf. page 73). An individual with a large k is likely to imitate "accidentally" the reaction exhibited by the minority. This, of course, will reduce the effectiveness of imitation behavior and, therefore, if k is large, a larger number N_0 is necessary to produce "crowd behavior."

The important point of the foregoing discussion is that such constants as A, a, k, and σ can be in principle, though indirectly, measured by appropriate psychobiological experiments. The value of N_0 thus could be calculated, and equation (22) checked experimentally. Thus from biological measurements on a number of individuals we could draw conclusions about their social behavior.

Once the social group has adopted a behavior, for example, R_1, what can bring forth a change toward the other behavior? First of all, such a change may be effected by a decrease of N_0, either due to death or to other causes. As soon as N_0 falls below the threshold given by the right side of expression (22), each individual will behave according to his own ϕ, and the reactions R_1 and R_2 will be equally represented.

Another possibility is a change in the distribution function $N(\phi)$, which we assumed to be originally symmetric with respect to $\phi = 0$. Possible causes of such changes will be discussed in the third lecture. Here we shall briefly discuss the effects of such changes.

Let the society have chosen first reaction R_1 as being exhibited by the majority. Subsequently, for some reason, let the innate preference ϕ shift toward negative values so that the $N(\phi)$ curves becomes displaced toward negative ϕ's, and the average ϕ now becomes negative instead of zero. This means that the preference of the group as a whole shifts toward reaction R_2. Such a shift of the distribution curve $N(\phi)$ results in a shift of the curve O''OO' of Figure 5 toward positive ψ's, so that it now assumes the position shown in Figure 6. The point of unstable equilibrium has now shifted from O to O_3. As the shift continues, the position represented in Figure 7 is eventually reached, in which the points O_3 and O_1 coincide, and the straight line is tangent to the curve at the point O_{31}. By an argument similar to the one used previously, we see that point O_{31} in Figure 7 corresponds to an unstable equilibrium, the only point of stable equilibrium being O_2. Hence at that time the social group will relatively suddenly change its behavior, and the majority will adopt reaction R_2. We have here a sort of "landslide."

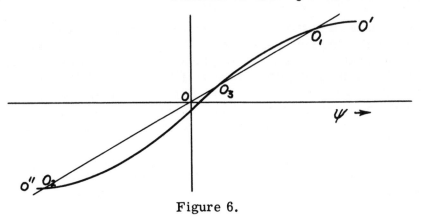

Figure 6.

    It is very important to remark that in Figure 6 point O_1 still
represents a stable configuration in which the majority exhibits
reaction R_1, in spite of the fact that the average is now negative
and, therefore, the majority, if freed from imitation effects, would
have chosen reaction R_2. We conclude that in very large groups
the majority may exhibit a behavior which they definitely dislike,
and yet this may be done without any physical or moral coercion,
as a result of the tendency of many human beings to imitate each
other.

    Thus *if* we assume certain neurological mechanisms, the
assumption of which has already proven fruitful in other branches
of mathematical biology, we can draw certain interesting conclusions abot the behavior of large social groups: conclusions that can
be verified by observation and experiment. Most likely our assumptions are too simple to lead to a correct representation

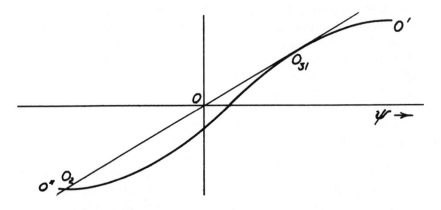

Figure 7.

of actual phenomena, and further generalizations are necessary. One obvious generalization is to introduce the effect of distance upon imitation as has recently been done[6]. We are more apt to imitate an individual who is near us than one who is far away. This study leads to very interesting conclusions about possible spatial distributions of different types of behaviors.

Another generalization, made by H. D. Landahl[7], considers the possibility that neither reaction R_1 nor R_2 is produced as long as the absolute value of ϕ is below a threshold h. Thus, in order to choose an activity, an individual not only must have a preference for that activity, but this preference must be sufficiently strong. Otherwise the individual remains undecided and does nothing.

Perhaps the most important generalization is to consider the case not of two, but of n mutually exclusive reactions, R_1, R_2, ... R_n. The problem offers very great difficulties, but an approximate approach to it has been made. It consists of reducing the situation to the case n = 2 by considering the alternative: "Either the reaction R_1 or any one of the other n - 1 reactions $R_k (k \neq 1)$." Some interesting results may be obtained in this way. Together with other problems of this kind, they are discussed in the author's recent book[8].

Of many other possible important generalizations we shall mention only one more. The possibility of imitating another individual depends on the amount of information we have about that other individual. Therefore, the theory of imitative behavior becomes closely related to the theory of transmission of information through social channels, as recently developed by the author[9].

Section II. DISTRIBUTION OF STATUS

The notion of social status is very important in sociology.
We shall use the word here in a very broad sense, broader probably than is customary. Under the term "social status" we shall
include also what is usually known as economic status. Problems
of distribution of wealth and income will therefore also fall within
the general scope of our discussion. This particular type of social
status is readily measurable: wealth is directly expressible in
dollars, income in dollars per year. Thus no conceptual difficulties confront the development of a mathematical theory of social
status in this case.

We observe other kinds of social status, which, although not
of economic origin, still can be readily measured. For example,
the political importance of an individual may be measured by the
number of votes which he controls. Similarly the administrative
importance of an individual may be measured by the number of
people whose activities he controls.

We thus not only can say that Mr. Jones is more wealthy
than Mr. Smith, but we can assert, for example, that Mr. Jones
is twice as wealthy as Mr. Smith. It may also be said that Smith
is three times as influential politically as Jones, or that he is
50 per cent more important administratively.

However, in our own society as well as in primitive societies
there are numerous situations in which statements are made that
"X is socially more prominent than Y" apparently without the possibility of indicating how much more prominent X is. In all such
cases it is possible to arrange all individuals in a certain order of
importance, as rated by every individual, in principle at least. We
shall then find that for any given pair of individuals, (X, Y), there
will be a certain percentage of ratings which will designate X as
the more prominent man, while others will designate Y as the
more prominent one. From the relative frequencies of these opposing ratings for different pairs we can then construct a psychophysical scale for the social status, by methods outlined in the
previous section. We merely consider the social status as the
intensity of a directly nonmeasurable stimulus, and apply the
reasoning given before.

Social statuses of different types may sometimes be correlated. Thus in some of the present day societies wealth also

means a high social prestige. This is, however, not a universal phenomenon.

Thus, whether we discuss the very tangible economic status or the more elusive social status proper, we deal with an opera-tionally measurable quantity.

The importance of the problem of social status in the mathe-matical biology of social behavior is increased by the fact that rudiments of social hierarchies are found in animal societies, notably in flocks of birds. One of the most studied of such pheno-mena is the so-called "peck order" or "peck right" in bird flocks[10]. In flocks of common chickens a peculiar relation is usually estab-lished. A bird pecks *some* of its fellow birds, while it is pecked by others. In some cases it is possible to arrange all birds in a flock into a linear row in decreasing peck order. In that case each bird in a row is pecked by every preceding bird while it pecks every bird following. Thus a simple hierarchy is established.

However, sometimes the following relation exists:

A pecks B; B pecks C, but C pecks A. The relation is known as "cycle."

Since in a peck order we have a primitive case of social hierarchies, it may be of interest for human sociology to develop a mathematical theory of this phenomenon. In a series of recent papers[11,12,13] Anatol Rapoport proposed an interesting mathematical approach to the problem of peck order. Referring the reader for details to the original papers, we shall outline here the general idea of the approach.

First of all let us introduce the notion of "structure" of a society. In a society composed of N individuals, the i-th indivi-dual has N - 1 peck relations with the other individuals. Of those N - 1 relations r_i will be of dominant type. That is, the i-th individual will peck r_i of the N - 1 individuals and be pecked by N - 1 - r_i remaining ones. Since there are N - 1 relations for each of the N individuals, there would appear to be altogether N(N - 1) relations. But in this way each individual is counted twice – first as the given individual, second as one of the N - 1 individuals for some other given individual. Therefore, we must divide the above number by 2, and find for the total number of dis-tinct peck relations (1/2) N (N-1). The society may now be charac-terized by the set R of numbers $(r_1, r_2, \ldots r_N)$. This set stands for the following verbal statement: "The first bird pecks r_1 other birds, the second pecks r_2 others, etc." This set is called the structure by A. Rapoport and score structure by H. G. Landau, to distinguish it from another type of structure. We have

$$\sum_{i=1}^{i=n} r_i = (1/2) \ N \ (N-1).$$ (1)

All possible score structures may be tabulated in some arbitrary
order and denoted by S_1, S_2, etc.

It is not definitely known what determines the peck order of
two birds. There is some evidence, however, that certain physiological and anatomical factors play a role. The existence of cycles
shows that the peck order is not a function of one variable only,
that is, it depends on more than one factor, whatever the nature of
those factors may be. If the peck order was determined by a function f(x) of one variable x, then the fact that A pecks B would
mean that the function f(x) for the individual A is either greater
than or less than f(x) for the individual B. Denoting by x_A and
x_B correspondingly, the values of the variable x for the two individuals, we would have one of the following statements:

$$A \text{ pecks } B, \text{ if and only if } f(x_A) > f(x_B)$$ (a)

or

$$A \text{ pecks } B, \text{ if and only if } f(x_A) < f(x_B).$$ (b)

Let us first consider the case (a). In that case, if B pecks C,
then $f(x_B) > f(x_C)$. But if $f(x_B) > f(x_C)$ then also $f(x_A) > f(x_C)$.
Hence if A pecks B, and B pecks C, A necessarily pecks C. A
cycle is impossible in this case. We arrive at the same conclusion in case (b).

The situation, however, becomes quite different if the peck
right depends on two factors and is therefore determined by a
function f(x,y) of two variables. For example, let A peck B, if,
and only if, $f(x_A,y_B) > f(x_B,y_A)$. We can easily construct such a
function f(x,y) that

$$f(x_A,y_B) > f(x_B,y_A); \qquad f(x_B,y_C) > f(x_C,y_B),$$

but (2)

$$f(x_A,y_C) < f(x_C,y_A).$$

All we have to do is to mark in the x,y plane the points x_A,y_B; x_B,y_A; x_B,y_C; x_C,y_B; x_A,y_C, and x_C,y_A, construct at each point perpendiculars of lengths f(x,y) such that the inequalities (2) are satisfied, and pass our arbitrary surface through the six points f(x,y).

But inequalities (2) now imply that A pecks B, B pecks C, and C pecks A.

It is possible to develop a theory of the peck order on this basis by choosing an appropriate function f(x,y) as well as appropriate distribution function of the quantities x and y in the flock. Because of the arbitrariness of the choices involved this method does not seem to be too hopeful. However, this approach acquires a different aspect if, by developing first a neurobiophysical theory of peck right, we express it as a function of some of the neurobiophysical parameters and thus first derive f(x,y) from a hypothetical neural mechanism. In that case the mechanism will determine both the number of variables as well as their biological meaning. Such an approach has, however, not yet been attempted.

We may consider with A. Rapoport[11] an entirely different approach.

Suppose that the peck order of two birds is once and for all time determined by the result of their first encounter, but that this latter result is determined by pure chance. That is, on the first encounter the probability for a given bird to become either aggressive or submissive is 1/2.

The structure of a small flock can be determined from these assumptions by simple inspection. Thus for two birds there is only one structure (1,0). One bird pecks, the other is pecked. Since it does not matter which bird pecks, the structure (0,1) is the same as (1,0). We are not interested in individual birds but only in the flock as a whole.

For N = 3 there are the following two structures: $S_1 = (2,1,0)$ and $S_2 = (1,1,1)$, shown diagramatically in Figure 8. In the first structure one bird pecks the other two; one of the others

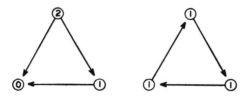

Figure 8.

pecks the third, while the third does not peck at all. The second
structure is a cycle. We can also determine the probabilities of
the two structures.

There are altogether three possible encounters with two
possible outcomes for each. For a given outcome of one encounter
there are two outcomes of the second encounter, and for each of
those outcomes there are two outcomes of the third. Thus there
are altogether $2^3 = 8$ possible sets of outcomes. Of these 8 sets,
6 correspond to the structure (2,1,0) and two to the structure
(1,1,1). Therefore the probabilities of the two structures are
correspondingly $6/8 = 3/4$ and $2/8 = 1/4$.

For N = 4 a somewhat more elaborate inspection establishes
four different structures with their corresponding probabilities[11].
For N = 5 there are nine structures. As N grows the task of es-
tablishing the number of structures becomes very difficult. Unfortunately no general expression for an arbitrary N has yet been
derived, though some interesting general theorems have been established by A. Rapoport[11].

The above considerations may be generalized by assuming
that the structure once established does not remain permanent but
that reversals of peck right occur occasionally. Not every reversal
of peck right will result in a change of structure. Thus a reversal
of peck right between the individuals 2 and 0 in diagram 1a
changes the structure 2,1,0 into 1,1,1. But a reversal of peck right
between individuals 2,1 in the same diagram does not change the
structure. It merely rotates the diagram as a whole.

We denote by a_{ij} the probability of a change from structure
S_i to structure S_j. In particular a_{ii} denotes the probability of
preservation of the structure S_i. Let us, for simplicity, assume
that encounters occur at regular intervals and let us take this
interval as a unit of time. Denote by $S_i(t)$ the probability of occurrence of the structure S_i at the time t. The structure S_i at the
time t may have occurred either from a structure S_i at t - 1
through no change, or from any structure S_j at the time t - 1
through a change $S_j \rightarrow S_i$. The probability of it having come
from S_i through no change is $a_{ii}S_i(t - 1)$; the probability of it
having arisen from S_j at t - 1 is $a_{ji}S_j(t - 1)$. Hence the probability $S_i(t)$ of occurrence of S_i at t from any of all the other
possible structures or through no change is

$$S_i(t) = a_{11}S_1(t-1) + a_{2i}S_2(t-1) + \ldots a_{ii}S_i(t-1) + \ldots \qquad (3)$$

$$+ a_{ni}S_n(t-1); \qquad\qquad i = 1,2, \ldots n .$$

If S(t) is the vector $\{ S_1(t), S_2(t), \ldots S_n(t) \}$, equation (3) may be written in vector-matrix form:

$$S(t) = (a_{ij})\, S(t - 1). \tag{4}$$

By iteration we find:

$$S(t) = (a_{ij})^t\, S(0). \tag{5}$$

Hence

$$S(\infty) = \lim_{t = \infty} (a_{ij})^t\, S(0). \tag{6}$$

By a rather involved mathematical argument A. Rapoport[12] shows that under specified, rather plausible, conditions the limit in equation (6) exists and is independent of S(0). This means that under those conditions the structure of the society will tend to a definite form which is independent of the initial conditions.

In a third paper[13], Rapoport studies for the case of N = 3 various, more general, cases, such as the effect of the previous reversals on the outcome of an encounter. The problems offer a fertile field to the mathematical biologist, mathematical sociologist, and, perhaps, pure mathematician.

An interesting general study for groups of any size has been recently made by H. G. Landau[14]. When the score structure is of the form

$$R = (r_1, r_2 \ldots r_n) = (N - 1, N - 2, \ldots, 0), \tag{7}$$

then the members of the society can be ordered in the following way

$$1 > 2 > 3 > \ldots > N,$$

so that each member dominates all the following members and is dominated by all the preceding members. Landau calls such a structure a hierarchy. On the other hand we may have an equality structure in which the elements r_i of the score structure R are equal to

$$r_1 = r_2 = \ldots r_n = \frac{N - 1}{2}. \tag{8}$$

This relation can, however, occur exactly only if N is an odd number.

Landau introduces what he calls a "hierarchy index" h which is defined by:

$$h = \frac{12}{N^2 - N} \sum_{j=1}^{n} \left(r_j - \frac{N-1}{2} \right)^2 . \qquad (9)$$

This hierarchy index h equals 1 when the score structure is given by expression (7) and is equal to zero when that structure is given by expression (9).

For intermediate structures the hierarchy index lies between one and zero.

Landau then proceeds to establish some interesting theorems which show how the hierarchy index depends on the *a priori* probability of the individual being dominant in an encounter, as well as on the size of the society. For details we must refer to Landau's original paper.

We now shall pass to a general study of social distributions in human society. We shall ask what general factors affect those distributions and what equations determine the distribution function if these factors are given. For this we shall first establish equations which govern the variations of a social distribution with respect to time and then investigate the conditions of stationary state when the rates of those variations vanish.

Any variation in the social status of an individual is caused by his direct or indirect interaction with others. Thus a wealthy man may become poor either through injudicious investments, through unfortunate speculations on the stock market, or because his fortune has been stolen. In all these as well as in other conceivable stiuations, the given individual interacts with one or more others. In the case of Mark Twain's *The Prince and the Pauper* the interaction between the prince and the pauper resulted in a temporary very drastic change of the social status of both, and, eventually, in a lasting change of the social status of the pauper. Thus, in general, as a result of a social interaction, the social statuses of both individuals may change by an amount Δ. In the case of economic status, the reason for such a possible change is obvious: one individual may gain at the expense of the other. But even if we consider a purely social status a similar thing may happen. Not infrequently the social status depends on a certain type of acquaintance. The individual with the lower status may increase his status if, as a result of his contact with an individual of higher status, he can make the necessary acquaintances. But, by the same process, the individual with the higher status may lower his status. Thus a person of an "upper" class may be introduced into "bad company" of thieves or gamblers and social degradation may follow. Or, position in society may be associated with certain manners and actions. The individual with a lower standing may acquire some of the manners of the individual with the higher standing and vice versa.

Hence one of the factors which determine the variation of the individual social status and, therefore, also the variation of its distribution is the frequency K of encounters between two individuals. The frequency $K(s,s')$ of encounters is the average number of encounters per unit time of a given individual of status between s and s + ds with any other individual of status between s' and s' + ds'. This frequency itself depends on the social statuses s and s' of the two individuals considered. A wealthy man is more likely to meet other wealthy men. A prince is more likely to meet other princes than to meet a pauper, and a pauper is more likely to meet other paupers. But, on a rare occasion, a prince may meet a pauper. Thus we would expect K to depend on the absolute value $|s - s'|$ of the difference s - s' of the social statuses of the two individuals in such a way that K decreases as $|s - s'|$ increases. However, quite generally K need not be a function of the social distance s - s' only. It may be any function $K(s, s')$ of the two social statuses, provided that it has a maximum for s - s' = 0 and decreases with $|s - s'|$. Since the frequency of encounters between Jones and Smith is the same as the frequency of encounters between Smith and Jones, therefore

$$K(s, s') = K(s', s) \tag{10}$$

always. Not every encounter results, however, in similar changes of the social status. Encounters between princes and paupers, though rare, may have occurred on other occasions than the one imagined by Mark Twain. The conceivable results of such encounters might have been drastically different. The individual with the lowest social status may after the encounter find his social status lowered even more. Such type of occurrence is particularly likely in the case of economic status.

Hence the next factor to be considered is the probability that in an encounter with another individual the social status of the first one will undergo a given change Δ, which may be either positive or negative. We shall denote this probability by p. The probability p is a function $p(\Delta)$ of Δ. It also depends in general on the social statuses s and s' of both individuals as well as on some personal characteristics a and a' of those individuals. For lack of better designation we shall refer to those personal characteristics as "abilities." The word *ability* is used here in a very broad sense. Without loss of too much generality we may consider all encounters to be of the same duration. In line with what has just been said we shall denote by

$$p(a, a', s, s', \Delta) \ d\Delta \qquad (11)$$

the probability of an individual with the social status s and ability a changing his social status by an amount lying between Δ and $\Delta + d\Delta$, when interacting with an individual of social status s' and ability a'.

The order of the arguments of the function p is important. Expression (11) refers to the probability of change of the social status s of the unprimed individual. If we write

$$p(a', a, s', s, \Delta) \ d\Delta$$

this will denote the probability of change of the social status s' of the primed individual.

Let the units measuring the social status s be chosen in such a way that s lies in the interval 0,1. We shall denote the number of individuals who have a social status between s and s + ds by N(s)ds. If N_0 is the total number of individuals in the society we have

$$\int_0^1 N(s) \ ds = N_0 \ . \qquad (12)$$

Let the units for the ability a be chosen so that $0 \leq a \leq 1$. Even if we may consider biophysically as large an ability as we wish and, therefore, have to introduce infinity as an upper limit we may always transform our units in such a way that in the new units the ability will measure 1, when in the old units it measures ∞. For instance a transformation

$$x' = \frac{2}{\pi} \ \tan^{-1} x \ ,$$

has the property that $x' = 0$ for $x = 0$; and $x' = 1$ for $x = \infty$. We shall denote the fraction of individuals with an ability between a and $a + da$ by $F(a)da$ so that

$$\int_0^1 F(a)\, da = 1. \tag{13}$$

Instead of saying "an individual with an s in the interval between s and $s + ds$", we shall sometimes say simply "an individual s." The same convention will be used for other variables such as a.

The relative frequency or probability $K(s, s')$ of encounters measures the number of encounters per unit time of a given individual of a status s between s and $s + ds$ with any other individual of a status s' between s' and $s' + ds'$. Therefore the total number of encounters of a given individual of status s between s and $s + ds$ with all other individuals whose statuses are different is given by

$$\int_0^1 N(s')\, K(s, s')\, ds' . \tag{14}$$

Expression (14) is a function $U(s)$ of s only. The number of encounters per unit time between all the $N(s)ds$ individuals of social status between s and $s + ds$ and all other individuals is therefore equal to

$$N(s)\ U(s)\, ds. \tag{15}$$

Since each individual of status s, $s + ds$ changes his status in general by some amount Δ as a result of each encounter, expression (15) represents the total decrease in the number of individuals with a status between s and $s + ds$.

Since we do not know *a priori* whether the social status s is or is not correlated with the ability a we cannot put for the number of individuals with a given s and a given a merely the product $N(s) F(a)\, ds\, da$. Instead we introduce a function $G(s, a)\, ds\, da$ which gives us that number. We have

$$N(s) = \int_0^1 G(s, a)\, da; \tag{16}$$

$$F(a) = \int_0^1 G(s, a) \, ds. \tag{17}$$

The number of individuals s',a', who encounter individuals s, a is given by

$$G(s, a) \, G(s',a') \, K(s, s') \, dada'dsds'. \tag{18}$$

The probability of their changing their s' to s, that is, the probability of having $\Delta = s - s'$; $d\Delta = ds'$ is equal, according to (11), to

$$p(a', a, s', s, s - s') \, ds'. \tag{19}$$

Hence the total number of individuals who originally have an s' between s' and s' + ds' and who pass per unit time from that interval into the interval s, s + ds is given by the integral of the product of expressions (18) and (19):

$$dsds' \int_0^1 \int_0^1 G(s,a) \, G(s', a') \, K(s, s') \, p(a,a',s,s',s - s') \, ds'dada' \tag{20}$$

and is an infinitesimal of second order.

A first order gain of individuals in the interval s,s + ds comes from encounters of individuals s' and s'' where both s' and s'' are different from s. The total number of such encounters is

$$N(s') \, N(s'') \, K(s',s'') \, ds'ds''. \tag{21}$$

Of the N(s') ds' individuals s' involved there are

$$G(s', a') \, ds'da' \tag{22}$$

individuals a'; while of the N(s'') ds'' individuals s'' involved there are

$$G(s'', a'') \, ds'' da'' \tag{23}$$

individuals a''.

The probability of those s' individuals to change their s'
so as to bring it into the interval s, s + ds is obtained by putting
$a = a'$; $a' = a''$; $s = s'$; $s' = s''$; $\Delta = s - s'$; $d\Delta = ds$ in (11). This
gives

$$p(a', a'', s', s'', s - s') \, ds. \tag{24}$$

Therefore the total number entering per unit time from interval
s', s' + ds' into the interval s, s+ds is given by

$$G(s', a') \, G(s'', a'') \, K(s', s'') \, p(a', a'', s', s'', s - s') \, ds \, ds' \, ds'' \, da' \, da''. \tag{25}$$

By a similar argument we find for the total number entering the
interval s, s + ds from s'', s'' + ds''

$$G(s'', a'') \, G(s', a') \, K(s', s'') \tag{26}$$

$$\text{x } p(a'', a', s'', s', s - s'') \, ds \, ds' \, ds'' \, da' \, da'' \ .$$

The total number entering the interval s, s + ds from all intervals
s', s' + ds' and s'', s'' + ds'' is obtained by integrating expressions
(25) and (26) with respect to s', s'', a' and a'' over the total range
of these variables, adding the results, and then dividing the sum
by 2. The latter is necessary because in integrating both (25) and
(26) with respect to s' and s'' we actually count each interval
twice since what was s', s' + ds' in expression (25) will now become s'', s'' + ds'' in (26).

We shall now introduce the following notations:

$$V_1(s) = \int_0^1 \int_0^1 \int_0^1 G(s', a') \, G(s'', a'') \, K(s', s'') \tag{27}$$

$$\text{x } p(a', a'', s', s'', s - s') \, ds' \, ds'' \, da' \, da'' \ ;$$

$$V_2(s) = \int_0^1 \int_0^1 \int_0^1 G(s',a')\ G(s'',a'')\ K(s'',s')$$

(28)

$$x\ p(a'',a',s'',s',s-s'')\,ds'ds''da'da''.$$

Remembering that $K(s',s'') = K(s'',s')$ [cf. expression (10)] and interchanging the primed and unprimed variables in expression (28) we see that $V_1(s) = V_2(s) = V(s)$.

We find for the total gain per unit time in the interval $(s, s + ds)$

$$V(s)\ ds. \tag{29}$$

The total rate of change

$$\frac{dN(s)}{dt}\ ds \tag{30}$$

in the interval $s,\ s + ds$ is obtained by subtracting the function $N(s)\,U(s)$ given by (14) from expression (29). Putting (30) equal to (29) less $N(s)\,U(s)$ and shortening by ds we find

$$\frac{dN(s)}{dt} = V(s) - N(s)\,U(s)\ . \tag{31}$$

Introducing for $V(s)$ and $U(s)$ their expressions (27), (28), and (14) we obtain a rather complicated nonlinear integrodifferential equation, a general solution of which would at present seem hopeless. *A priori* we cannot even say whether $N(s)$ approaches a steady state which does not vary with respect to time or whether it varies indefinitely. In the second case, obviously, $N(s)$ is not a constant and a nonuniform society exists. In the first case we may investigate the stationary state which is defined by the equation

$$V(s) - N(s)\,U(s) = 0. \tag{32}$$

Suppose $p = $ const. $= 1$ so that the probability of a social shift of an amount between Δ and $\Delta + d\Delta$ is simply $d\Delta$, independent of either Δ, s, s', a, or a'. Let us also assume a uniform distribution of abilities a so that $F(a)$ = const. = 1. Also let $K(s, s')$ = 1. In other words, assume not only a uniform distribution of abilities but also a complete independance of the probabilities of encounter or of their results on either the ability or the social status.

Introducing $p = 1$, $K = 1$ and $F = 1$ into (14), (27) and (28) and then the latter into (32) we find, remembering (12);

$$N_0^2 - N(s) \, N_0 = 0 \qquad (33)$$

or

$$N(s) = N_0 . \qquad (34)$$

Thus with the above assumptions all social statuses will be equally frequent.

If, however, $F(a) = 1$, $K(s, s') = 1$, but $p(a, a', s, s', \Delta)$ is not constant and contains at least s as a variable, then we obtain a different result. In that case $U(s) = N_0$ because of (12) and equation (32) gives

$$N(s) = \frac{V(s)}{N_0} . \qquad (35)$$

This equation cannot in general be satisfied by $N(s)$ = const. because even if $N(s)$ = const., V still remains in general a function of s as is seen from (27) and (28), except for some very special and usually rather implausible choice of the function $p(a, a', s, s', \Delta)$.

A similar result is obtained if p = const. but $K(s, s')$ is not a constant and contains s as a variable. In that case V is constant but $U(s)$ is not and $N(s)$ is given by $N(s) \, U(s) = C$, where C is a constant.

Thus we find the following important result: Even if the distribution of any innate ability which may affect the social status is uniform, the social status will in general be distributed nonuniformly as long as either one or both of the following conditions hold — the social status affects the probability of social encounters or the probability of an individual's traveling a certain social distance is a function of that distance.

But these two conditions are practically always met. Therefore we see that in general nonuniform distributions will be the rule so that some social statuses will be more frequent than others. We cannot say, however, that there will be more individuals with a low social status than with a high one. It is possible that solutions representing the opposite relation exist.

Thus, barring mathematical difficulties connected with the solution of equation (32), we may calculate the social distribution N(s) if we know K and p. Since K and p can in principle be determined by observation we have here again an "if . . . . , then . . . ." statement which is verifiable.

The nonuniform distribution of any quantity in a society may lead to some discontinuities in the social structure. This discontinuity will be due to the fact that individuals frequently associate in more or less closed groups, according to their similarity in one or more respects. In general the tendency for two individuals to associate will be the greater the more similar the individuals. We may, however, also consider cases of association between individuals with greatly varying characteristics. For the present we shall restrict ourselves to the former case.

The simplest possibility is that two individuals associate only when the absolute value of the difference of their characteristics is less than a certain amount. If we consider the social status s as the only variable we shall have as the condition of association of two individuals whose social standings are s and s':

$$(s' - s)^2 < \Delta^2; \quad (s' - s)^2 - \Delta^2 < 0. \qquad (36)$$

Consider the formation of an association of individuals including those having the highest value s_m of s. How far down the scale of s's will individuals still be included in that association? The answer may be given by the requirement that the sum total of $(s' - s)^2 - \Delta^2$ for the whole group would remain negative. If s_x is the lower limit of s still admissible into the association, then:

$$\int_{s_x}^{s_m}\int_{s_x}^{s_m} [(s' - s)^2 - \Delta^2] \, N(s) \, N(s') \, ds \, ds' < 0. \qquad (37)$$

The left hand side of expression (37) is a function $P(s_x)$ of s_x; s_x then is the root of the equation

$$P(s_x) = 0. \qquad (38)$$

Individuals with $s < s_x$ are not admitted into the "social class" of the larger s's. Similar relations can be established for other variables characterising an individual.

An expression similar to (37) but in which the integration is carried out between the limits s_x and $s_{x'}$ determines the size of the next class in which the maximum value of s is s_x and the minimum is $s_{x'}$. Both $N(s)$ and Δ determine the total number of "classes" in a given society. If $N(s)$ is known we can calculate Δ from the (usually small) number of "classes."

Two individuals may, however, be different in more than one respect. They may differ with respect to the social status s, as well as with respect to some ability x which is distributed in a different way than s. Let us denote any given characteristic of the individual by ξ_i. Then ξ_1 may denote the social status, ξ_2 the given ability, ξ_3 some other characteristic, etc. Let the total number of variables be n. Denoting by η_i appropriate co-efficients we may now consider as condition of association the requirement:

$$\sum_{i=1}^{i=n} \eta_i \left(\xi_i - \xi_i'\right)^2 < \Delta. \tag{39}$$

Let $N_i(\xi_i)$ be the distribution function of the variable ξ_i so that $N_i(\xi_i)d\xi_i$ denotes the fraction of all individuals who have ξ_i between ξ_i and $\xi_i + d\xi_i$ and

$$\int N_i(\xi_i)d\xi_i = 1, \tag{40}$$

where the integration is extended over the whole range of the variable ξ_i. If we denote by N_0 the total number of individuals in the society and by ξ_{im} the highest values of ξ_i and by ξ_{ix} the lowest value still admissible in the "upper class," then the size of that "upper class" is given by

$$N_0 \int_{ix}^{\xi_{im}} \cdots \int_{kx}^{\xi_{km}} \left[\sum \eta_i(\xi_i - \xi_i')^2 - \Delta^2\right] N_1(\xi_1) N_1(\xi_1') \cdots$$

$$\tag{41}$$

$$\cdots N_n(\xi_n) N_n(\xi_n')d\xi_1'd\xi_1' \cdots d\xi_n d\xi_n' .$$

Instead of considering the difference between two character-istics, as we did in equation (36), it may be more natural to con-sider their ratios. An individual with an income of $100,000 is likely to associate with another individual whose income is $75,000, but an individual with an income of $26,000 is not likely to associate with an individual whose income is $1,000. The dif-ference is the same but the ratios are different. Similarly, an executive or politician who controls directly or indirectly 10,000 individuals will associate with another one who controls 6,000 in-dividuals, but a person having a control over 4,000 individuals will not associate with one having a control over only 25 individuals.

In such cases we must substitute for equation (36) the following one:

$$(\log s' - \log s)^2 < \Delta^2 . \tag{42}$$

We then can use again the same argument as before.

3. An Expository Analysis of some of Rashevsky's Social Behavior Models[1]

By JAMES S. COLEMAN

Bureau of Applied Social Research

INTRODUCTION

This paper is an expository analysis of some models of social behavior constructed by Nicolas Rashevsky. The models we shall examine are taken from his book, *Mathematical Biology of Social Behavior*.[2] Professor Rashevsky is a mathematical biophysicist, who with his associates at the University of Chicago has developed extensive theoretical models of the activity of the central nervous system. In the past several years, he has become increasingly interested in social behavior, and in groups of interacting individuals.

These models that we shall examine have made frontal attacks on some of the problems that sociologists have been chipping at the flanks of for many years. Such an approach, setting up and making deductions from specific models of complex systems of behavior, necessarily entails many simplifications and assumptions which may not be true in actual societies. Many will feel that this is not the best way for developing social theory. Perhaps not; but who is to say? At the present stage of sociology, we need to explore not one but many paths to the development of a sound science. This path has as yet been little explored. Partly because of this, partly because of the abundant rewards this approach has reaped for other sciences, we feel it is quite important to explore it at least until we see where it can lead us. This paper is designed primarily for those persons who want to help in this exploration, to provide for them a general orientation by laying bare the structures of these models.

Because we feel that the valuable things the models have to say are not easily found, and because we do not wish them to be lost to sociologists, we shall make an attempt, in this exposition, to make them more accessible to understanding, bringing out what

we consider to be of potential value to sociology. This will largely
take the form of a systematization[3]: classifying and comparing
parts of the models and the models as wholes. In this way one may
begin to understand what the models do and what they don't do; how
the parts of a model fit together; and just what the relation is between the sociology of a model and the mathematics of the model.
We will still not be in a position to say with assurance, "This approach is valuable for social theory," or "This approach has no
value for social theory." Only time may tell us that efforts might
better have been expended in one direction than another. But, once
understanding this approach, we can then give it as fair an evalua-
tion as we do those which are easily examined, and we can make
our decisions more rationally, rather than to applaud or condemn
because of an irrational reverence for or prejudice against a mathematical equation.

In Section I of our analysis, we shall describe -- verbally
and unsystematically -- the four models which we are to examine
later in more detail. This shows us intuitively what the models are
"about," but gives us little insight into what is similar and what is
different about the models. It is probably best not to try to understand the models fully at this point, but rather to simply get an impression of what they are about. In order to carry out our analysis,
we must be able to compare the various parts of the models, so in
Section II we attempt a classification scheme which will allow such
a comparison. We shall first classify characteristics of individuals and groups, then the processes of the model, then the model as
a whole.

After this, in Section III comes the systematic analysis of
each of the four models, which lets us see more clearly the structures[4] of the models. Section IV is a short discussion, with the
model of imitative behavior as an example of the way in which general deductions are made from the model.

Finally, in Section V, to show how the structures of these
models are adaptable to various types of behavior, we shall adapt
two of the models to quite different behavior areas. For example,
beginning with the model of "altruistic and egoistic societies," we
adapt the basic structure to produce a resulting model of "conformity in a group situation."

Thus this analysis is meant: 1) to make the models more
understandable by giving a simpler introduction to them and by
making explicit the types of processes they represent; 2) to sep-
erate the formal mathematical model from its specific social content, in order to compare the various models and the processes

within them, and thereby to increase our knowledge of how mathematical models of social behavior may be constructed; and 3) to suggest alternate sociological meanings for the formal models, which may stimulate other ideas for still different meanings, or which may stimulate creation of different models using some of the parts of these.

This paper may be used in conjunction with a study of the book from which the models are taken, or alone, without the original presentation.[5] We have attempted to make the analysis self-sufficient, so that reference to the original is not necessary for its understanding. Also, most of the mathematics beyond simple algebraic equations occurs, not in the postulates of the model, but rather in the operations carried out in making deductions from them. Since most of this paper will not be concerned with these operations, there will be mathematics of any difficulty only at a few points.

The reasons we shall concentrate our analysis upon the postulates of the models rather than upon the mathematical operations which derive deductions from them are two: 1) these latter operations become fairly involved mathematically, at the same time having little relevance for models other than the particular one being examined; and 2) more important, we feel that the greatest present stumbling block to mathematical model building is the inability of sociologists to formulate their ideas and their problems in mathematical terms without divesting them of their sociological relevance. Once this difficulty is overcome, a common meeting ground with the mathematician is found, and his aid may be enlisted. It is not suggested that Rashevksy's models, or this analysis of them, will go far toward solving this complex and difficult problem. There are many facets to the problem, that of successful measurement being an important one which we do not touch upon.

There are a number of quite different approaches among those who construct and use mathematical models in social science, of which Rashevsky's is only one. The purpose of this paper is not to evaluate this approach, nor even to examine Rashevsky's general purpose in constructing these models, but to use them for a different purpose, that of examining how certain kinds of models are constructed.

This paper is not intended for those who are sophisticated in the use of mathematical models, but rather for those who are interested though inexperienced in this field, to aid in the ways mentioned above.

Section I. VERBAL DESCRIPTIONS OF FOUR MODELS

IMITATIVE BEHAVIOR (p. 86, R.)[6]

This is one of the most complete and detailed of Rashevsky's models. The equations which form the basis of the model are derived from his theory of the central nervous system, with an added assumption about stimuli from other individuals, which makes it a model of social behavior. We will not examine nor question the derivation of these equations – this will be our rule throughout – but will take them as given, and proceed from that point. Of course, we will verbally interpret the equations, to see what they mean in the context of the model. Because this model is built from an underlying theory, it is rather fully developed. Others of the models (e.g., a general theory of social distributions) are left in a rather tentative form, with only the basic outlines of the model constructed.

In the present model, it is assumed that there are two mutually exclusive activities occuring in society. Everyone does one, but not both. Suppose there are two songs so popular that everyone goes around humming the tune of one of them. Humming one tune would be one activity (designated R_1 in the model), and humming the other would be the second (designated R_2 in the model).

It is postulated that everyone has some innate, unchanging tendency or disposition toward doing each of the activities (ϵ_1 is a measure of the disposition toward R_1, and ϵ_2 a measure of the disposition toward R_2).[7] These two dispositions are of course conflicting, and the difference between the two ($\epsilon_1 - \epsilon_2 = \phi$) determines in a probabilistic sense what the individual will do. The equations which show how they determine the probability of doing R_1 rather than R_2 are:[8]

$$P_1 = 1 - \frac{1}{2} e^{\phi} \qquad \text{(if } \phi > 0\text{)} \qquad (1.1)$$

and   (p. 88, R)

$$P_1 = \frac{1}{2} e^{\phi} \qquad \text{(if } \phi \leq 0\text{)} \qquad (1.2)$$

where P_1 is the probability of doing R_1. These equations mean simply that if ϕ is large and positive, then P_1 will be near one, and the individual will very likely do R_1. If it is large but negative, then by the second equation, P_1 will be near zero, and the individual will likely do R_2.

If there were no outside stimulus, the individual would act in accordance with these two equations. But besides his innate disposition, each person has a temporary tendency toward R_1 and one toward R_2, which are produced by an outside stimulus. These variable tendencies (ϵ_1' and ϵ_2') together with the innate disposition then come to form the final tendency toward R_1 or R_2. ($\epsilon_1' - \epsilon_2' = \psi$, so $\phi + \psi$ is the final resulting tendency toward R_1 or R_2. $\phi + \psi$ then plays the same role in the two equations that ϕ along played before the outside stimulus was included.)

From what sources does this outside stimulus come? In answering this question, we finally arrive at imitative behavior. Each individual who is doing R_1 acts as a stimulus on every other individual, so that the outside stimulus which determines ψ is the cumulative effect of everyone's behavior.[9] (The mechanism through which this variable component, ψ, of the tendencies to R_1 and R_2 is determined by the behavior of others will be examined in the more systematic analysis.)

This now gives an interesting situation: an individual's behavior is partly determined by the behavior of others in society. But their behavior is itself affected by his behavior, for each individual plays an equal role in the society, no one being *a priori* immune to imitation. What will happen in this situation? Will the society do predominantly R_1, or predominantly R_2, or will both activities be done about equally? How large a role will imitation play? These things of course cannot be determined without knowing the distribution of ϕ, as well as knowing the stimulus effect of each individual's behavior, and the total number of individuals who are in the society and who act as stimuli.

The deductions which Rashevsky makes from the postulates of this model attempt to answer the above questions, showing just how the final behavior depends upon these quantities. We will not examine these deductions in detail in our analysis, but will be more concerned with how the several processes of the model relate to each other to produce the model as a whole.

DISTRIBUTION OF WEALTH (p. 58, R.)[10]

Before beginning, let us caution against dismissing the model as trivial because one feels that distribution of wealth doesn't really occur in this way. This has little relevance here, for it is the formal aspects of the models we are most interested in.

Basically, the situation which the model represents is this: There is a system of interacting people, each of whom has two distinguishing characteristics: his *ability* x, and his *wealth* w. The individuals interact in pairs, at equal intervals of time. As two people interact, one will gain and the other will lose wealth, depending upon how much wealth the poorer of the two already has and upon the abilities of each. Thus after a number of interactions, a great deal of wealth will have changed hands, and the distribution of wealth in the society may be quite different from what it was at first.

But in this model there are two other ways in which individuals may gain and lose wealth. They may be called "production" and "consumption." The wealth one gains from production is considered as input to the system, a gain in wealth without taking away from anyone else. It is dependent upon one's ability and his already existing wealth. Consumption, on the other hand, is considered as output from the system, drawing on the individual's supply of wealth, again without any interaction with other individuals. The amount of consumption is dependent only upon the existing wealth of the individual.

Thus each person has three processes for gaining and losing wealth: interaction with other individuals, production, and consumption. The production and consumption occur continuously, with equations being given for production and consumption per unit time (p. 59, R., eq. 6, 7). For the other process, all interactions are considered as being of the same length of time, so each individual has the same number of interactions per unit of time, regardless of who he is.

With the situation as given, the problems posed are as follows: Is there an equilibrium state for the system, so that after some period of time the distribution of wealth will remain constant? If so, can the distribution of wealth be expressed solely as a function of the distribution of ability? If this is so, what form will it have if the distribution of ability has a certain form? It turns out that there is an equilibrium state, wealth can be expressed as a function of ability, and the distribution of wealth is quite skewed when the distribution of ability is symmetric. But again, we will not focus upon these deductions, but upon the basic structure of the model.

A GENERAL THEORY OF SOCIAL
DISTRIBUTIONS (Chap. 8, R.)

This model is quite tentative, since neither of the two processes which form its foundation are completely specified. Thus very little can be deduced about the situation to which this model will lead. However, the model's structure is of interest, for it seems to be amenable to a number of social situations, as we shall show in Section V.

We are given a society of constant size N_0, in which each individual is characterized by two factors: an innate ability, a, which remains constant, and a status, s, which may change. It is assumed that on contact, two individuals with given abilities and statuses will each change some slight amount in social status. The specific mechanism for that change is not stated, but it is postulated that the amount of status changed, Δ, is a random variable whose distribution depends upon the abilities of both individuals, a and a', and the statuses of both, s and s'.

This is a "probability process," which means that upon contact, there is some indeterminacy concerning just how much one's status will change. There is a certain probability distribution of Δ for each individual in contact with another particular individual. That is, each combination of (a, a', s, s') will have, in general, a different distribution of Δ. The process is left quite general in that both individuals need not change the same amount (as was true in the case of distribution wealth, where one individual's gain was another's loss). The process can be thought of as a generalization of the equivalent process of the distribution of wealth model. It generalizes that one in two ways: the amount of change is a random variable, not strictly determined; and the gain of one is not necessarily the loss of the other.

A second process is one concerned with the frequency of interaction: symbolically, $K = K(s, s')$.[11] This frequency of interaction between two individuals is assumed to be a function of the statuses of the two individuals, decreasing as the statuses of the individuals differ more widely. This process can be regarded not as a generalization of the parallel one of the model of distribution of wealth, but instead as a closer approximation to reality. There all people were assumed equally likely to meet, which is a kind of first approximation. Here the frequency of meeting is assumed to be a function of one characteristic of the individuals, which may be considered a second approximation to reality.

Since this model is in such tentative form, very little is deduced by Rashevsky concerning the situations to which it will lead. There are a number of mathematical operations carried out on p. 66-68 R., to bring the model part of the way to quantitative deductions, but as long as the functions are not specified somewhat more fully, little can be done. We do not even know whether there will be an equilibrium state reached, in which the distribution of s is constant. As more is specified about the relationships, more deductions are possible. Rashevsky carries the model somewhat further in elaborations which will not be considered here.

The model can be regarded as a kind of generalization of the model of distribution of wealth, although there are other differences between the two.

ALTRUISTIC AND EGOISTIC SOCIETIES (Chap. 14, R.)

Here, as in the other models we are examining, we shall not consider all the generalizations and modifications of the model, but just the basic model itself. The model is included primarily to show the structure of a model quite different from most of the others.

An individual i is characterized by a "satisfaction," S_i. This satisfaction is a function of some other characteristic of the individual, x_i (which we may call "effort"[12]), and of the "efforts," x_1, x_2, . . . x_n, of all others with whom he is in contact:

$$S_i = a_i \sum_{j=1}^{n} p_{ji} x_j - b_i x_i^2 .$$

This equation says that his satisfaction decreases with the amount of effort he expends, but increases with the effort of everyone in society. This can be thought of as corresponding to a factory situation, where each individual's satisfaction decreases the more he works, but increases with an increase in total work output (due to the increased pay, etc., because of the increased production). (See p. 45-46 R., for derivation of the equation.) The coefficients a_i, b_i, and p_{ji}, will be examined later in the analysis.

The individual isn't concerned only with his own satisfaction, but is also concerned with that of others in society. The degree to which individual 1 is concerned with individual   2's satisfaction is k_{12}. The society or group may be characterized by the matrix of these terms (which may be "1", representing concern, or "0", representing no concern). An "egoistic" society would be one with this kind of matrix of k's:

$$\begin{pmatrix} 1 & 0 & . & 0 \\ 0 & 1 & . & 0 \\ . & . & . & . \\ 0 & 0 & . & 1 \end{pmatrix}$$

which shows that each has concern only for himself. An "altruistic" society would be characterized by:

$$\begin{pmatrix} 1 & 1 & . & 1 \\ 1 & 1 & . & 1 \\ . & . & . & . \\ 1 & 1 & . & 1 \end{pmatrix}$$

which shows that each has concern for all.

Some "higher satisfaction," $\overline{S}_i$, of the individual results from seeing the satisfaction of all those with whom he is concerned. This higher satisfaction is the sum of the amount of each person's satisfaction times the degree to which individual is concerned with that person's satisfaction, or: $\overline{S}_i = k_{i1}S_1 + k_{i2}S_2 \ldots + k_{in}S_n$. If we thing of S as "comfort" or material satisfaction, then this characteristic, $\overline{S}$, can be though of as a higher satisfaction or happiness which results from not only one's own comfort, but also that of others.

The general problem is this: How much effort should this individual spend to maximize his $\overline{S}$? This is not a simple matter for the individual, for his effort, x_i , affects not only his own material satisfaction, but also, to some extent, everyone else's. Since his higher satisfaction depends upon at least some of these other person's material satisfactions, he must take this fact into account when changing his x_i . And he must know not only that his effort affects the satisfaction of others, but also just how it affects them, and how much it does so.

Assuming that he knows this, it is not a difficult problem mathematically to deduce how much effort (x_i) he will put forth. The problem becomes one of maximizing $\bar{S}_i$ with respect to x_i. We will examine the further aspects of this model in Section III.

Section II. DESCRIPTION OF THE CLASSIFICATION SYSTEM

Here, then, are the four models. The outlines of each have been described, so that we have a feeling of what each model is about. The descriptions have also given us some idea about whether the model seems useful or not; That is, in reading the descriptions, we tend to accept or reject the model as it does or does not conform to what we know about behavior, and our intuitive notions about the relations between the characteristics which the models postulate.

But it is exactly this judgment which we should *not* make at this point. In making such a judgment we are requiring the model-builder to carry out the whole task: to provide us with a finished model, which gives exact meaning to each variable and relates them in such a way that they accurately mirror real behavior. This is a great deal to expect of mathematical models at present; such hopes will probably seldom be satisfied. If one is searching for finished models which can predict how particular systems of individuals will behave, he will likely be disappointed with most mathematical models.

But at the outset we decided that this was not to be our purpose here. We want to use these models, not for what they can tell us about social behavior, but for what they can tell us about the *relations between* mathematical models and social behavior. Our main purpose, then, is equipping ourselves, so that we will not require the model-builder to do the whole job; so that we can take a partially formulated model and complete it, or take a model and change it slightly to conform more nearly to what we know about social behavior, or so that we can translate vague social theory into forms more amenable to precise model-building.

If we are to accomplish this, we must examine the models much more fully than we have done so far. This requires that we have a systematic way of examining and comparing the models; that is, some orderly method of analysis. This part of the paper is intended to give us such a method. It consists of a classification of the various parts of the models, which will allow our analysis to be carried out quite simply, and in such a way that we can easily compare the models.

THE STRUCTURE AND THE CONTENT OF A MODEL

Before the classification itself, let us examine more closely a premise which is implicit in our whole approach. This is the independence of the two parts of any mathematical model: the *structure*, which is completely mathematical, devoid of any social or physical meaning, and the *content*, which consists of the meaning given to the various parts of the structure. In these models, the content always concerns social behavior of some sort, but the structure of the models differs quite markedly in some cases. Our analysis is concerned with divorcing at least part of the content from the structure, both to see what the structure itself is like and to allow us to adapt this structure to different content areas.

There seem to be at least two levels on which we can transfer the structure from one content area to another. The less drastic change is to keep the same meaning for the elements of the system, but to consider different aspects of them; that is, change the meanings of the variables without changing the units which they characterize. This is what is done in the last part of this paper, where we change the meanings of the variables of two models to obtain in one case a model of *attitude* distribution from a model of *status* distribution, and in the second a model of *conformity* behavior of individuals from a model in which *satisfaction* of individuals is the main characteristic. Here the elements of the system remain individuals, while the meanings of the variables which characterize them are changed. This is ordinarily the kind of change we as sociologists might make in the content of these models, for they concern behavior of systems of individuals, and our primary concern is with various aspects of this same general area.

It is also possible, however, to make a more radical change in the content of a model. This would be to let the elements of the system be of a different kind. In all four of these models, the elements are individuals. If we wanted to use one of them, say the model of "altruistic and egoistic societies," for representing the behavior of competing firms in an economic system, we would let the elements be firms rather than individuals. Or if we were studying a book of physical chemistry with a view toward applying some of the models there to social behavior, then we would want to divorce the content entirely from the formal model and change from molecules as elements to individuals as elements. In fact, this is just what Rashevsky has done in one of his models (not included here -- p.72,R.). This model was derived by Boltzmann, a physical chemist, to describe the most probable distribution of energy among molecules of a gas in an equilibrium state. Rashevsky substitutes individuals for molecules (the elements of the system) and wealth for energy (the characteristics of the elements).

Even remaining in the area of social behavior, however, we might want to change the elements of the system. For example, *families* might be considered the elements of the system in a model which represents inter-family friendship patterns in a community. In such a model, not individuals but families would be considered the basic units of description and analysis. Composite units would be made up of two or more families in certain relations.

In the models which we are considering, individuals are always elements of the system. Therefore, in classifying the parts of these models to provide a basis for comparison, we need only divorce the first level of content from the structure. This means that the classifications will be on the basis of mathematical differences, but that we can refer to "characteristics of individuals" and "characteristics of groups" rather than having to talk about "characteristics of elements of the system" as would be the case if we intended to consider only the mathematical structure of the model.

Thus there are two kinds of units characterized in the models: individuals, and the "group" or "society," which constitutes the system of individuals included in the model. First we shall make some distinctions between different kinds of characteristics of individuals, then consider characteristics of societies.

CHARACTERISTICS OF INDIVIDUALS

Properties and Relational Characteristics: Our first distinction between types of characteristics of individuals is according to whether they refer to a single individual or to two or more individuals. Any characteristic like age, height, occupation, religion, which we ordinarily think of as being a characteristic of the individual is of the first type, for there is reference only to the single person. On the other hand, some characteristics have reference to two individuals: one person's attitude toward another, the frequency of interaction between two people, the dominance relation between two people, and the distance between their homes are examples of such characteristics. These characteristics refer not just to a single individual, but to the individual and another individual.

The relational characteristic might be more than pairwise, referring, say, to three people rather than two. For example, a characteristic representing the difference between the combined power of a coalition of two individuals and the power of a third would necessarily have reference to three individuals. But these models confine themselves to pairwise interactions, so that we need not consider such a case. To distinguish characteristics of a single individual from those referring to two individuals, we shall call the former *properties* of individuals, and the latter *relational characteristics* of one individual with respect to a second.

Types of Relational Characteristics: All the relational character- istics of these models are quantitative; nevertheless, at some points there is an analogy between these and such qualitative binary relations as "is equal to," "is dominated by," etc. Specifically, we can ask about the *symmetry* of these characteristics. An ex- ample of a symmetric characteristic occurs in the model of a gen- eral theory of social distributions. The frequency of contact be- tween individuals s and s' necessarily is symmetric [K(s, s') = K(s';s)], for the second person meets the first as often as the first meets the second. On the other hand, in the model of altruis- tic and egoistic societies, k_{ij}, the concern of individual i for indi- vidual j, is not symmetric, since individual i's concern for j is not the same as j's concern for i. That is, in general $k_{ij} \neq k_{ji}$.

We may secondly ask whether the characteristic is *reflex- ive:* that is, whether it is meaningful to talk about the relation be- tween the person and himself. In the case of k_{ij}, above, it is; the concern of individual i for his own satisfaction (k_{ii}) not only is meaningful, but plays a part in the model. The other example, however, K(s, s') is not reflexive: the individual's frequency of contact with himself K(s, s) is not of use in the model nor is it meaningful.

The Correspondence Between Properties and Relational Charac- teristics: Although there is a clear difference between properties and relational characteristics, a property of an individual may be derived from relations between him and others. The derivation is purely mathematical, and consists of some function of his relation with every other person in the society. For example, K(s, s') is the frequency of interaction between individual s and s' in the model of a general theory of social distributions. Let us change the notation slightly, to let it be K_{ij}, where i and j refer to the individuals. If we sum over all j

$$\left(\sum_{j=1}^{n} K_{ij} = K_{i}, \right)$$

the resulting characteristic of individual i would be his total frequency of interaction, his "gregariousness."

This kind of operation ordinarily results in a meaningful
property of the individual, one which is no different from other of
his properties, except that it is only valid within the context of the
given group. Such a characteristic has been called a *contextual*
characteristic of the individual in a paper by Lazarsfeld and
Barton.[13]

Endogenous and Exogenous Variables: If a characteristic is modified by the processes of a model, it is *endogenous* to that model.
Otherwise, being independent of the system, it is an *a priori* condition upon which the resulting state of the system depends, and
therefore may be labelled an *exogenous* variable. Although ordinarily constant over time, an exogenous variable is not necessarily
so. The important point is that if it changes, it does so independently of the rest of the system. It is often arbitrary whether exogenous variables are assumed to be constant or some prescription is given whereby they change. As long as this change does not
depend upon other processes of the system, the variable remains
independent, or exogenous.

Because of the importance of this classification, exogenous
variables will be noted by an asterisk (*) in the later systematic
analysis of the models. This property of a variable, its dependence on the system, holds true for characteristics of individuals
and groups alike, and therefore will not be re-examined when classifying characteristics of groups.

Stimulus Variables: This distinction is, as is the previous one, in
terms of the part the variable plays in the processes of the model.
But this will have reference to only certain processes of the
model. When any characteristic of one individual or a characteristic of the society acts to affect a characteristic of another individual, we shall call that characteristic a stimulus variable. An
example will show better what we mean. In the model of a general
theory of social distributions, the individual's status, s, is
changed as a function of his own ability, a, his status, s, the ability of the person with whom he is in contact, a', and that person's
status, s'. In this process, then, the two characteristics of the

other individual, a' and s', are stimulus variables. Similarly, in
the equivalent process for the other individual's status change, a
and s would be stimulus variables.

The reason we characterize these certain variables in this
way will become evident later, when we examine the processes of
the model. Essentially, the reason is this: since individuals are
discrete elements, it is important to see what the model says
about the way these elements interact. When we determine which
characteristics provide the causal connections between the discrete elements, we are better able to characterize the structure
of the model.

Continuous Variables and Attributes: Some of the characteristics
of individuals in these models are assumed to be measured by a
variable which may take on any value within a given real interval.
These characteristics we will call *continuous variables* to distinguish them from characteristics whose measure may take on only
discrete real number values. In these models, only a particular
case of the latter occurs, in which the number of values is two.
Such characteristics we will call *dichotomous attributes*, or simply
attributes. Most of the characteristics in these models are continuous variables, the one major exception being the behavior R_1
and R_2 (R_2 is the same as the negation of R_1, since everyone does
one but not both activities) in the model of imitative behavior. It is
an all-or-none proposition, with no question of intensity (e.g., he is
either asleep or awake, votes or does not vote in an election, etc.).
In the next section, we will see that the characteristics of society
which correspond to continuous variables are quite different from
those which correspond to attributes.

Variation With Time: There are characteristics which are *constant*, those which are *changing*, and those which occur at intervals
of time, as *events*.[14] This, of course, is within the context of the
given model. A constant characteristic may be one which changes
in real life, but because the change is negligible for the time span
which the model is to represent, is considered constant in the
model.

Any constant characteristic is exogenous to the system of
the model, although the converse is not true as we noted previously. The constant characteristics as well as the changing ones may
vary from individual to individual (but do not necessarily do so),
but only the changing ones will vary with respect to time.

Some characteristics such as acts of behavior may not change with time in the way mentioned above, but exist only as discrete events in time. We may characterize the individual by a single act; for example, his vote in an election or his eating a meal in a restaurant.[15] However, often we are interested in the pattern of acts or repetition of acts over a period of time. Thus we may characterize the individual by his "usual" action, or his frequency of doing a certain act. The correspondence between the event (the single act) which characterizes the individual at a given point in time, and the repeated event, which characterizes him over a given period of time, is simply a statistical correspondence like the correspondence between characteristics of individuals and those of groups.

Other Distinctions: Besides these distinctions between types of variables which tell us about the structure of the model, there are others which we shall not use in the systematic classification, but which we shall use in discussing the models, to give better intuitive meaning to them. For example, some characteristics of individuals are overt behavior, while others are latent dispositions. Some models deal with possessions, such as wealth. Often characteristics are simply probabilities – produced by some disposition – that certain behavior will occur. We shall sometimes use these terms in defining the variables, but they are not of aid in comparing the structure of one model to that of another.

Before leaving the classification of characteristics of individuals, we must be careful to distinguish between two kinds of uses of a given datum. The first usage is as a "variable" or "characteristic" in its own right, used as either an independent or a dependent variable. This is the usage presupposed in all the above classifications, and is the way in which all these models use any datum which is part of the model. But there is another usage in which a given datum cannot be so rigorously classified. This is use as an "indicator" of another variable, which cannot itself be directly measured. All psychological variables must be measured in this way, by means of behavioral indicators, since they are not directly measurable. Also, we often do not directly measure behavior, but obtain a "report" of the behavior, using this report – usually, from the individual himself – as an indicator of the behavior.

However, these models will not be concerned with the problem, for it is assumed that the variables which are part of the models are measured; measurement is not problematic, but it is taken as given.

In summary, our classification of characteristics of individuals is to be as follows:

A. 1. *Properties:* refer only to the single individual.

   2. *Relational characteristics:* refer to two individuals.

     a. *symmetric:* the relation in one direction is the same as in the other.
     b. *reflexive:* the relation holds toward the individual himself.

B. 1. *Endogenous* variables: modified by the processes of the system.

   2. *Exogenous* variables: act as conditions for the system, unaffected by the processes.

C. 1. *Stimulus* variables: characteristics of one individual or the group, acting to change the state of another individual.

D. 1. *Continuous* variables: characteristics whose measure may take on any real number value within specified limits.

   2. *Attributes:* dichotomous characteristics.

E. 1. *Constant* characteristics: constant over time.

   2. *Changing* characteristics: changing over time.

   3. *Events:* discrete occurrences which affect the system.

CHARACTERISTICS OF GROUPS OR SOCIETIES

Corresponding to characteristics of individuals are characteristics of the group or society itself. Many of these characteristics of society are directly derived from characteristics of individuals. The derivation is usually something like this: all the individuals in society are characterized by say, "ability," symbolized by x. The society is characterized by the *distribution* of ability throughout society. Thus for a property of an individual which is a continuous variable, there is a distribution curve as the corresponding characteristic of society.

In the first three of these models, a very large society is postulated, and a continuous distribution curve is assumed, so that the methods of calculus are used. Thus the density function of x, symbolized by p(x), is such that $\int_a^b p(x)dx$ represents the proportion of individuals whose x lies between a and b.

Certain parameters of this distribution curve may be considered as characteristics of the society also. In the above example, the mean value of x in society would be such a parameter, as would the variance.

The above type of correspondence applies to characteristics of society derived from individual characteristics which are continuous variables. When the individual characteristic is an attribute, then the derived characteristic of society is usually the proportion (or number) of the total society possessing the attribute. If the attribute is one such as "being left-handed," a derived characteristic for society is, for example, the proportion (or the number) of left-handed people in society. If the attribute is simply "being in the society or group," then a derived characteristic of the society or group is its size. When the attribute is also an event in time, such as the act of suicide, or marriage, then a derived characteristic of society is a rate, familiar to all sociologists.

The above kind of derived characteristic of society is the kind which occurs most often in these models. Any characteristic of the individual has a corresponding distribution throughout the society, which we shall call an *analytical* characteristic of society. An analytical characteristic of society, as we shall use the term here, is a statistical aggregate throughout the society or group, of some characteristic of individuals.[16]

Both the above derivations begin with *properties* of individuals. But it is not only properties of individuals which have their correspondence in characteristics of societies. Relational characteristics may also. Let us examine p_{ij} in the model of altruistic and egoistic societies. It is defined as the effect of individual i's effort on j's satisfaction. The characteristic of society corresponding to p_{ij} would be the matrix of p_{ij}'s of size N x N (N = number of people in society). Since p_{ij} is reflexive the diagonal elements are meaningful, and since it is not symmetric, the matrix will not be symmetric.

By first reducing this relational characteristic to a property, as we showed could be done, we would obtain either: $p_{i\bullet}(=\sum_j p_{ij})$: the effect of individual i's effort on everyone's satisfaction or $p_{\bullet j}$

$(= \sum_i p_{ij})$: the effect of everyone's effort on individual j's satisfaction. Then the distribution of either of these over society would be just like that of any other property of an individual.

There are also characteristics of societies or groups which cannot be derived from characteristics of individuals as statistical aggregates. The laws of a town and municipal property, for example, are not directly reducible to characteristics of individuals. Similarly, the time of a crew in a boat race is not statistically derivable from any characteristics of individuals. Such a characteristic of a society we shall call a *primary* characteristic.

Among these models, we find only a few primary characteristics of societies. In the model of "distribution of wealth," there is an equation for "production" by individuals, which has proportionality constants A, B, and C (page 59, R., eq. 6). Although it is not possible to interpret these without ambiguity, one interpretation would seem to be that they are primary characteristics of the society which indicate what factors count most in gaining wealth in the society (for instance, the relative sizes of B and C show the relative effectiveness of accumulated wealth and ability as factors in gaining more wealth in the particular society under consideration). It is important to note that this is not a *distribution* as in the previous case, but simply a single, unitary characteristic which indicates a property of the society.

It is important to note that such characteristics as these presuppose a society which is more than simply a certain number of people who happen to be included together. That is, they presuppose a society which is unitary enough to have single production characteristics, holding throughout the society, A, B, and C.

This comprises the classification we shall make of characteristics of the society. Once again, they are:

Analytical characteristics derived from primary characteristics of individuals. These are in general density functions, but in the case of attributes are usually proportions. If instead of a property of individuals, we begin with a relational characteristic, there are two paths:
a) to go directly: relation → matrix, an analytical characteristic of society;
b) to follow the course: individual relation → individual property → analytical characteristic of society.
As with individual characteristics, they may be constant, or changing. They may be exogenous or endogenous.

Primary characteristics, which are not derivable from individual
characteristics alone. Most examples of this kind of
characteristic in these models come about as constants
or coefficients in various equations which represent processes in the model.

UNDEFINED COEFFICIENTS

While some of the variables in these models are explicitly
set forth as essential parts of the models, others, often left undefined, are introduced as "coefficients" or "constants" in the equations. Although they are not explicitly defined, their usage in the
model gives them some psychological or sociological meaning, and
whenever such meaning can be deduced, we will attempt to do so.

We can illustrate how these interpretations may be made by
using a part of the model of imitative behavior which we have not
yet mentioned. This is the equation representing the effect of other
people doing R_1 upon an individual's latent tendency to do R_1. The
variable part of this tendency is ϵ_1', and the rate of change of ϵ_1',
when X other persons are doing R_1 and thus acting as stimuli
upon him is:

$$\frac{d\epsilon_1'}{dt} = AX - a\epsilon_1' . \tag{2.1}$$

This means that as X increases, the rate of change of ϵ_1' will
increase, but as ϵ_1' itself increases, the rate will decrease.

But what are the meanings of A and a? These are the "undefined coefficients" of this equation. We can see intuitively what
they mean by noting what would happen to the equation if they
changed in value. If A were to increase, the rate of change of ϵ_1'
would increase for a given number, X, of people doing R_1. If A
became negative, the stimulus effect of each individual would tend
to decrease ϵ_1' rather than increase it. If A were zero, then other
persons' behavior would have no effect at all on ϵ_1'. It seems, then,
that A is a kind of "effectiveness coefficient," showing the effectiveness of others' behavior in changing ϵ_1'.

When we examine a, we see that it does not "operate upon"
the number of stimuli, X, as does A, but rather upon ϵ_1' itself. If
a were to increase, then for the same value of ϵ_1', the rate of change
would decrease. If a were zero or negative, then ϵ_1' would

continue to increase with no limit, for $d\epsilon_1'/dt$ would remain positive for all (positive) values of ϵ_1'. This second term on the right hand side of the equation then seems to act as a limiting force upon ϵ_1', so that we might call a an "inhibition coefficient," or a "limiting coefficient."

There is another way to determine the meaning of these coefficients, and to do it much more precisely than we have done. The formal name for the method is "dimensional analysis" and its fundamental rule is that each term of an equation must have the same dimensions. Put very simply, it says that an equation: "9 apples = 4 bananas + 5 oranges" is just as incorrect as another equation: "9 apples = 4 apples + 4 apples." While in the second case the *numbers* are incorrect, in the first, the *dimensions* are incorrect. The equation can have no physical meaning as long as the dimensions of each term are not the same. Therefore, in the equation we are examining, each term, $d\epsilon_1'/dt$, AX, and $a\epsilon_1'$, must have the same dimensions, or the equation is incorrect.

The variables which are already defined are t, which has the dimension *units of time,* X, which has the dimension *individuals doing* R_1, and ϵ_1', which has simply the dimension *units of* ϵ_1'. If we use this knowledge, we can determine what the dimensions of the two coefficients must be if the equation is to be dimensionally correct. Looking first at the left hand side of the equation, we see that the dimensions are:

$$\frac{\text{units of } \epsilon_1' \text{ changed}}{\text{unit time}}.$$

The two terms on the right, AX and $a\epsilon_1'$, must each have these same dimensions. Examining first AX, we know that X has simply the dimension *individuals doing* R_1, so A must have dimensions which will complement this to give a resulting dimension

$$\frac{\text{units of } \epsilon_1' \text{ changed}}{\text{unit time}}.$$

A therefore must be:

$$\frac{\text{units of } \epsilon_1' \text{ changed}}{(\text{individuals doing } R_1)(\text{unit time})},$$

so that the dimension *individuals doing* R_1 cancels out. In words, this means that A is defined as the change in ϵ_1' per unit time due to the stimulus of one individual doing R_1.

Proceeding similarly, we find that the other coefficient, a, must have the dimensions:

$$\frac{\text{units of } \epsilon_1' \text{ changed}}{(\text{unit of } \epsilon_1' \text{ existing})\ (\text{unit time})},$$

which makes the product, $a\epsilon_1'$ dimensionally the same as the two other terms. This tells us that a is simply the decrease in ϵ_1' per unit of ϵ_1' existing per unit time, or the proportionate decrease in ϵ_1' per unit time. Intuitively, this means that a is an "extinction coefficient," or as found previously, an "inhibition coefficient."

Thus we see that by finding the dimensions of these coefficients, we have also found definitions for them. The definitions have not only intuitive meaning such as "effectiveness coefficient," or "inhibition coefficient." They also give us precise quantitative definitions, telling us exactly what to measure in order to determine values for a and A (assuming we knew what ϵ_1' was, and had instruments to measure changes in ϵ_1' as well as its absolute value).

The procedure we have just gone through, although simple, may be unfamiliar to many, but it is what we often do implicitly. It is used explicitly in the physical sciences, having proved quite valuable there.[17] We may note that dimensional analysis, which has more valuable uses than that indicated above, is a tool which has heretofore been little used in mathematical models for social and psychological processes, and which might be useful.[18]

CLASSIFICATION OF PROCESSES

Just as the *variables* of a model, mathematically defined (as real numbers, etc.) correspond to individual and group characteristics, considered in the previous section, the *equations* of the model correspond to psychological and social processes.[19] The equations express certain functional relationships between the mathematical variables, and when the variables are given social or psychological meaning, the equations express postulates about causal relations between the individual or group characteristics.

Before we discuss social processes and psychological processes, it is well to point out an essential difference between the way one ordinarily would go about constructing models for the two types of processes.

In model-building in the physical sciences, a common problem has been to infer the underlying structure of a substance so as to explain why it acts the way it does. For example, the chemical elements, such as oxygen, carbon, etc., were devised as constructs to explain physical and chemical behavior of matter. It was not possible to see or measure the microscopic particles and processes which produced the macroscopic effects. Thus the model-building was in essence inferring a latent or underlying structure to explain the behavior of the system, which was the only thing which could be observed.

In psychological model-building, the procedure is much the same: there is an underlying structure which cannot be directly seen, although the resulting behavior of the total system (the individual) is observable. The model is an attempt to explain this behavior by inferring a particular structure of the component parts of the system.

The problem of building models of social processes is different from this. The problem is not that we cannot see each minute process, but that we cannot relate them to each other in our minds to reproduce the actual operation of a system of behavior of a group. In this case it is not that our measuring instruments cannot "get inside" to see what goes on, but rather that we cannot fit together all the discrete and separate processes which we see around us in order to know much about how these will ultimately affect the system. It is as if we are tiny observors down among the molecules who can see a few molecules bumping each other around now and then, without being able to relate what was happening to the molecules near us to the behavior of the total system.

Of course, as will become evident in this analysis, in order to build a model of social behavior, it seems necessary to either explicitly include or imply one or more types of psychological processes, and to the extent that these processes are not yet well understood, a model of social behavior must overcome both kinds of problems: setting up models of processes to "get inside" at unobservables, and models which organize observable events concerning one or a few individuals into large-scale systems.

Now we will proceed to consider the processes of these model more precisely. Just as we needed a "way of looking" at the types of variables in a model, we need a way of looking at the equations of a model which constitute its processes. Our ways of looking at these processes will be three: (1) whether they include *time* as an explicit variable; (2) the types of variables which they contain: individual characteristics, group characteristics, etc.; (3) whether they include indeterminacy or not.

Equations of State and Equations of Change: Some of the equations in these models explicitly include time as a variable while others do not. Those which do include time are capable of showing the *rate of change* of one variable as a function of another while the others show only that a change in one variable produces a change in another. That is, they show only the *state* of one variable as a function of the state of another. The state equations say essentially either: (1) the change in the dependent variable comes about so quickly that the new equilibrium state is reached almost immediately; or (2) although the new state might not be reached quickly, the rate of change is not important to the model, and can be disregarded.[20]

We shall not use this distinction in our examination of single equations, but only in examining the "overall process" of the model. The distinction will be valuable at that point, in helping us characterize the model as a whole. However, this is a distinction which it is useful to keep in mind in examining each equation, for it sensitizes us to what the model postulates about the situation.

Unit Processes and Interaction Processes: There is a simple but important distinction we can make between the processes of these models. This distinction is according to whether the variables of the equation are all characteristics of the same individual, characteristics of the group, or characteristics of several individuals. In models like these, we may have the following combinations (if we assume only pairwise interaction or interaction with the total group, with no intermediate).

There are equations containing:
1) Characteristics only of the single individual.
2) Characteristics of two individuals.
3) Characteristics of the single individual and the group.
4) Characteristics only of the total group.

We can look at these models in a different way, one which will prove to be exactly the same for our purposes as the above. The conjunction of these two ways of looking at the processes of a model will prove quite valuable. Let us consider the model as representing a set of discrete elements (individuals)

within the system (the society or group). We may have several
types of processes occurring to produce change. First, a process
within an element, labelled (1) in the diagram below; then a process between two elements, labelled (2) below; a process between
the element and the entire system, labelled (3) below; and finally
a process within the system as an entity, labelled (4) below.

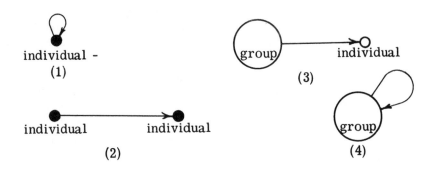

individual -
(1)

individual   individual
(2)

group ——— individual
(3)

group
(4)

The intuitive meaning of such types of processes will soon become
clear. Meanwhile, it is sufficient to note that processes (1), (2),
(3) and (4) are identical to the distinctions 1, 2, 3, and 4 made
on the basis of the types of variables included in the equation. For
example, if the process takes place completely within the individual
(process (1) on diagram) it will contain characteristics of the individual alone, and similarly for the other cases.[21]

Individual Unit Processes: The type process diagrammed:
taking place within the single individual, we shall call an *individual
unit process*. This process includes, as we have noted, only the
characteristics of the single individual. Although such a process
may be of a number of different kinds, the models we are examining contain only one such process.[22] The model is that of imitative
behavior, and the process is one in which the individual's underlying disposition to do R_1 determines the probability with which he
will do it. Symbolically,

$$P_1 = 1 - \frac{1}{2} e^{-k(\phi + \psi)} . \qquad (2.2)$$

$\phi + \psi$ is the underlying disposition to do R_1 as opposed to R_2 (including both the innate component, ϕ, and the imitative component, ψ), while P_1 is the probability of doing R_1. Both of these characteristics as well as the other one in the equation are properties of the single individual himself. The process is one of moving from the underlying disposition $(\phi + \psi)$ to the overt act (R_1).

Many other variations of this process can occur. It is empirically often the case that an act may affect an underlying disposition; for example, the act of running may make one hungry. Or one disposition may affect another: hunger may produce irritation. There are other types of variations also. The variables of the equation need not be properties of the individual: they may be relations, as long as they are "attached to" the individual himself rather than to the other individuals to whom the relation refers. For example, a process showing change in a sociometric choice of individual 1 for individual 2 could occur within individual 1, through no outside influence, while it could not occur within the second individual. The choice, although a relation between the two individuals, is a part of individual 1, and not of individual 2.

We might intuitively think of this type of process, which we have called an individual unit process, as a "psychological process," for it does not necessitate social behavior at all, but simply shows the effect of some characteristics of the individual upon another of his own characteristics. This type of process we shall symbolize in our later diagrams as $P \longrightarrow P$, meaning simply that some characteristics of the person affect other characteristics of the same person. Such symbolic diagrams will be a convenient shorthand in characterizing the models later.

Interaction Process: The second kind of process, of which there are many in these models, we shall call an "interaction process." Both (2) and (3) in the diagram above we shall include under this general heading, for both concern the effect upon an individual in an interaction, either with another individual ((2) in the diagram) or with the total society or group. They signify interactions between elements, in which stimulus variables of one individual affect characteristics of another.

An example of the first type, a two-person interaction process, occurs in the model of distribution of wealth. In this process, the abilities, x and x', of both individuals, and the wealth of the poorer, W', determine the exchange of wealth between them. Therefore x' and W' are stimulus variables for the first individual, while x is a stimulus variable for the second. The equation is

$$\Delta W = \gamma(x - x')W', \qquad (2.3)$$

where ΔW is the amount of wealth gained by one and lost by the other in the interaction.

This type of process we shall call $S_1 \longrightarrow P$, meaning that characteristics of one individual act as stimulus variables (S_1) to affect some characteristics (P) of another.

The other variation of the interaction process is one in which characteristics of all the rest of the group or society act upon one individual. Such a model consists not of two-person interactions, but of interactions between the group and individual.

There are several other important variations of the inter-action process. In one of these, every other person in the society acts as a stimulus upon the single individual at the same time. When they act *differentially* upon him, one man affecting him more than another, the process is like two of those in the model of altruistic and egoistic societies. For example, in the equation:

$$\bar{S}_1 = k_{11}S_1 + k_{12}S_2 \ldots + k_{1N}S_N, \qquad (2.4)$$

the k_{ij}'s are coefficients determining the effect of each man's S on individual 1's $\bar{S}$. Such processes are equivalent to many two-person interactions occurring simultaneously. In other interaction processes, the individuals do not act differentially upon the individual, but all have the same amount of influence. In such a case, when all are acting upon the individual at the same time, and all affect him the same amount, we can consider either that the analytical characteristic of society corresponding to the distribution of the individual characteristics is acting upon him, or that each individual is acting upon him separately, but all interactions occur at once. The interaction process in the model of imitative behavior is like this: the stimulus which affects each man is X, the number in the society doing R_1, and Y, the number doing R_2. We could consider this as many separate two-person interactions, or as a single interaction of the individual with an analytic characteristic of society. In our diagrammatic representation of these two variations of the interaction process, both of which are characterized by the simultaneous effect of everyone in the group upon the single individual, we shall use the following symbol: "$S_N \longrightarrow P$" where the subscript N indicates that N individuals are acting as stimuli.

In another variation, the stimulus which affects the individual is not a characteristic of another individual nor an analytical characteristic of the total group, but a primary characteristic of the group or society. The equations of "production" and "consumption" in the model of distribution of wealth are two such processes. The coefficients A, B, C, D, and E, in these equations (production: $\Delta_1 W/\Delta t = A + BW + Cx$; consumption: $\Delta_2 W/\Delta t = D + EW$) are characteristics of the society which determine the effects of one's ability and existing wealth in gaining wealth, and the effect of one's existing wealth in losing it through consumption. In these equations, the term "stimulus" no longer corresponds to the ordinary meaning of the word, but the meaning we have given to it for our purpose remains: a characteristic of an individual or of the society which acts to affect a characteristic of another individual.

When the interaction process is one of this sort, in which one or more primary characteristics of the society act to affect an individual, then we shall use the symbol: $S_s \longrightarrow P$, with the subscript s standing for "society."

This comprises all the various interaction processes which we shall consider, and includes all those in these models. Such a classification as this may seem to be quite divorced from reality, but this is simply because we have been considering only the structural properties of the processes. If we were to examine these processes from the point of view of what kinds of things they "mean," we would find some interesting similarities and differences among them. All correspond to what we might intuitively think of as "social psychological processes," and they correspond to things which happen to us each day, as we are confronted by interaction with another individual, with many other individuals, or with some primary characteristic of the community such as its laws. There are of course other more complex types of interaction, but models including just the types included here become complex enough to keep us busy. Also, they seem capable of enough complexity to represent real situations with some accuracy, although few models including them at present are able to do this.

Social Unit Processes: Corresponding to the individual unit process (in which only characteristics of the individual appear) is the "social unit process," in which only characteristics of the society or group appear. This corresponds to (4) in the above diagram. In such a process as this, there is no reference to individuals, but only to the social unit. None of the models included here contain such processes, but another in Rashevsky's book does. It is a process of population change, stating the rate of change of population of a social unit to the existing population; simply an exponential growth equation: $dn_a/dt = \beta_a n_a$ (p.207,R), where n_a is the size of the group, and β_a is a "growth" coefficient.

A "purely sociological" model would contain only such processes as this, relating various characteristics of the social unit, with no reference to the separate individuals within the system. Economic models ordinarily contain only processes of this type, the social unit in these models being the firm, or in some cases, the total economy.[23]

These four models, all of which contain interaction processes, are in a midway position between models which deal only with characteristics of the single individual -- psychological models -- and those which deal only with characteristics of the group. They relate individual behavior to behavior of the total group, which few mathematical models existing at present attempt to do.

Summarizing this way of classifying processes, we have:

a. Individual unit process: $P \longrightarrow P$.

b. Interaction process:

    1) One individual affects another: $S_1 \longrightarrow P$.
    2) All individuals affect an individual at one time: $S_N \longrightarrow P$.
    3) A primary characteristic of the society affects an individual: $S_s \longrightarrow P$.

c. Social unit process: (not included in these models).

Postulate of Communication or Contact: In a model which contains an "interaction process," there must be an additional part which we have not yet mentioned. The interaction process ordinarily says, in effect, "Given that these two or more people are in contact or communication, they will change each other in this way." The whole model may consist essentially of one such process, as the model of distribution of wealth (the production and consumption equations are not essential to the operation of the model), or a general theory of social distributions. What is it that allows these models to continue in operation with the system reaching an equilibrium, rather than being simply a discrete process which tells what happens when two people are in contact? It is another part of the model, just as important as the interaction process, which supplies the "given" in the interaction process. It is a postulate which says, "This is how people come into contact or communication."

It supplies the missing link in any model which contains an interaction process (as all of these here do), so that the changes
described by the interaction process can occur. If we put it another way, the postulate of contact is necessary in order to translate any ordinary characteristics of an individual (e.g., his behavior) into a stimulus variable for another individual. Without
this postulate, the characteristic would remain simply a characteristic of the first individual, and not become a stimulus for the
second. In the two models mentioned above, which contain two
person interaction processes, it is a postulate which regulates the
order and frequency of interaction among various individuals in
the society. In the other two models, imitative behavior, and
altruistic and egoistic societies, it says in essence that everyone
is in contact at all times.

The only model in which this "postulate of contact" is an
explicit process is the general theory of social distribution. In
this model there is not only postulated a certain frequency of interaction between two persons, but this frequency changes as a function of a property of the individuals.

The important point about this "postulate of contact" is that
it is a necessary part of any model which contains an interaction
process and which purports to describe the behavior of a system
of individuals. This is because individuals are discrete elements,
with no systematic and continuing contact between them, so that a
model which describes the behavior of a system of interacting individuals must not only make explicit a process by which they
change each other upon contact, but also make explicit the assumptions about how often they come into contact.

Since, as we noted above, a model such as these cannot represent the behavior of a system of interacting individuals without
some such postulate as this, we shall use a symbolic representation for this in our later examination of the models: "$P \dashrightarrow S$",
meaning simply that the characteristic of the Person is translated
by some contact or communication into a Stimulus for another
individual. The broken arrow is used to stand for the term
"becomes," or "is translated into." The solid arrows for the processes indicate a *causal* connection, and stand for the term "affects." In the case that the model postulates that all are in contact
at all times, so that everyone acts as a stimulus for a person at all
times, the S will become S_N, and where the interaction is only a
two-person one, the S will become S_1, in accordance with these
distinctions made previously.

Probability Processes: We shall examine one more aspect of these processes. It is this: some of the equations introduce an element of probability, while others do not. A process we have examined before will indicate the distinction:

$$P_1 = 1 - \frac{1}{2}e^{-k(\phi + \psi)} \quad (\phi + \psi > 0) \tag{2.5}$$

Here P_1 is the probability of doing R_1, so unless it is very near one or zero, we cannot be completely sure whether the individual is doing R_1 or R_2.

If, however, k were large, then the exponential term would be very small, and the probability would vanish from the process. P_1 would always be 1, (or zero if $\phi + \psi < 0$) and the sign of $(\phi + \psi)$ would completely determine the behavior: R_1 if $\phi + \psi > 0$, and R_2 if $\phi + \psi < 0$.

This distinction is a valuable one, for if a model contains a process of the probability type, then under ordinary conditions we cannot calculate exactly the position of a given individual in the structure of the society, even at an equilibrium position of society. The greater the indeterminacy in any one process, or the greater the number of "probability processes" in the model, the less sure we are about the position of individuals in the system at any one time. The extreme case of this occurs in another of Rashevsky's models, "distribution of conservative quantities due to chance" (not one of those models examined here). In that model, we know exactly what the equilibrium distribution is, but we know nothing about any specific individual's position.

It is also important to note in which kind of an equation the probability occurs. The equation in the example above refers to a single individual; because of this, and because the society is assumed to be quite large, the indeterminancy with respect to the society vanishes, although a particular individual's behavior remains indeterminate. If the probability occurs in an equation for the behavior of the total group or society, the structure of the society would not become deterministic, and would have to be treated by stochastic methods.

To distinguish those processes which include an element of probability, we shall impose a lower case p upon the symbol for the process: for example, the above equation would be designated by $P \xrightarrow{p} P$. If this p does not appear, the process is deterministic.

OVERALL PROCESS OF THE MODEL

We want not only to look at the separate processes of each model, as indicated above, but also to examine the interlocking of these processes to form the complete model.

To show what we mean, let us use as an example the model of altruistic and egoistic societies. In this model, the overall process is one in which each individual's satisfaction is affected by the efforts of everyone in the group. Then this in turn affects the "higher" satisfaction of everyone. Each individual then changes his effort until this higher satisfaction is maximized. In this model, the overall process is the combination of these three steps, which correspond to the three equations of the model.

This is only one kind of overall process; each model has its own particular kind of overall process, but there are certain features of them which allow us to characterize the model as a whole.

Self-Generating Models: In a model such as the one mentioned above, the state of the system at a given time is determined only by the previous state and by certain constants. Certain variables within the system feed back and change other variables in the system. The distinguishing feature of this kind of model is that all characteristics which are not constant are dependent upon other variables *within* the system. There are no *independent* variables which change with time. We shall call such a model "self-generating," for once the system is set up, it depends upon nothing from the outside; all changes occur from within.

Partially Self-Generating Models: Other models may have a "feedback" mechanism which is a primary feature of the type considered above, but it is this feedback plus changes due to exogenous variables which determine subsequent states of the system. For example, if in the model of imitative behavior we considered as the system which the model was to encompass a society which imported movies from abroad, there would be not only stimulus from other people within the system, but also stimulus from without, independent of the system; that is, stimulus from the imported movies. Such a model we would call "partially self-generating," for subsequent states of the system are determined partly by previous states of the system itself and partly from variation due to outside factors. We shall see presently that the model of "distribution of wealth" is like this.

Externally-Generated Models: Finally, there are models which
have *no* feedback mechanism, which are completely dependent
upon changes due to exogenous variables. A model for the imitative behavior of one individual would be of this sort. In such a
model, changes in his behavior would be due entirely to changes in
the behavior of others, not included in the model. Such a model
might be called "externally-generated." None of the models we
are examining here are of this sort.

Dynamic And Static Models: There is another way of looking at
the overall process. This is in terms of whether any of the processes within it include time as an explicit variable. In every
equation for a causal process, time is at least an implicit variable,
but it is not always included explicity. For example, in the model
of "altruistic and egoistic societies," there is the process by which
an individual's "higher satisfaction," $\bar{S}_1$, is a function of the satisfaction of all those in the group:

$$\bar{S}_1 = k_{11}S_1 + k_{12}S_2 + \dots + k_{1n}S_n \quad . \qquad (2.6)$$

In this process, time is not an explicit variable. The process
evidently postulates that with a shift in any S_i, the shift in $\bar{S}_1$ will
be almost immediate. Such equations we have called equations of
state, as contrasted to equations of change.

   For those models which include equations of change, it is
possible to deduce not only what states will be reached, but also
the time path by which they are reached. For the type of model
which does not explicitly recognize time, this is not possible.

   However, for some models which do not explicitly recognize
time, it is possible to determine succeeding states of the system in
terms of number of trials or number of steps. Those models on
the other hand which do not recognize time, nor trials, and nor
steps are quite different from those which do. They say, in effect:
Given these initial conditions, this final *state will be reached*. The
models which do recognize time, trials, or steps, say: Given these
initial conditions, this *path will be followed*.

   All of the models here examined except the model of
"altruistic and egoistic societies" are of this latter type, while
that model, like most game theory models, is of the former type.
This "final state" type of model we shall call *static,* as opposed to
the "path" type of model, which we shall call *dynamic* (following
the usage of these terms in economic models). This distinction is

independent of the previous one of self-generating, partially self-generating, and externally-generated, made above. The way these two distinctions relate will become more evident when we examine the overall process of each model. For example, we shall find that the model of "altruistic and egoistic societies" is self-generating, but static, for it postulates that the individuals involved will bring about a certain state, with no question of how they will bring it about. That is, they will change the x_is to maximize the $\bar{S}_i$s. Given the initial conditions, a certain state will result, but we have no knowledge of what will happen in between.[24]

The previous symbolic notation of processes (e.g., "$P{\longrightarrow}P$", etc.) was used not only to enable us in the analysis to recognize each type of process more easily, but also to enable us to represent the overall process of the model. Let us use the model of "a general theory of social distributions" as an example. The processes of this model are:

$P{\dashrightarrow}S$: $K = K(s,s')$ (The frequency of contact between two people is a function of their statuses.)

$S{\xrightarrow{P}}P$: $p = p(a,a',s,s',\Delta)d\Delta$. (Given that there is a contact, the probability distribution of the first individual's change in status is a function of the abilities and statuses of the two.)

Together, the processes are: (for the individual a,s)

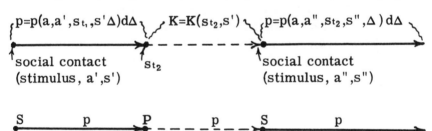

In words, it is: Contact with another person (a',s') acts to change one's own status, s_{t_1}, by an amount dependent upon the abilities and statuses of oneself and the other, and on random factors. The new status, s_{t_2}, then determines the frequency of contact with other individuals, and acts to select the next interaction partner (a'',s''). The first process then repeats itself, and so on.

All appearances to the contrary, we are not using these diagrams and symbolic notations to complicate matters, but rather to make clearer the way the model operates. The solid arrows simply represent lines of causal relationship, the broken arrow represents translation to a contact situation, and the diagram shows what happens to one individual through a short period of time. A diagram showing the processes for many people would probably defeat itself through its complexity; however, in the analysis, it will be easier with one of the models to show what happens for two people, assuming they are the only ones in the group.

This overall process in the model diagrammed above is of the self-generating type, and contains a probability process, as the above diagram shows. We shall see later what the diagrams for other types of overall processes look like.

DEDUCTIONS FROM THE POSTULATES

In presenting a systematic analysis of the model, we shall mention not only its variables and the processes, but also something about the deductions made from the basic structure. This should serve two purposes: to give some idea of what kinds of resulting situations the model predicts, telling what kinds of initial information are necessary if it is to make such predictions; and to allow one to compare the various types of deductions made concerning the different models. For some of the models, the deductions concern the state of the society at equilibrium, for some they concern not only this, but also a given individual's position in the society. We shall not classify precisely the various types of conclusions drawn from the models, but simply describe them.

Section III. A SYSTEMATIC EXAMINATION OF THE FOUR MODELS

Although this section is small in size, it constitutes the heart of the analysis. The charts on the following pages consist of a systematic presentation of the variables and processes of the several models we are studying. The classification schemes presented in the preceding sections are used to show the part each variable and each process plays in the model, and how the model as a whole is "put together."

The chart for a given model will seem rather bare as it is presented, just as the descriptions of the models given previously are imprecise and vague by themselves. The two are to be used to complement each other, so when studying the chart for a model, it will probably be useful to refer to the description given previously. While the other sections of this chapter are written to be read, this one is written to *studied*.

A cursory reading of this section will help little in understanding the models. The variables and the processes of the models will be labeled according to our classification system, as follows:

Individuals: property - relation
               attribute - continous
               constant - changing - events
               stimulus - (others)
               exogenous - endogenous

               (see page 117 for elaboration)

Groups: primary - analytic
               constant - changing

               (see page 122 for elaboration)

Processes: $S \longrightarrow P$
            $P \longrightarrow P$
            $P \dashrightarrow S$ (with subscripts s, N, and 1 for
                   the S's)

            (see page 127 for elaboration)

Since most characteristics of individuals are properties and continuous variables, they will be labeled with respect to these two factors only if they are not properties, or not continuous variables.

The important distinction of exogenous and endogenous variables will be denoted by an asterisk (*) in the left margin for exogenous variables. All others are modified through the processes of the model in some way.

After each chart will be a short description of the overall process of the model, and a few statements concerning the deductions which Rashevsky makes from the postulates of the model.

IMITATIVE BEHAVIOR (p. 86, R.)

1. *Characteristics of individuals:*   *of society:*
   a) *Explicitly introduced:*

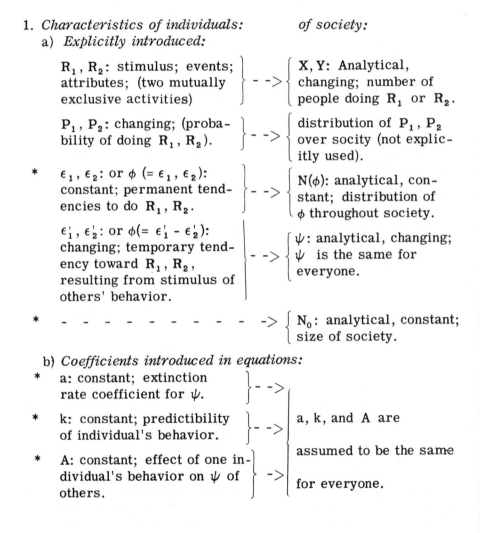

R_1, R_2: stimulus; events; attributes; (two mutually exclusive activities) - -> X, Y: Analytical, changing; number of people doing R_1 or R_2.

P_1, P_2: changing; (probability of doing R_1, R_2). - -> distribution of P_1, P_2 over socity (not explicitly used).

* ϵ_1, ϵ_2: or ϕ (= ϵ_1, ϵ_2): constant; permanent tendencies to do R_1, R_2. - -> $N(\phi)$: analytical, constant; distribution of ϕ throughout society.

ϵ_1', ϵ_2': or $\phi(= \epsilon_1' - \epsilon_2')$: changing; temporary tendency toward R_1, R_2, resulting from stimulus of others' behavior. - -> ψ: analytical, changing; ψ is the same for everyone.

* - - - - - - - - - - -> N_0: analytical, constant; size of society.

b) *Coefficients introduced in equations:*
* a: constant; extinction rate coefficient for ψ. - ->
* k: constant; predictibility of individual's behavior. - -> a, k, and A are
* A: constant; effect of one individual's behavior on ψ of others. -> assumed to be the same for everyone.

2. *Processes:*

$$S_N \longrightarrow P : \frac{d\psi}{dt} = A(X - Y) - a\psi$$ (tendency toward R_1 and R_2, produced by stimulus of others' behavior, X and Y)

$$P \xrightarrow{p} P: P_1 = 1 - \frac{1}{2} e^{-k(\phi + \psi)}$$ (if $\phi + \psi > 0$) (probability of R_1 is a function of basic tendency, ϕ, and added tendency, ψ.)

$$P_1 = \frac{1}{2} e^{-k(\phi + \psi)}$$

(if $\phi + \psi \leq 0$)

$P \dashrightarrow S_N$: everyone is in contact at all times, so that everyone's behavior acts as a stimulus for everyone else.

3. *Overall Process:*

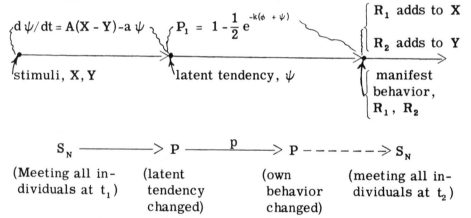

$d\psi/dt = A(X - Y) - a\psi$ $P_1 = 1 - \frac{1}{2} e^{-k(\phi + \psi)}$ R_1 adds to X

R_2 adds to Y

stimuli, X, Y latent tendency, ψ manifest behavior, R_1, R_2

$$S_N \xrightarrow{\hspace{2cm}} P \xrightarrow{\quad p \quad} P \dashrightarrow S_N$$

(Meeting all in-
dividuals at t_1)

(latent
tendency
changed)

(own
behavior
changed)

(meeting all in-
dividuals at t_2)

The model of imitative behavior is completely *self-generating,* since none of the exogenous (*) variables are assumed to change with time, and the model operates through the feedback process shown above. The model is *dynamic,* for time is an explicit variable, and the time path of the system could conceivably be deduced. It is *deterministic* with respect to the system, since the society is assumed to be quite large, and the probability process concerns the behavior of the single individual. This converges to a strictly determined number, X, for a very large society as is assumed here. However, the model is *probabilistic* with respect to the individual, for his behavior is only probably determined at equilibrium.

The deductions made from the postulates above concern the type of behavior to be found in the society at equilibrium. X^* (the number in society doing R_1 at equilibrium) will under some conditions be equal to $N_0/2$, for unless a certain inequality is met, there will be no effect of imitation. This condition of inequality is: $a < AN_0(k\sigma/\sigma + k)$.[25]   What this means in effect is this: Since A is the stimulus effect of each individual, and N_0 is the total population, then AN_0 is the total stimulus effect for the system. a is the extinction rate, or "death rate" for the imitative tendency, ψ, so if the "death rate" of ψ is greater than the total stimulus effect times the quantity in parentheses (which we shall not discuss since it has a rather complex effect), then there will be no imitation effect, and everyone will do what his own tendency tells him.

There is no exact solution made for the equilibrium value of X, that is, X^*, for the final equation can be solved only by approximate methods. However, it is shown that as size, N_0, of the population is larger, the behavior will tend more toward the extreme, either $X^* \approx N_0$ or $X^* \approx 0$. Other investigations are made, for varying distributions of ϕ, but we shall not consider them.

DISTRIBUTION OF WEALTH (p. 58, R.)

1. *Characteristics of individuals:*   *of society:*
   a. *Explicity introduced:*

   W: stimulus, changing; ⎫   ⎧ distribution of W (no
   total wealth of individual. ⎬ - -> ⎨ symbol used): analytical,
                             ⎭   ⎩ changing.

   *   x: stimulus, constant; ⎫ _ _ _> ⎧ p(x): analytical, constant;
     ability of individual.   ⎬   ⎩ distribution of ability
                                   ⎭

   * - - - - - - - - - - - - - -> ⎧ N_0 : analytical, constant;
                                  ⎩ size of society.

   * - - - - - - - - - - - - - -> ⎧ τ : primary, constant;
                                  ⎩ length of interaction.

   b. *Coefficients introduced in equations:*

   * - - - - - - - - - - - - - -> ⎧ γ : primary, constant;
                                  ⎨ coefficient of exchange
                                  ⎩ in interaction.

* (γ and τ, above, could be considered relational characteristics of individual, while A,B,C,D, and E could
* be considered properties of individuals, but being invariant over society are considered primary characteristics of the society.)

$\}$ - - -> $\begin{cases} \text{A,B,C,: primary, constant; coefficients in equation for production.} \end{cases}$

- -> $\begin{cases} \text{D,E,: primary, constant; coefficients in equation for consumption.} \end{cases}$

2. *Processes:*

$S_1 \longrightarrow P: \Delta W = \gamma(x - x')W'$ (change of wealth upon interaction as a function of abilities of two, and wealth of poorer, W'.)

$S_s \longrightarrow P: \Delta_1 W/\Delta t = A + BW + Cx$ (production per unit time is proportional to ability and to present wealth.)

$S_s \longrightarrow P: \Delta_2 W/\Delta t = D + EW$ (consumption per unit time is proportional to wealth.)

$P - \overset{p}{} - \gg S_1:$ frequency and duration of interaction is assumed constant over time and throughout society.

3. *Overall Process:*

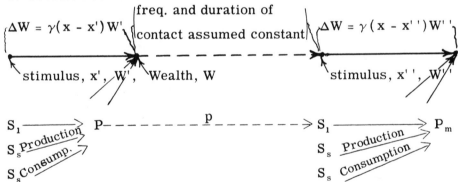

The model is only *partially self-generating,* for the processes of production and consumption are assumed to add or subtract wealth from outside sources. It is not only the interactions which determine subsequent states of the system, but also these processes which feed from the outside. The model is completely *deterministic,* containing no probability process. It is *dynamic,* although the specific deductions made are for the equilibrium state rather than the time path to this state.

We will say just a word about the mathematical methods used for solving the model. The very first step is that of summing up all the loss and gain of wealth per unit time through interactions. This is done in equations 4, and 5, p. 59, R.. In this model, as in most of the others, the society is considered as very large so that the methods of calculus may be used, so instead of a summation of all the losses and gains, it is an integration over the total society. The distribution of ability through society is assumed to be normal about x = 0. Although there are a number of mathematical operations carried out, the final deduction concerning an equilibrium state is not given in any terms which are specific enough to show how the distribution of W varies with changes in the other characteristics.

The solution for the equilibrium state, if it were carried to its conclusion, would be seen to depend upon these characteristics: $p(x)$, τ, γ, A, B, C, D, and E. All but the first of these are primary characteristics of the society, with meanings something like what we have suggested above. According to the model, the distribution of wealth will, as is stated in the book, be highly skewed toward individuals of high ability.[26]

A GENERAL THEORY OF SOCIAL DISTRIBUTIONS
(p. 64, R.)

1. *Characteristics of individuals:*   *of society:*
   a. *Explicitly introduced:*

   a: stimulus, constant; learn- ⎫   ⎧ F(a): analytical, con-
   ing ability of individual.   ⎬ -> ⎨ stant; distribution of a
                                   ⎭   ⎩ over society.

   s: stimulus, changing;   ⎫   ⎧ N(s): analytical, chang-
   status of individual.   ⎬ -> ⎨ ing; distribution of s
                                   ⎭   ⎩ over society.

   $p(\Delta)$: relational, (not re- ⎫ -> ⎧ none explicitly con-
   flexive nor symmetric),   ⎪   ⎩ sidered.
   changing; probability distri-   ⎬
   bution of change in status   ⎪
   upon interaction.   ⎭

K: relational, (symmetric, not reflexive), changing; frequency of contact between two individuals. $\left.\vphantom{\begin{array}{c}a\\a\\a\\a\end{array}}\right\}$ -- ->$\left\{\vphantom{\begin{array}{c}a\\a\end{array}}\right.$ none explicitly con-sidered.

* - - - - - - - - - - - - - -> $\left\{\vphantom{\begin{array}{c}a\\a\end{array}}\right.$ N_0: analytical, constant; size of society.

b. *Coefficients introduced in equations:* none

2. *Processes:*

$S_1 \xrightarrow{\ p\ } P$: $p = p(a,a',s,s', \Delta)\, d\Delta$ (probability of changing a cer-tain amount, Δ , upon inter-
       (specific form is not   action is a function of abilities
       given)   and statuses of two individuals and of Δ .)

$P \xdashrightarrow{\ p\ } S_1$: $K = K(s,s')$ (frequency of two individuals meeting is a function of their statuses.)

3. *Overall Process:*

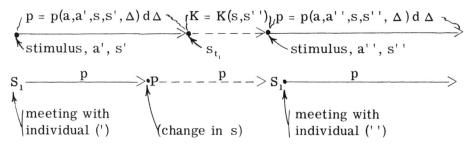

The model of "A General Theory of Social Distributions" is *self-generating,* since the only changing characteristics (s and K and $p(\Delta)$) are changed by the system itself, and act through feedback processes to change each other. The model is *dynamic,* for it can show how the state of the system changes with time; and it is *probabilistic* to a greater to a greater extent than any other model we are examining. Both processes are probability proc-esses, the first one explicitly, and the second implicitly, but no less so. For in the second process, even if we consider the fre-quency of meeting as strictly determined by the s of the two indi-viduals, the initial order of meeting is evidently random (subject to the frequency restrictions), and upon the order will depen'd the subsequent state of the system.

No specific deductions are made by Rashevsky concerning this model, although some operations are carried out to show how such deductions would be made. Few deductions can be made concerning the model in its present state, since the specific forms of the processes are not given. The great interest the model holds for us lies in the fact that it contains a process of voluntary association, which none of the other models here (and few other models anywhere) do, and in its conjoining this with the other type of process which it includes. These two processes in conjunction seem to produce a system similar to a number of situations in social behavior. One such situation we shall examine in Section 5. Since the further implications of the model are dealt with there, we shall not consider them here.

ALTRUISTIC AND EGOISTIC SOCIETIES (p. 119, R.)

1. *Characteristics of individuals:*   *of society:*

   a. *Explicitly introduced:*

   x_i : stimulus, changing; effort of individual i. $\left.\right\}$-->$\left\{\right.$ none explicitly considered.

   S_i : stimulus; changing; satisfaction of individual i. $\left.\right\}$-->$\left\{\right.$ none explicitly considered.

   $\overline{S}_i$: changing; undefined but corresponds to a "higher" satisfaction. $\left.\right\}$-->$\left\{\right.$ none explicitly considered.

   * k_{ij} : relational, (reflexive not symmetric), constant; concern of individual i with individual j's satisfaction. $\left.\right\}$--> $\left|\right.$ matrix of k_{ij}'s which defines society as altruistic or egoistic, or some combination of the two. analytical, constant.

   b. *Coefficients introduced in equations:*

   * a_i : constant; increase in satisfaction per unit of reward (e.g., pay) . $\left.\right\}$-->$\left\{\right.$ none explicitly considered.

* b_i : constant; decrease in satisfaction from expending one unit of effort. $\left.\vphantom{\begin{array}{c}a\\b\\c\end{array}}\right\}$ -->$\left\{\vphantom{\begin{array}{c}a\\b\end{array}}\right.$none explicitly considered.

* p_{ij} : relational, (reflexive, not symmetric), stimulus effect of individual i's effort on individual j's satisfaction. $\left.\vphantom{\begin{array}{c}a\\b\\c\\d\end{array}}\right\}$ -->$\left\{\vphantom{\begin{array}{c}a\\b\end{array}}\right.$none explicitly considered.

2. *Processes:*

(1) $S_N \longrightarrow P : S_i = a_i \sum_{j=1}^{N} p_{ji} x_j - b_i x_i^2$

(each individual's S is a function of the reward resulting from everyone's effort (first right hand term) and the "punishment" resulting from his own effort (2nd right hand term).)

(2) $P \text{ - ->} S_N$: (implicit); each individual knows the satisfaction of every other individual.

(3) $S_N \longrightarrow P : \overline{S}_i = k_{i1} S_1 + k_{i2} S_2 + \dots + k_{iN} S_N$

(each individual's $\overline{S}$ is a function of the satisfaction of all others times his concern for their satisfactions)

(4) $P \longrightarrow P$: Individual i changes x_i to maximize $\overline{S}_i$; that is, until

$$\frac{\partial S_i}{\partial x_i} = 0 \ .$$

(5) $P \text{ - ->} S_N$: (implicit) everyone's effort affects others.

3. *Overall Process:*

(We shall consider, in the diagram, the total group to be two individuals; the lines represent the points at which each affects the other. The S's in the upper diagram are variables of the model, not related to those in the lower diagram, which symbolize the type of process.)

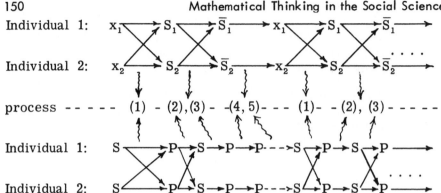

Individual 1: x_1 $\longrightarrow$ S_1 $\longrightarrow$ $\bar{S}_1$ $\longrightarrow$ x_1 $\longrightarrow$ S_1 $\longrightarrow$ $\bar{S}_1$ $\longrightarrow$

Individual 2: x_2 $\longrightarrow$ S_2 $\longrightarrow$ $\bar{S}_2$ $\longrightarrow$ x_2 $\longrightarrow$ S_2 $\longrightarrow$ $\bar{S}_2$ $\longrightarrow$

process $- - - - -$ (1) $-$ (2),(3) $-$ $-$(4, 5)$- - -$ (1)$-$ $-$ (2), (3) $- - - - -$

Individual 1: S $\longrightarrow$ P $\longrightarrow$ S $\longrightarrow$ P $\longrightarrow$ P $- - ->$ S $\longrightarrow$ P $\longrightarrow$ S $\longrightarrow$ P $\longrightarrow$

Individual 2: S $\longrightarrow$ P $\longrightarrow$ S $\longrightarrow$ P $\longrightarrow$ P $- - ->$ S $\longrightarrow$ P $\longrightarrow$ S $\longrightarrow$ P $\longrightarrow$

This model is quite different from any of those we have yet studied. It is *self-generating,* just as most of the others, but it differs from them in that it predicates only a final state, and does not show behavior processes operating through time. (In the diagram of the overall process, we have showed the processes operating through time, but only because the fact that there is a final state different from the initial state necessitates it.) Process (4) says only that the individual will change his x to maximizing his $\bar{S}$, and does not tell *how* he will do so. Therefore, the model is *static,* and in this respect is quite similar to game theory models and other maximization or minimax problems. They are problems in rational behavior, which set up a system, and then ask what is the rational way for the individual to maximize his gains (or minimize his losses).

The model is completely *deterministic*.

In solving the maximization problem, the individual must know characteristics of other individuals such as S_j, p_{ij}, and a_j for all j's who affect his higher satisfaction. This means that the model predicates not the kind of interaction in the imitative behavior model, which was superficial, with no memory effect, but rather a fairly close relationship. It might be noted that not only a group which was egoistic (concern for others is zero), but also a group which was "atomistic" in that no one knew how his effort affected others (i.e., no one knew p_{ij}'s or a_j's of others), would act without regard for others. Altruistic behavior in this model presupposes both *concern for* others' material satisfaction, and *knowledge* of how one's behavior will affect their satisfaction.

But this is not reckoning with a further complication. The model seems to be a special case of an n-person, non-zero sum game, in which the solution (if one exists) is not nearly so easily determined as Rashevsky's presentation suggests. The basis of the difficulty is that each $\bar{S}_i$ is a function of $(x_1, x_2, \ldots x_n)$, so that a simple maximization with respect to x_i is not sufficient.

Section IV. THE MATHEMATICAL OPERATIONS USED TO MAKE DEDUCTIONS FROM THE POSTULATES

So far we have dealt primarily with one aspect of these models: the postulates which form their structures. We have also mentioned what kinds of deductions are made from the postulates. But one large area we have not touched: how to get from the postulates to the final deductions. It is here that the real mathematics of a model occurs, for the deductions are drawn from the postulates through mathematical operations upon the postulates.

Each model will in general require its own particular methods for making deductions, determined by its postulates. It would seem, therefore, that nothing in general could be said about the methods of making such deductions. This is not true, because (1) one man's models will reflect a certain type of mathematics, that to which he is most accustomed. For example, Rashevsky's mathematics is that of classical physics, leaning heavily on calculus, having little to do with stochastic processes or matrix algebra, which are the primary tools of some other model-builders. (2) It is quite easy to set up postulates from which few deductions can be made because the mathematics for making the deductions do not exist. Therefore, the postulates of a model are not ordinarily set up without thinking about how deductions are to be made from them, but are usually modified in order to allow deductions to be made.

We shall show how deductions are made concerning an equilibrium state in one of the models; for the above reasons, this will suggest how they are made in some of Rashevsky's other models. At the same time, this will show how the systematic presentation of the models in the previous section may be used to aid in making deductions. The model is that of imitative behavior, for which the overall process is:

$$
\left\{ \frac{d\psi}{dt} = A(X - Y) - a\psi \right. \quad \rightsquigarrow \quad \left/ P_1 = 1 - \frac{1}{2} e^{-k(\phi + \psi)} \right. \quad \rightsquigarrow \quad \left\{ \begin{array}{l} R_1 \text{ adds to } X \\ R_2 \text{ adds to } Y \end{array} \right\}
$$

$$
\begin{array}{cccc}
X, Y & & \psi & R_1, R_2 \qquad X, Y
\end{array}
$$

$$
S_N \longrightarrow P \xrightarrow{\quad p \quad} P \dashrightarrow S_N
$$

We shall carry out deductions concerning the equilibrium state, asking the question: If there is an equilibrium state, with the number of people doing R_1 (say X^*) constant, then what variables will determine this state, and in what way? We shall not carry out the deduction in detail, but only indicate the essential steps.

1. *Setting Up The Problem:* The endogenous or dependent variables of the system are those indicated as such in the previous section. They are:

for the individual: ψ, P_1, R_1, R_2

for the society: ψ, X, Y.

We want, if possible, to solve the equations for X^*, the equilibrium value of X, in terms of the independent variables, eliminating the other dependent variables. That is, to solve for X^* in terms of A, a, k, N_0, $N(\phi)$.

2. *Determining the Equilibrium State for One Person:* Since the two processes, $S_N \longrightarrow P$, and $P \xrightarrow{p} P$, are sequential, and represent processes occuring for a single individual, we can combine them to eliminate a P. That is, $S_N \longrightarrow P \xrightarrow{p} P$ can be collapsed to $S_N \xrightarrow{p} P$.

$$S_N \longrightarrow P: \quad \frac{d\psi}{dt} = A(X - Y) - a\psi \tag{4.1}$$

$$\text{transposing, } \psi = \frac{A(X - Y) - d\psi/dt}{a} \tag{4.1a}$$

$$P \xrightarrow{p} > P: \quad P_1 = 1 - \frac{1}{2} e^{-k(\phi + \psi)} \tag{4.2}$$

(this equation holds for an individual whose $\phi + \psi > 0$, a similar one holding for those whose $\phi + \psi \leq 0$).
At equilibrium,

$$X = X^* \text{ and } Y = Y^* = N_0 - X^*,$$

so

$$X^* - Y^* = 2X^* - N_0 \tag{4.3}$$

Also at equilibrium, $d\psi/dt$ must equal zero, since this equation determines the shift in P_1 over time, which is zero for everyone at equilibrium. Therefore, using this fact and (4.3), and (4.1a), at equilibrium, we obtain

$$\psi^* = \frac{A(2X^* - N_0)}{a} \tag{4.4}$$

This ψ^* is the same for everyone. Substituting this in (4.2), we collapse the two equations into one, giving

$$P_1^* = 1 - \frac{1}{2} e^{-k(\phi + \frac{A(2X^* - N_0)}{a})} \tag{4.5}$$

This gives us the probability that an individual with $\phi + \psi^* > 0$ will do R_1 at equilibrium. But as it stands it is dependent upon X^*, which is determined by all the P_1^*'s for everyone in society. Therefore, the next step is to relate the individual back to society, showing how his behavior contributes to the equilibrium.

3. *The Individual's Behavior Related to Society:* So far, we have the probability that a person with a certain ϕ will do R_1 at equilibrium. Since at equilibrium the only factor which varies throughout the population besides P_1^* is ϕ, then we can write P_1^* as a function of ϕ, $P_1^*(\phi)$. This means that one person's P_1^* differs from that of another only as their ϕ's differ.

Further, we know that the number of people who have ϕ's between ϕ_1 and $\phi_1 + d\phi$ is $N(\phi_1)d\phi$. Suppose, for example, this number is ten. Then the expected number of these who will do R_1 at equilibrium is $P_1^*(\phi)\cdot 10$. If P_1^* for these people is .9, then the expected number of the ten who will do R_1 is $.9\cdot 10$, or 9. In general, the expected number of people in such an interval who will do R_1 is $P_1^*(\phi)N(\phi)d\phi$. If we integrate this over the population, then we will get the expected number of people in the whole society who will do R_1 at equilibrium. Since the population is assumed to be quite large, the expected number will equal the actual number; that is, it will equal X^*. Written as an equation,

$$X^* = \int_{-\infty}^{\infty} P_1^* (\phi)N(\phi)d\phi. \tag{4.6}$$

This now allows us to eliminate one of the two dependent variables which are still remaining; that is, to eliminate X^* or P_1^*, just as we previously were able to eliminate all the dependent variables but these two. By combining equations (4.5) and (4.6), we do this. First, we multiply both sides of equation (4.5) by $N(\phi)\,d\phi$, to get:

$$P_1^*(\phi)\,N(\phi)\,d\phi = \left\{ 1 - \frac{1}{2}\,e^{-k\left[\phi + \frac{A(2X^* - N_0)}{a}\right]} \right\} N(\phi)\,d\phi \qquad (4.7)$$

If we now integrate both sides of equation (4.7) with respect to ϕ, we get for the left hand side, $\int P_1^*(\phi)\,N(\phi)\,d\phi$, which is equal to X^*, so that by integrating the right hand side, we obtain the value of X^* as a function of all the exogenous variables of the system, with P_1^* eliminated. This is essentially the way the last step is carried out. However, for three reasons, it gets complicated, so we shall not carry it further.

The first reason is that, as we mentioned before, the equation for P_1^* with which we began, equation (4.5), holds only for those people $\phi + \psi > 0$. A similar equation holds for the rest of the population, but this divides up the integration into two parts, which makes a formidable looking integration. Second, we must assume some distribution of ϕ, that is, some form for $N(\phi)$, and the form which Rashevsky has assumed makes the integration even more formidable looking. Most important, however, is the the fact that even after integration, the equation cannot be solved explicitly for X^*, since X^* occurs both in an exponential term and algebraically, so that approximations must be made to find the value of X^*.

In principle, however, we have carried the deduction through, showing the principal steps which are necessary to solve for one of the dependent variables (X) at equilibrium, in terms of the exogenous variables of the system. The principal steps were: setting up the equilibrium conditions; eliminating all possible variables while dealing with the equations for one person alone; and eliminating the final dependent variable (P_1^*) by relating the individual behavior at equilibrium to the state of the whole society.

Section V. SUBSTITUTION OF DIFFERENT CONTENT IN SOME OF THE FORMAL MODELS

GENERAL THEORY OF SOCIAL DISTRIBUTIONS BECOMES: ATTITUDE CHANGE AND VOLUNTARY ASSOCIATION

We have already suggested the application of the model of "A General Theory of Social Distributions" to a different behavior area – that of attitude change. We suggested that while the basic process might not be especially good for representing change in status, it may be better for representing change in attitude.

Let us look at the two processes of the model again. The process of change, given contact with another individual, as indicated on page 147 is of the following form: The probability of changing s a certain amount is a function of two primary characteristics of the individuals and of the predicated amount of change. Symbolically, it is: Probability of changing s an amount Δ is $p(a, a', s, s', \Delta)d\Delta$. The form of the function is not specified further. As it stands, the process is quite general: It says that there is a certain probability distribution of attitude change (i.e., change in s) given certain values for the two characteristics of the individuals. For example, for particular values a_1, a_1', s_1, and s_1', the probability distribution for change in attitude of the first individual (that is, individual a, s) might look like this:

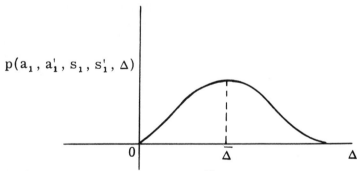

Here the most probable amount of change is $\bar{\Delta}$. On simple intuitive grounds, remembering the way attitudes seem to change, we see that this might represent a situation in which the other individual (a', s') has an attitude more positive than (i.e., more to the right of) the first, and thus upon interaction the attitude of the first would change in the direction of the second, the most likely amount of change being $\bar{\Delta}$.

We see that as long as the process is left as it stands, it is quite general, and also, as in the case of any very general proposition, not of much use in a particular case. About the only restrictions it makes on the interaction is that the attitudes are made manifest, and that the way in which they are made manifest, as well as the way in which the other individual's attitude is received, are dependent on one other characteristic., a, of each of the individuals besides their attitudes, s. By selecting this characteristic with care, we can keep the indeterminacy of the model to a minimum, making the distribution of Δ closely concentrated about some value, $\bar{\Delta}$. For there are actually many characteristics of the individuals which affect the amount of change, and if we knew them all and the way they operate to produce this change, we could eliminate the uncertainty from the process. We could calculate exactly what the amount of change would be. We are far from such a happy prospect, however, and the best we can do is to select some one of those characteristics which might be measured somehow and which does have an important effect on the amount of change. In a more complex model, we might add another variable, to reduce the uncertainty still further.

The second process of Rashevsky's model of distribution of status, the process which regulates frequency of interaction, is this: $P \longrightarrow S$: $K = K(s, s')$. It specifies only that K, the frequency of interaction between two people, is a function of their statuses (in our case, now, their attitudes). This fits in quite well with a process of attitude change. It has been often observed that there is a process which tends to counteract potential attitude change in informal social situations. The process is this: those whose attitudes on a relevant subject are similar tend to associate with each other, while those whose attitudes differ stay apart as best they can.

Changing the symbols of the model now, let a_i represent the attitude position of individual i. The second characteristic of the individual which enters the process as affecting change is the attitude's *relevance* to him which we shall call r_i. We will postulate that as the relevance of the attitude increases, his attitude change upon interaction will decrease. Then we want the first process – attitude change – to say that given an interaction between individuals i and j, the difference in attitude, d_{ij} ($= |a_i - a_j|$), after the interaction will be less than before the interaction. That is, $\Delta d_{ij}/\text{contact} < 0$. Further, since the process depends upon r_i and r_j, we want to say that Δa_i = decreasing $f(r_i)$, and similarly for

a_i . That is, we say here that as the relevance of the attitude to him is greater, the attitude will be affected less by influence of others. If we let k_{ij} be the frequency of interaction between i and j, then the first process is to conform to: Δa_i = increasing $f(k_{ij}, 1/r_i)$.

The second process says that as d_{ij} is greater, frequency of interaction is less, or symbolically, k_{ij} = decreasing $f(d_{ij})$. Also, we want it to say that as the relevance increases, the change in frequency brought about by attitude similarity or conflict will be more pronounced. That is, k_{ij} = increasing $f(r_i, r_j)$. Or altogether, the process is to conform to: k_{ij} = increasing $f(1/d_{ij}, r_i, r_j)$.

We shall give specific form to these processes shortly, to show how they might operate in an extremely simplified situation. But first, it is worthwhile to consider for a moment some aspects of the second process, regulation of interaction. The process might include an element of indeterminacy. For example, suppose there are ten people in the group which the model is to represent, say tenants in a small apartment building, and suppose that according to the model, the frequency of contact between any two of them is, to begin with, exactly once per day. It would seem that such a process would be deterministic, for it states definitely that to begin with each pair meets once a day. However, the process is certainly not deterministic, for it does not state the *order* in which they would meet, and in general a person's attitude at the end of the day would be different, depending upon the order in which he met the nine others. It would be possible to "doctor up" the process for attitude change, so that the order of meeting would make no difference, but this might be at the expense of having the process reflect any real process of attitude change.

We see that one must be quite stringent in setting up the conditions for the frequency-regulating process (the P - -> S process). If he is not, then indeterminacy is introduced into the model, perhaps preventing any deductions from being made. The reason Rashevsky was able to have processes of interaction without specifying in the postulates the order of meeting along with the frequency is that the operations used to carry out the deductions introduced this assumption implicitly. Since he assumed very large societies, the final deductions may be the same as if this restriction had not been introduced. For a small group such as we would like to consider here), to allow indeterminacy is to postulate a stochastic process which might be quite difficult to solve for an equilibrium state (if one exists).

This model of attitude change and change in association then is of this sort, to recapitulate: Two people have some initial frequency of meeting through propinquity. They meet; if their attitudes are fairly close together, they will reinforce, coming closer to the same. This similarity in attitudes will make them see each other more frequently, further strengthening their attitude similarity. If their attitudes are quite different, the model says that the initial contact would bring them closer together, but at the same time, if it did not bring them close enough, the difference in attitudes would tend to make them reduce the frequency of meeting. If the attitudes of each were reinforced in their own direction later, through meeting others, then the model would say that their frequency of meeting would grow even less, and thus their chance to influence each other less.[27]

Let us give these processes specific form, to show how they would operate in a simplified version of the model. We shall make both processes deterministic, for the reasons mentioned before.

Suppose there is a new apartment building into which ten single men have just moved, and suppose it is during the heat of an election campaign. Three of the men are strong Democrats, and seven strong Republicans. They see each other exactly once the first day, and in no special order (the process for attitude change is doctored so that the model remains deterministic). We assume that they make known their attitudes upon each contact. Attitude change is presumed to take place overnight, taking into account all the influences which have been operating during the day. The process by which the change in frequency of interaction comes about happens immediately as the attitudes change. More precisely:

1. *Characteristics of Individuals:*
   a_i: stimulus, changing; political
   attitude, Democratic or Republican

   $-1 \leq a_i \leq + 1$, with:

   $(-1 \leq a_i \leq 0)$ = Republican, with greatest
   strength at - 1.

   $(0 \leq a_i + 1)$ = Democratic, with greatest
   strength at + 1.

 * r_i : stimulus, constant; relevance of attitude (Assume
   $r_i = r = .45$ for all i.)

k_{ij} : relational, (symmetric, not reflexive), changing: frequency of interaction between individuals i and j. k_{ij} = 1 meeting per day for all i,j before attitudes are known.

2. *Coefficients Introduced in Equations:*

* b_{ij} : *relational,* (symmetric, not reflexive), *constant;* frequency of interaction in absence of any attitude effect. b_{ij} = b = 1 meeting/day for all i, j.

* g_i : *constant;* effect of other's attitude in changing own attitude; g_i = g = .0225 units of a_i changed times units of relevance / units of others' attitude, for all i.

3. *Processes:*

$$S_1 \longrightarrow P: \quad \Delta a_i/day = \frac{g}{r} \sum_{j=1}^{10} k_{ij} a_j \quad (i \neq j)$$

(attitude change per day is cumulative effect of all influences in that day).

$$P \text{ - - - >} S_1 : \quad k_{ij} = be^{r^2 a_i a_j}$$

(interaction frequency is a function of position and relevances of attitudes of two individuals).

4. *Overall Process:*

$$\left\{ \Delta a_i = \frac{g}{r} \sum_j k_{ij} a_j \quad k_{ij} = be^{r^2 a_i a_j} \right.$$

stimuli, a_j a_i stimuli, a_j

$S_1 \longrightarrow P \text{ - - - - - - >} S_1 \longrightarrow$

The above postulates fulfill the conditions set forth previously concerning the relations between the variables. The attitude change is dependent upon meeting others, and it decreases with the relevance of one's own attitude, while increasing with the number of contacts. The interaction frequency increases as attitudes are more nearly alike (but having little effect where attitudes are almost neutral, most effect where they are most pronouced in one direction or the other), and becomes more pronounced as the relevance increases.

Now, with the specific values we have given the variables, what will happen to the seven Republicans and the three Democrats?

If we assume that when they move into the apartment building,
their attitudes are -1 for the Republicans and +1 for the Democrats; that is, maximum on both sides, then let us see what happens to each group after the first day. Substituting values of a_i,
g, r, and k_{ij} into the equation for the first process, we find that
when they get up the next morning, each Democrat finds his attitude is now .75 rather than +1, while the Republicans maintain
their attitude at -1. The frequency of contact between each two
Democrats has increased, however, to 1.13 (this is actually meaningless, since the model is deterministic, and k_{ij} can take on only
integral values, but we will continue to use it because of complications which would occur by restricting k_{ij} to integral values.
There would be no difficulty if the model were not deterministic.).
Meanwhile, the frequency of contact between any one of them and
a Republican is reduced to .86. The frequency of contact between
two Republicans, however, is increased to 1.22, where it remains
from this point hence.

After the second day, the Democrats are faring even worse.
Now their attitudes are down to .56, and they are not strong enough
to keep the previous level of interaction up, so it is down to 1.06
now, while their frequency of meeting Republicans is up to .89.
The Republicans, strong enough in numbers and now stronger in
attitude than the Democrats, continue at the same attitude level and
interaction level as before (these are limited by the attitude relevance, r, and by the upper limit on a).

By the third day, the Democrats are down to an attitude of
.36, with a faster eroding of their attitudes now. Their interaction
reduces to 1.03, only a little above the propinquity level, and their
interaction with Republicans now up to .93, only a little below the
propinquity level.

Soon we find that all the Democrats are as staunch Republicans as the original Republicans, their attitudes having been completely changed. Although for simplicity we dealt with only two
groups, it is easy to see that if we had allowed r_i to vary among
the individuals, we would have had different individuals ending up
at different places. Some of the Democrats would have been converted, while some would have continued in the old attitude, while
if we had allowed the a_i's to take on different values from the two
poles, +1 and -1, we might have had some of the Republicans converted to Democrats. The value of r_i is quite important in the
model, for in the above example, if r_i had been +1 for all i,
rather than +.45, the Democrats would have been able to increase
their rate of interaction among themselves enough to counteract

the seven Republicans in the building, so that they would have remained Democratic. At equilibrium, they would associate with
other Democrats 2.7 times a day, and with the Republicans only
.36 times, little enough to insure that they will not be converted.

Of course, the specific form we have given the model comes
far from conforming to actual forms of the processes in real life.
However, it serves as an example to show how the model operates,
and what kind of generalizations of the model it can lead to.

ALTRUISTIC AND EGOISTIC SOCIETIES BECOMES
CONFORMITY IN A GROUP SITUATION

We shall introduce this model differently from the preceding
one, beginning by describing a social situation which is fictional
but of a familiar type. Then we shall take one of the processes
from the model of altruistic and egoistic societies and show how it
fits an important aspect of the situation we have described.

Suppose there are six people working in a certain shop of a
large company. One of the six is foreman of the group. Management has decided to attempt to introduce Negroes into its working
force, but in doing so has a plan in which the members of each
shop vote on whether to allow a Negro in that particular shop. Let
us single out one individual in the shop, and investigate his reactions when this situation arises.

This man feels that Negroes should be allowed into the shop,
for he reacts unfavorably to the general discrimination against
Negroes. In talking to the others, he finds that one of his fairly
close friends is strongly against allowing a Negro to come in,
while two others of his friends are strongly for it. The foreman,
a rather opinionated man, is strongly against the whole idea. Our
man notes all this, and it affects his own basic attitude somewhat,
but he continues to feel not much differently than he did at first.
He plans to vote for allowing the man into the shop.

But when it comes time to vote, he finds that it won't be by
secret ballot, as he had thought, but that he will have to say yes or
no in front of all five of his fellow-workers, including the foreman.
For him this certainly changes the situation. Now he must re-
assess his decision, for what might the foreman do if he votes contrary to the foreman's expressed wishes? And what about his
friend who strongly opposes the idea of a Negro in the shop? Will
a vote for the Negro alienate this man? He must weigh all these
things; no longer will he be able to vote the way he really feels.

These other factors complicate the situation greatly. After much deliberation, he decides to vote against the Negro.

But then when the vote is about to be taken, the foreman reads again the instructions from management, and finds he must not be present for the vote because of the possible influence of a foreman in swaying the vote. Now our tortured man must once again re-evaluate the situation. One of the factors, an important one, is gone from the situation. This time, and for the final time, he decides to vote for the Negro, since his basic attitude together with the chance of alienating his two friends who are for the Negro counterbalance the possibility of alienating his other friend who is against the Negro.

As we can see, this man had a pretty difficult time of it, and was no doubt glad when the vote was finally over. The difficulty however, was not for him alone, because each of the other man in the shop had to make similar decisions. We should recognize that this is not an isolated and uncommon kind of process. Much of our social behavior contains the basic elements which entered into this process. And the very terms in which it is stated invite some mathematical formulation. The man "weighs" these "factors," finds that one group "counterbalances" the other, and so behaves one way rather than the other. The man we singled out was attempting, in making his decision, to measure according to some standard, each factor. In setting up a mathematical model for the process, we will be doing nothing more nor less than attempting to reproduce the process which the man himself carried out.

We postulate that the structure of the process is similar to $\bar{S}_1 = k_{11} S_1 + k_{12} + \ldots + k_{16} S_6$, with appropriate meanings for the symbols. The meanings: S_i (we shall substitute the symbol A_i) is the direction and intensity of individual i's *attitude* on the question. Since there are only two possible positions, for or against, then this one variable can represent both the position and intensity of the attitude. Here the absolute value of A_i is the intensity, while the sign, plus or minus, is the position, for or against.

$\bar{S}_i$ (we shall substitute the symbol B_i) is the *behavior* of individual i on the question. In our shop example, this could have only direction (a vote for or against), not intensity. In general, however, it could have both intensity (denoted by absolute value) and direction (denoted by sign).

k_{ij} is the degree to which individual i feels he must conform to the attitude of individual j. All the k_{ij}'s for individual i sum up to one; that is

$$\sum_{j=1}^{6} k_{ij} = 1.$$

We should note that k_{ii} has a special significance. The size of k_{ii} as compared to the sum of all the rest of the k_{ij}'s (for that same individual) is the degree to which the individual is "inner directed" rather than "other directed" within this particular group. Or we may think of it as his "self-confidence" within this group. The k_{ij}'s can be thought of as "coefficients of influence," for they are a measure of the influence of individual j on individual i.

The process, then, which we have postulated to exist in the fictional situation we described, and in others like it, is: (using the substituted symbols)

$$B_1 = k_{11}A_1 + k_{12}A_2 + \ldots + k_{16}A_6$$

and equivalently for the other members of the group. This, we suggest, is the form of the decision process through which the man finally cast his vote. When the further variations occurred, the man altered his "equation" accordingly. For example, when the foreman (6) left, the sixth term of the equation dropped out.

The six behaviors, B_i, written as a vector, would be equal to the matrix of k_{ij}'s times the vector of attitudes, A_i. That is:

$B = KA$, where B is the vector of B_i's, K is the matrix of k_{ij}'s, and A is the vector of A_i's.

Let us compare now, in diagrammatic form, the process for conforming behavior to the process taken from altruistic and egoistic societies: (using only two individuals for simplicity)

$$S_i \qquad \overline{S}_i \qquad k_{ij}$$
$$\text{is} \qquad \text{is} \qquad \text{is}$$
$$\text{equivalent} \quad \text{equivalent}$$
$$\text{to} \qquad \text{to} \qquad \text{to}$$
$$\downarrow \qquad \downarrow \qquad \downarrow$$
$$A_i \qquad B_i \qquad k_{ij}$$

$$(\overline{S}_i = k_{ii}S_i + k_{ij}S_j)$$

$$(B_i = k_{ii}A_i + k_{ij}A_j)$$

We see that the two processes are structurally just the same, although the specific meanings of the variables are different.

But in examining this process previously (Section IV) we showed that it actually represents two processes, P - ->S, and S ——→ P; that is, first there is the process by which the S_i's (or A_i's) become stimuli for other individuals, then the process through which, as stimuli, they affect an individual's $\bar{S}_i$ (or B_i). This sensitizes us to the fact that in the present situation there must be communication of some sort if A_i is to affect B_j. This then leads us to ask what will happen if the individuals are not able to communicate. Let us consider such a situation, (with only two people for simplicity) in which an individual must infer the other's attitude through noting his behavior, and he assumes that this behavior directly reflects that person's attitude. That is,

$$B_{1(\text{time } 1)} = k_{11} A_1 + k_{12} B_{2(\text{time } 0)}$$

In the same way that the first individual infers the second's attitude, the second infers the first's:

$$B_{2(\text{time } 1)} = k_{21} B_{1(\text{time } 0)} + k_{22} A_2 \, .$$

Now the model takes on added interest: What will happen at time 2? Of course, we don't know what will happen in various kinds of actual situations, but we shall construct the model for a situation in which the same thing occurs the second time as occurred the first time. That is,

$$B_{1(\text{time } 2)} = k_{11} A_1 + k_{12} B_{2(\text{time } 1)}$$

$$B_{2(\text{time } 2)} = k_{21} B_{1(\text{time } 1)} + k_{22} A_2$$

With this step we have a *dynamic* and *self-generating* model. The behavior keeps changing with each step, as long as the individuals are in contact, until an equilibrium is reached. Let us compare the structure of this model now with that of the satisfaction model:

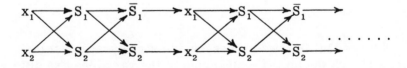

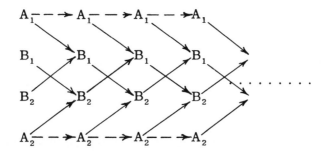

The structure of the new model with these further changes is more than a little different from the satisfaction model. In the first place, it postulates only one type of process, while the satisfaction model has three. Secondly, although B_i plays a role similar to $\overline{S}_i$, it is dependent not on the A's of everyone, but on one's own A and on others' B's; $\overline{S}_i$, on the other hand, is dependent on the S's of everyone.

This, above, is the essential structure of the model, modified for a situation with no verbal communication. Now we might ask: According to the model, what will happen? Will an equilibrium be reached? If so, what are the equilibrium values of B_i? Are they the same for everyone in the group? That is, does $B_1 = B_2$ at equilibrium? How long, under various conditions, will i take to reach an equilibrium if one is reached?

Although most of these questions are fairly easily answered, we shall not investigate them here, but rather finish the consideration of this model by asking more fundamental questions, such as: How well does the basic model itself agree with any actual situations? Or, concerning the k_{ij}'s, are they useful characteristics by which to describe an individual in such a situation? If so, how much do they vary from one situation to another, and from one type of activity to another? What relation do they have to what sociologists call "reference group behavior?" One interesting point concerning them is this: While the sum of k_{ij}'s over j equals 1, the sum of k_{ij}'s over i for a given individual j does not in general equal 1. This sum seems to be a measure of the individual's status in the group: more precisely, it is the totality of his influence in setting the norms of the group, or in directing the behavior of the group.

4. Probability in the Social Sciences

By JACOB MARSCHAK

University of Chicago

Section I. PROBABILITIES AND THE NORMS OF BEHAVIOR

Recently,[1] the U. N. forces in Korea faced the choice between two decisions: (I) to cross the 38° parallel or (II) not to
cross it. Their commanders did not know whether, if the parallel
were crossed, the Chinese adversary would or would not answer
by counter-attacking in superior power, from across Korea's
Northern border. In the language of current newspapers, our officers did not know whether the Chinese did or did not have "aggressive intentions." This is a vague term. The following table gives,
however, an implicit definition that is precise enough. The intentions of the adversary are defined by their results, as follows:

Table I

Chinese behavior \ Our behavior	(I) Cross the parallel	(II) Don't cross the parallel
(a) "aggressive"	U. N. Losses	Stalemate
(b) "non-aggressive"	U. N. Gains	Stalemate

We shall assume that, from the U. N. point of view, gains
are preferable to stalemate, and stalemate is preferable to losses.
We shall use the phrase "probability is equal to one" as equivalent
to "it is certain." Now suppose the probability of the Chinese being "non-aggressive" is one. Then policy (I) produces a result
(gains) preferable to the result (stalemate) of policy (II). The U.
N. commander "should" choose (I). If the probability of (b) were
not one but zero – i.e., if the probability of (a) were one – he

166

"should" choose (II). Thus if we know that our commander was
sure (rightly or wrongly) of his opponent's intentions and has done
what he "should" have done, then his opinion about those intentions
– his assignment of probabilities to (a) and (b) – would be revealed
by his action.

A similar inference from action to opinion, under the assumption that the acting person is doing what he "should" be doing, can
be made also in a more general case: namely, in the case when
our commander is not necessarily sure as to the adversary's intentions, and thus associates them with probabilities that are not
necessarily 1 or 0 but may be intermediate between 1 and 0. Such
fractional probabilities we have not yet defined. Yet you have no
doubt acted on the basis of judgments such as "an assertion is almost certain to be true" (= "is very probable"), "almost certain
to be untrue" (= has small probability), "as likely as not to be
true" (= has probability 1/2).

Let us look into this more carefully. To avoid terminological
confusion, let us call the probabilities assigned by our commander
to the alternatives (a) and (b), his "subjective probabilities." We
are not interested at present in how they originate – whether the
commander derived them from some systematic observations, or
based them on some vague experience, or even possibly on mere
prejudice. We shall explore, instead, *whether these subjective
probabilities can be defined in terms of his action*. The suspicion
that this can be done is suggested by the following. Suppose our
commander is "almost certain" (subjective probability "a little
below one") that (b) is true; then, is it not right to say that he
"should" cross the 38° parallel? If he is "almost certain" that (b)
is not true (subjective probability "a little above zero"), he "should"
not cross. One may therefore be tempted to say that there exists
a certain critical level for the subjective probability of (b), with
the following property: if the subjective probability of (b) is above
this level, our commander chooses (I); if it is below, he chooses
(II). "Man is the measure" – if not of all things then, at least, of
his own subjective probabilities, as revealed by his action.

A little reflection shows, however, that the commander's action cannot have been determined by his subjective probabilities,
unless some – equally subjective – "values" or "utilities" had been
attached to the outcomes of his actions – to the "gains," "losses"
and "stalemates" entered in our table. As a matter of fact, we had
already made a statement about the utilities of these outcomes,
when we said that gains are preferred to stalemate and stalemate
is preferred to losses. If the three outcomes are thus "completely

ordered," we can attach to them "utility numbers" which would be ordered in a corresponding fashion: for example, 7, 5, 1; or 6, 4, 2; or log 6, log 4, log 2; — in short, any decreasing sequence of three numbers. If any such sequence is used to designate utility numbers, the outcome with a higher number will be preferred to one with a lower number. Yet such ordering of the outcomes is not sufficient to determine choice of action, even if the subjective probabilities of outcomes of a given action are fixed.

Suppose, for example, that two U. N. officers, an American and a South-Korean, agree that the Chinese are as likely as not to counter-attack if we cross 38° parallel. Yet the American may disfavor the crossing, while the South-Korean may advocate it. That is, the American may prefer a stalemate to a 50-50 chance of gains or losses; while the South-Korean (possibly reflecting his government's eagerness to re-unite the country) has an opposite preference. Thus, choice is determined by the complete ordering (the "order of preferences") of probability distributions of outcomes, not by the complete ordering of the outcomes themselves.

The complete ordering of probability distributions is consistent with (though not necessarily equivalent to) assigning "utility numbers" to probability distributions of outcome, as well as to the outcomes themselves, according to the following rule: the utility number attached to a given probability distribution of outcomes equals the average of the utility numbers of the outcomes, weighted with the respective probabilities of those outcomes.[2]

In our example, both the American and the South-Korean may assign the same utility numbers to the best and the worst outcome: say 100 to "gains," 0 to "losses." If they both want to maximize the expected utility, then their assumed disagreement about what to do reveals that, for the American, the utility of a stalemate is larger than 50 — namely, larger than $(1/2)(100) + (1/2)(0)$ — while for the South-Korean it is less than 50. One can, in fact, imagine an experiment in which a commander has to make (hypothetical) decisions, being faced not only with the choice "a stalemate or a 50-50 chance of gains or losses," but also with choices such as "a stalemate or a 60-40 chance of gains or losses," "a stalemate or a 70-30 chance of gains or losses," etc. Suppose one would thus find a break-even point: for example, suppose that the commander has decided to cross the parallel if he felt that the chance of gains is larger than or equal to 65 percent; and not to cross if he felt the chance of gains is smaller than 65 percent. Then we can say that, for him, stalemate is equivalent to a 65-35 chance of gains or losses. Consequently, on a scale of utilities in which 100 and 0 are, respectively, assigned to gains and losses, the utility of stalemate (for that commander) will be 65, because (100) (65%) + (0) (35%) = 65. Thus, if we fix the "0" and "100" points in any arbitrary way (this is similar to the "0" and "32" points of the Fahrenheit scale, or the "0" and "100" of the centigrade scale of temperature), and if we assume that the man is "doing what he should do" and that he "should" maximize expected utility, then his actual responses to given probabilities of outcomes of his actions can be interpreted as revealing the utility numbers attached to each of those outcomes.[3]

Conversely, if the utilities attached by the decision-maker to alternative outcomes are known, it is possible to infer from his decisions the subjective probabilities that he attaches to alternative outcomes — provided that he "is doing what he should do" and that he "should" always maximize expected utility.

It is historically interesting that Thomas Bayes, one of the founders of the theory of probability, used just this kind of inference in order to define probability: In his posthumous essay (famous for another reason) we read[4]

> "The probability of any event is the ratio between the value at which an expectation depending on the happening of the event ought to be computed, and the value of the thing expected upon its happening" (Definition 5); and

> "If a person has an expectation depending on the happening of an event, the probability of the event is to the probability of its failure as his loss if it fails to his gain if it happens" (Proposition 2).

Note Bayes' phrase "ought to be computed." His definition is a norm of behavior. To your gain (a_1 dollars, say) that is contingent upon an uncertain event, there "ought to" correspond in your mind a smaller but sure gain (a dollars, say) such that you are indifferent between gaining a_1 upon the happening of the uncertain event, or gaining a with certainty. Hence, there is (or rather ought to be) in your mind also a ratio of these two numbers, $a/a_1 = p_1$, say. It is called by Bayes, probability of the event; while he calls a the "expectation." Suppose further that, if the event fails to happen, you neither gain nor lose: Then clearly $a = a_1 \cdot p_1 + 0 \cdot (1 - p_1)$ is the average of gain and loss, weighted with their respective probabilities. You "ought to compute" this weighted average before making a choice. Of two uncertain gains choose the one with the higher value of expectation.

In Bayes' second quoted statement the person must have chosen to conclude a fair bet – that is, the expectation value $p_1 a_1 + p_2 a_2 = 0$, where the loss (taken as a positive number) equals to $- a_2$ and has probability $p_2 (= 1 - p_1)$. Hence $p_1 / p_2 = - a_2 / a_1$.

No problem of ascertaining utility arises for Bayes because his gains and losses are money amounts. We can reformulate his definition of probability as the following normative statement (which we shall call "Bayes' norm"):

Let the possible decisions be numbered $1, \ldots, n$; let the possible states of the world be numbered $1, \ldots, m$. Denote by a_{ij} the gain that the person will obtain if he takes the j-th decision, and the world is in its i-th state. Then, if the person behaves "as he should," there exists a set of m non-negative numbers p_i which add up to unity

$$\sum_{i=1}^{m} p_i = 1$$

and have the following property: one decision (say the j-th) is not preferred to another (say the k-th) when and only when

$$\sum_{i=1}^{m} p_i a_{ij} \leq \sum_{i=1}^{m} p_i a_{ik} \quad (j,k = 1, \ldots, n) \tag{1.1}$$

A number p_i is called the (subjective) probability of the i-th state of the world; the two sums in (1.1) are called expected gains associated with, respectively, the j-th and the k-th decision.

As an example (with $m = n = 2$), the possible gains of a man who has decided between buying and not buying stocks are tabulated on the following page.

If the subject decides according to the norm there postulated, then there must exist subjective probabilities p_1, $p_2 (= 1 - p_1)$, with the following property: $p_1 a_{11} + p_2 a_{21} \leq p_1 a_{12} + p_2 a_{22}$ if the subject does not prefer buying to not buying; and such that $p_1 a_{11} + p_{21} a_{21} \geq p_1 a_{12} + p_2 a_{22}$ if he does not prefer not buying to buying. Consequently, if he is indifferent between buying and not buying, both these relations are true so that

$$p_1 a_{11} + p_2 a_{21} = p_1 a_{12} + p_2 a_{22}$$

$$\frac{p_1}{p_2} = \frac{a_{22} - a_{21}}{a_{11} - a_{12}} \text{ , where } p_1 + p_2 = 1. \tag{1.2}$$

(Note that if we had put, for simplicity, $a_{12} = a_{22} = 0$, we would obtain Bayes' "Proposition 2"). Thus by confronting the subject with varying quadruplets of prospective gains one can estimate the subjective probabilities he assigns to the stocks' rise or fall, respectively. For example if (1.2) is satisfied for $a_{11} = -100$ dollars, $a_{21} = +300$ dollars, and $a_{12} = a_{22} = 0$, then "the odds are" $p_1 : p_2 = 3:1$, in favor of falling stocks; or $p_1 = 3/4$, $p_2 = 1/4$.

Table I.2

States of the world i= \ Decisions j=	1. Buy	2. Don't buy
1. Stocks will fall	a_{11}	a_{12}
2. Stocks will rise	a_{21}	a_{22}

It is empirically ascertainable whether a subject's behavior is consistent with this norm. If it is, the subjective probabilities themselves are ascertainable. Consider, for example, the following "payoff matrices" – each being simply the Table I.2, with captions omitted and letters a_{ij} replaced by dollar figures:

Table I.3

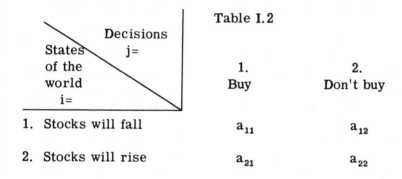

$$\begin{pmatrix} -100 & 0 \\ 300 & 0 \end{pmatrix} ; \begin{pmatrix} -1 & 0 \\ 3 & 0 \end{pmatrix} ; \begin{pmatrix} -2 & -1 \\ 4 & 1 \end{pmatrix} ; \begin{pmatrix} -1 & 0 \\ 2 & 0 \end{pmatrix} .$$

Suppose that the subject is indifferent between buying and not buying when the gains are as in the first matrix. This is simply the case already studied; it has revealed subjective odds 3:1 in favor of falling stocks. Now, the norm implies that if he is indifferent between buying and not buying when faced with the first matrix, he should also be indifferent between buying and not buying when faced with the second and third matrices, but should not buy when faced with the fourth matrix of Table I.3: because not only

$(- 100) (3/4) + (300) (1/4) = (0) (3/4) + (0) (1/4)$ but also

$(- 1) (3/4) + (3) (1/4) = (0) (3/4) + (0) (1/4)$ and also

$(- 2) (3/4) + (4) (1/4) = (-1) (3/4) + (1) (1/4)$; while

$(- 1) (3/4) + (2) (1/4) < (0) (3/4) + (0) (1/4)$.

Such empirical tests of consistency of a man's behavior with some given norm have been occasionally described as meaningless; with the consequence drawn that the (approximate) measurement of subjective probabilities has no meaning. The argument is as follows. Suppose the subject is indifferent between buying and not buying when faced with the first matrix of Table I.3, and also when faced with the fourth matrix. This need not imply that his behavior is inconsistent with Bayes' norm. The subject may have merely changed, during the time required by the experiments, his subjective odds, from 3:1 to 2:1 [since $(-1) (2/3) + (2) (1/3) = 0$]. Suppose, on the other hand, that the subject, when faced with different payoff matrices, almost always makes the same choices as he would make if he maintained unchanged subjective odds and obeyed the Bayes' norm. Yet the subject may have behaved in contradiction with Bayes' norm; he may have changed his opinion about the odds, from experiment to experiment, in exactly such a fashion that the contradiction was masked.

This objection makes it necessary to reformulate every behavior norm by requiring that it should be "approximately" valid during a specified period of time. But what is meant by "approximate," and how to determine the time interval over which the norm is valid? This will depend on the use that has to be made of the norm in practice. The next two lectures give several illustrations of how the merely "approximate" description of human behavior is used for prediction and policy.

What we called the Bayes' norm is quite innocent of the concept of utility. Herein lies its limitation. Most decisions do not result in monetary gains and losses. The military gain, or loss, in our Korean example (Table I.1) is not expressible, either as a money amount or as any other single quantity. It is, at best, a combination of quantities (a "vector"): so and so many guns, prisoners, villages

taken. To be sure (and this will help us later), even when the alternative outcomes differ only because of the presence or absence of
some "qualitative" attributes ("to live in the corn-belt," "to die in
New York") one can express them as a combination of quantities,
each possibly having only a finite number of values: e.g., life or
death = 1 or 2; corn-belt or New York or West Coast = 1 or 2 or 3;
so that life in the corn-belt = vector (1,1). But this may be incon-
venient. For our purposes, it is unnecessary. Our Korean example has shown, in a preliminary way, that we can interpret choices
by assigning subjective "utility numbers" to alternative events, the
events themselves not having been expressed either as values of
single objective variables (such as the number of guns or of prisoners) nor as combinations of such values (the number of guns and of
prisoners). We have seen that, *given the probabilities* of outcomes,
one can infer from manifest decisions to underlying subjective utilities, provided the subject has chosen "as he ought to." To formalize this statement, let us replace Bayes' norm by the following one:

Let A be the set of all possible outcomes of the sub-
ject's decisions. Let a_{ij} ($i = 1, \ldots, m$; $j = 1, \ldots, n$) be
that element of A which he associates with the i-th state
of the world and his j-th decision. If the probability assigned by the subject to the i-th state of the world is

$$p_i \ (p_i \geq 0; \Sigma p_i = 1; i = 1, \ldots, m)$$

and if he behaves "as he should" then there exists a real
valued function $u(a_{ij}) = u_{ij}$ such that one decision (say, the
j-th) is not preferred to another (say, the k-th) when and
only when

$$\sum_{i=1}^{m} p_i u_{ij} \leq \sum_{i=1}^{m} p_i u_{ik} \ (j, k = 1, \ldots, n). \tag{3}$$

The function u( ) is called utility function; its value
u_{ij} is called the utility of the outcome a_{ij}. The two sums
in (3) are called expected utilities associated, respectively,
with the j-th and the k-th decision.

The norm just stated presupposes that probabilities are given
to the subject; and his actual decisions reveal his system of utilities.

This is, in a sense, opposite to Bayes' norm because, if a subject acts according to Bayes' norm his actual decisions reveal his subjective probabilities; while the utilities are given, and are simply identical with amounts of money. We may call the norm just stated, the "Daniel Bernoulli norm."[5] His concept of "moral expectation" is, in fact, identical with the "expected utility" of the statement just formulated, at least for the special case when each a_{ij} is a number, viz., the monetary wealth of the subject. More generally, the a_{ij} may denote any kind of situation which the subject expects to be the result of a given decision of his.

To exemplify Bernoulli's norm we may use the captions of Table I.2 but replace monetary gains a_{ij} by utility numbers u_{ij}. We can, similarly, interpret the numbers entered in Table I.3 as utility numbers. Note that, in the case when these numbers measure the utilities associated with the monetary gains, it is the utilities not the dollar amounts that have, for example, in the first column of the first matrix, the ratio - 1:3. If the person knows (or thinks he knows) the odds to be 3:1 in favor of stocks falling, he will be indifferent between buying and not buying if faced with the first three matrices; and will not buy if faced with the fourth.

If the probability estimates of the subject are known, and if he behaves according to the "D. Bernoulli norm," it is possible to ascertain the utility numbers he assigns to various events, although only (as with centigrades and Fahrenheit degrees) up to two arbitrary constants. For example, suppose the subject is indifferent between buying and not buying stock when faced with the payoff matrix in dollars, given on the left part of the following table:

Table I.4

Payoff in dollars		Payoff in utilities	
$a_{11} = -100$	$a_{12} = 50$	$u_{11} = u(-100) = 0$	$u_{12} = u(50) = ?$
$a_{21} = 200$	$a_{22} = 50$	$u_{21} = u(200) = 1$	$u_{21} = u(50) = ?$

Suppose (as before) that the odds are 3:1 in favor of the first row (falling stock prices). On the right side of Table I.4, we have fixed arbitrarily the zero and unity of the utility scale: 0 = utility of -\$100; 1 = utility of \$200. What is, on this scale, the utility of \$50? From the subject's indifference between the two decisions (represented, respectively, by the first and second column) we conclude, using D. Bernoulli's norm: (0) $(3/4)$ + (1) $(1/4)$ = u (50) = 0.25. Thus, by varying the odds on which the subject is supposed to base his decision, and finding dollar payoff matrices such that the subject is indifferent between two decisions, one obtains the subject's utility scale for various outcomes of his decisions having arbitrarily fixed two points on this scale. This has been essentially the procedure of Mosteller and Nogee, already mentioned. The experimental difficulty includes, in particular, the ascertaining that the subject has "learned" the odds that he is told are prevailing. Moreover, analogous to the discussion we had on the occasion of the Bayes' norm, one has to meet the objection that the person may change his behavior parameters (his utility numbers, in the present case) during the experiment.

In the example just used, the outcomes a_{ij} were dollar amounts; it was shown that the utility number corresponding to any given dollar gain or loss – and thus the "utility function of money gains" – can be ascertained from the actual choices of a subject assumed to obey a certain norm. Instead, the a_{ij} might equally well have been, not dollar gains or losses, nor the values of any other single variable (number of prisoners taken), but vectors of quantities, or "qualitative" outcomes. Our example illustrates, incidentally, that Bayes' norm is not serviceable, not only because it has to deal with outcomes that are values of a single variable only, but also because it disagrees with the experience that people who can be expected to behave "as they should" may have non-linear utility functions of money: the gain of $50 is half-way between - $100 and + $200; yet the choice has proved consistent with the utility of $50 being not half-way but one-quarter of the distance between - $100 and + $200. It seems that Bayes overlooked the reasons which had led his predecessors (Daniel Bernoulli, Cramer) to insist on the difference between "physical wealth" and "moral wealth": the latter not being, in general, proportional to the former. Present day economists call the latter, "utility" (of a given monetary wealth or, more generally and precisely, of a given combination of goods in one's present and future possession). Even for the directors of a corporate firm, who decide on the basis of monetary profits and losses and not of ultimate "pleasures and pains," it is not true that a dollar has the same weight in the decision regardless of the dollars already earned. A loss leading to bankruptcy subtracts more from the utility than a profit of equal size adds to it – the utility function is non-linear. For an attacker bent on destruction, the utility is not a linear function of the physical damage inflicted upon the enemy; rather, destruction beyond a certain point is useless to the attacker. And so on.

The D. Bernoulli norm, formulated in its essence around 1730, was accepted by modern economists like Alfred Marshall. But the assumption that a person computes and compares expected utilities associated with his alternative decisions may appear as complicated and artificial (not more or less, though) than does the computation of expected monetary gains which seemed so evident to Bayes as to make him base on it his definition of probability! In our days, von Neumann and Morgenstern, the authors of the *Theory of Games*, improved on their predecessors by providing a set of postulates, equivalent to, but in some sense simpler, more appealing than the postulate of maximizing expected utility. More recent writers have tried to propose postulates that are still more "transparent."

It is a remarkable psychological fact that a proposition may be equivalent to a set of intuitively appealing propositions and yet be not itself intuitively appealing. There would be otherwise no need for mathematical textbooks! This is a human limitation. For God, of course, the simplest axioms and the most difficult theorems are equally obvious, and their roles interchangeable. Let us, then, look at behavior postulates that are logically equivalent to but "psychologically" simpler than the Bernoulli norm.

Let A, B, C, . . . denote probability distributions of outcomes; (in a special case a "distribution" may assign probability 1 to one event, and 0 to all others; it is, in this case, identical with that single event). Denote by ABp the following probability distribution: "probability p that the distribution is A; probability 1-p that the distribution is B." Let $A \leq B$ mean "A is not preferred to (or "not better than") B." "$A = B$" will be written instead of "$A \leq B$ and $B \leq A$" and will mean "the subject is indifferent between A and B." "$A < B$" will be written instead of "$A \leq B$ and not $B \leq A$" and will mean "A is worse than B." Then the subject "should" obey the following rules:

I. The A, B, C, . . . are "completely ordered" by the relation $\leq$; that is,

   1) $A \leq B$ or $B \leq A$ ("comparability");

   2) if $A \leq B$ and $B \leq C$ then $A \leq C$ ("transitivity").

II. If $A = B$ then $CAp = CBp$.

III. If $A < B$ and $B < C$ then there exists a unique p such that $B = ACp$.

Rule I needs no explanation. A verbal comment on Rule II can be provided as follows. If A is not preferred to B and B is not preferred to C, I am indifferent as between the two. I am now offered two lotteries – one promising either C or A, with odds p:(1 - p), and the other promising either C or B, with the same odds. Thus the same outcome, C, with probability p, will occur on both lotteries; and if C does not occur then the first lottery will give me A, while the second will give me B. But I am indifferent between A and B. Hence, there is no reason for me to prefer one lottery to another.

Rule III asserts, in a rather strong form, the "continuity" of the preference relation. Actually a milder formulation of Rule III, and also of Rule II would suffice to obtain the needed result, viz., the "D. Bernoulli norm."[6] Our stronger formulation gives an easier, though more superficial, insight into the matter, although, even so, I shall have merely to hint at the proof. Note first that our rules permit us to "calibrate" a utility scale as one does a thermometer. Choose three prospects A, B, C such that I am not indifferent between any two of them. Then, by Rule I, they can be ordered in a unique fashion. Suppose this order is: B is preferred to C, and C to A. On a horizontal straight line, plot them in the order (from left to right): A, C, B (Fig. I.5). Call a number $u(A)$ the utility of A; this will be also the utility of all prospects A', A", which, for me, are neither better nor worse than A. Similarly call $u(B)$ the utility of B and its equivalents. What number $u(C)$ shall we then have to assign to the utility of C and of its equivalents? By Rule III there exists a unique probability p such that, to me, C is equivalent to BAp. Call $u(C)$ the number equal to $pu(B) + (1 - p) u(A)$. In particular if we arbitrarily fix $u(A) = 0$ and $u(B) = 1$ then $u(C)$ is simply equal to p. We can now place C on our scale (Fig. I.5), making the distance AB to represent one utility unit, and the distance AC to represent p utility units $(0 < p < 1)$. By Rule II, the number p will also measure the utility of all lotteries such as A'Bp, AB'p, A'B'p, where A' is equivalent to A and B' is equivalent to B. We can thus "calibrate" the utility scale for all prospects which are not better than B and not worse than A: they will be expressed by appropriate numbers ranging from 0 to 1. If a prospect D is worse than A, then A lies on our scale between D and B. Suppose the odds (those required by the Rule III) which make A equivalent to a lottery promising B or D are q:(1 - q); that is, I am indifferent between A and BDq. Then call the utility of D, $u(D)$, a number such that $u(B) \cdot q + u(D) (1 - q) = u(A)$. With $u(A) = 0$ and $u(B) = 1$ this makes $u(D) = - q/(1 - q)$.

Fig. I.5

Outcomes: D   A   C   B   E

$\vdash$————————$+$————————————————$+$————$+$————$\dashv$

Utilities: $- q/(1 - q)$ 0 p 1 $1/r$

$\overline{AC}$: $\overline{CB} = p{:}(1 - p); \; u(C) = u(B){\cdot}p + u(A){\cdot}(1 - p)$

$\overline{BA}$: $\overline{AC} = q{:}(1 - q); \; u(A) = u(B){\cdot}q + u(D){\cdot}(1 - q)$

$\overline{AB}$: $\overline{BE} = r{:}(1 - r); \; u(B) = u(E){\cdot}r + u(A){\cdot}(1 - r)$

By an analogous procedure utility numbers are assigned to prospects – such as E in our figure – that are better than B. We have
thus calibrated the utilities of all possible prospects. If we now assign the numbers 0 and 1 to the utilities not of A and B, but of
some other pair of (non-equivalent) prospects, the origin and the
unit of measurement of utilities is changed (just like we can measure the altitude of a mountain from the sea level as well as from a
lake level, in yards as well as in feet). But in any case, the Bernoulli norm will follow. For, to take up first the case when a prospect involves only two alternative outcomes, we have seen (see Figure I.5) that the utility of such a prospect equals the sum of the
utilities of the outcomes, multiplied by respective probabilities; i.
e., the utility of a prospect equals its "expected utility." And since
higher utilities are preferred to smaller ones, a prospect will not
be preferred to another one unless its expected utility is higher.
To extend this to the case of prospects involving more than two alternative outcomes is a matter of easy algebra. We shall skip it.
     Our Figure I.5 could be also used to explain the approach of
Bayes, if we reverse the problem and consider the outcomes as
represented by given distances from the zero-point, measured in
money units: A = 0 dollars, B = 1 dollar. Then Bayes defines the
probability of, say, C, by the ratio of the distances $\overline{AC} : \overline{AB}$. This
"calibrates" probabilities.
     We can say that in the Bayes norm the utilities were assumed
objectively given (viz., identical with money amounts), and the probabilities were derived as parameters of the subject's behavior, as his
"degrees of belief." Contrariwise, the Bernoulli norm assumes
probabilities to be objectively given and derives subjective utilities.
We had criticized Bayes' norm for its identifying the outcomes of
decisions with the values of a single variable (such as the money
gain) observable without reference to the subject. But a similar

criticism applies to the Bernoulli norm. The probabilities on
which the subject bases his action need not be identical with some
objective properties of chance devices (cards, dice) which the ex-
perimenter uses. This was observed by the English mathematician
and logician, F. P. Ramsey. He shows that manifest decisions can
be thought of as revealing *both* the subject's probabilities *and* utilities. We can call "Ramsey's norm" the following statement:

> Let A be the set of all possible outcomes of the
> subject's decisions. Let a_{ij} (i = 1, . . . , m; j = 1, . . . , n)
> be that element of A which he associates with the i-th state
> of the world and with his j-th decision. If the subject be-
> haves "as he should," then there exists a unique set of num-
> bers $p_i (p_i \geq 0; \Sigma p_i = 1; i = 1, . . . , m)$ and a real valued
> function $u(a_{ij}) = u_{ij}$ such that one decision (say, the j-th)
> is not preferred to another (say, the k-th) when and only
> when

$$\sum_{i=1}^{m} p_i u_{ij} \leq \sum_{i=1}^{m} p_i u_{ik} \, (j, k = 1, . . . , n).$$

The numbers p_i are called subjective probabilities (or degrees of belief). The function $u(a_{ij})$ is called utility function; its value u_{ij} is called the utility of the outcome a_{ij}.
The two sums in (3) are called expected utilities associated,
respectively, with the j-th and the k-th decision.

A set of behavior rules, equivalent to Ramsey's norm but
"psychologically" more appealing was proposed by Ramsey himself
and, in our days, by de Finetti and, especially, by Savage.[7] It would
be difficult to convey their proofs in this lecture. But it is possible
to indicate that subjective probabilities can be defined on the basis
of observable decisions of a subject, even if one rejects the identification (practised by Bayes) between utilities and money gains; and
to indicate how this definition of probability is related to the norm
requiring maximization of expected utility. Consider the matrix in
Table I.6 of outcomes a_{ij}, with m = n = 2. Suppose I am indifferent
between the two decisions. Then Ramsey will define the degrees of
belief in (or the subjective probability of) each of the two states of
the world as $p_1 = p_2 = 1/2$. For example, suppose an urn contains
white and red balls and I am given the choice between the following
two options: (1) if I draw white, I die; if red, I live; (2) if I draw red,

Table I.6

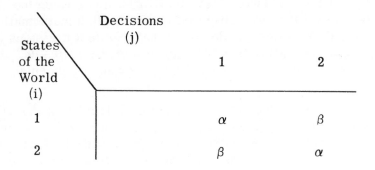

States of the World (i) \ Decisions (j)	1	2
1	α	β
2	β	α

I die; if white, I live. If I am indifferent between the two options
(but not between life and death) I have equal degrees of belief (defined as 1/2) that the ball drawn will be white or red. We postulate
that the subject has consistent degree of belief. That is, he will remain indifferent between any two options represented by the matrix
of Table I.6, regardless of what meaning is given to the outcomes
α and β. Having thus defined subjective probability = 1/2 (but not
yet any other probabilities) enables Ramsey to define a scale of
measurable utilities, as follows. An outcome γ is said to be "half-
way" between α and β if the subject is indifferent between γ
and the prospect of having α or β with subjective odds 1/2 : 1/2.
It is again postulated that the subject is consistent, in the sense that
γ will remain "half-way" between α and β regardless of the particular pair of the states of the world to which the subjective probabilities 1/2, 1/2 are attached. Now Ramsey can define the utility
of α as zero, the utility of γ as 1, the utility of β as 2, and (with
the help of some further axioms on order and continuity) he can
construct the scale of utilities. This brings him to the same point
at which Bayes had made the start, except that Bayes' money
amounts are replaced by utility numbers. Like Bayes, Ramsey can
now calibrate probabilities: these are ratios between certain differences between utilities – as on our Figure I.5. The norm that
prospects with higher expected utilities should be preferred to
those with lower ones follows immediately.

It is worth noting that the logic of connecting between "measurable," (and not merely "completely ordered") utilities as required by
the Bernoulli and the Ramsey norm has been patterned, to a large
extent, after Hilbert's "Foundations of Geometry"[8] in which the relation was established between points ordered along a straight line

and the real numbers measuring distances. In a more general
sense, too, discussion of behavior norms is similar to that of foundations of geometry. Various geometries – various internally consistent sets of axioms and theorems – are possible. So are various
sets of behavior rules. Such consistent systems do not assert anything about empirical reality – e.g., about physical or psychological
phenomena. Yet they do help to order these phenomena, by comparing facts with ideals. The normative discussion of behavior shares
this feature with mathematics and logics. In addition, it shares
with logic another feature: certain modes of thinking *and* acting
may be "preferable" to others. For example, it is preferable,
when one is told that all men are mortals, not to conclude that all
mortals are men; and it is preferable, when choosing A in preference to B, and B in preference to C, not to choose C in preference to A. We are warned against "bad logic" as well as against
"inconsistent behavior" (the latter is even called sometimes "illogical behavior"). The warning is of a pragmatic nature: bad logicians
won't survive. In the last lecture, we shall return to this practical
aspect of normative social science, and of probabilities in social
science.

The approach of Ramsey and of D. Bernoulli is more congenial to social scientists than that of Bayes because Bayes con-
fined himself to outcomes which are money gains. But still more
important, the common feature of the approach of both Ramsey and
Bayes, is particularly congenial to social scientists. It permits us
to deal with "probabilities of single events." While the XVIII century Continentals, in Paris or Petersburg, indulged in dice and
cards, and watched the frequencies of repeated events, the English
seem to have thought more of horses and fighting cocks and wrest-
lers. The betting books of Oxford colleges are full of guesses such
as "Napoleon is dead" (dated November 1812) accompanied by the
betting ratios – whether in guineas or in bottles of port. This is
right after the social scientist's taste! He is often unable to observe repeated events.

But, then the following question arises: if I happen to be able
to observe repeated events, how shall I use those observations in
computing my "degrees of belief," which are my guide in decision-
making? Shall I, for example, equate my degree of belief in drawing a white ball from an urn, to the relative frequency of such drawings in the past, at least as an approximation? In short: *is there
any relation between subjective probabilities and the statistical
method?* Is there any sense in the statement: "The chances that I
shall survive the operation are the same as getting a royal flush"?

(These questions are important for our future discussion, because in the two remaining lectures, statistical methods will be applied to human and social phenomena and to policy decisions.)

These questions were, in essence, answered in the affirmative by Bayes himself, and again, in our time, by Ramsey. To justify the affirmative answer, one first shows that the "law of large numbers," properly interpreted, does follow from the properties of subjective probabilities. To do this, it will be convenient to use the concepts of "conditional probabilities" and of "independence." We shall define them as we proceed. (These concepts will also prove useful in Lectures 2 and 3.)

Let $\overline{W}$ be the negation of the state of the world W, and let $\overline{V}$ be the negation of the state of the world V; and suppose that the subject is indifferent between the following options:

$$
\left.\begin{array}{l}
\alpha \text{ if } \overline{W} \\
\beta \text{ if } W
\end{array}\right\} \text{ and } \left\{\begin{array}{l}
\alpha \text{ if } \overline{W} \\
\beta' \text{ if } W \text{ and } V \\
\beta'' \text{ if } W \text{ and } \overline{V}
\end{array}\right.
$$

For example: let α = death, β = survival; β' = early arrival; β'' = late arrival; $\overline{W}$ = plane has engine trouble; V = plane is fast. Then the option on the left hand is: to die if the plane has engine trouble; to survive if it has not. The option on the right hand is: to die if the plane has engine trouble; to survive and arrive early if the plane has no engine trouble and is a fast one; to survive and arrive late if the plane has no engine trouble and is a slow one.[9] Our assumption is, then, that I am indifferent between the option on the left hand and the option on the right hand. That is, by Ramsey's postulate, the expected utility of the left-hand option is equal to that of the right-hand option. But the expected utility of the left-hand option is clearly

$$
u(\alpha)p(\overline{W}) + u(\beta)p(W),
$$

where $u(\alpha)$, $u(\beta)$ are the utility numbers attached to the outcomes α and β, respectively, and $p(\overline{W})$ and $p(W)$ are the probabilities of the alternative states of the world $\overline{W}$ and W respectively. In a similar notation, the expected utility of the right-hand option is

$$u(\alpha)\,p(\overline{W}) + u(\beta')\,p(W \text{ and } V) + u(\beta'')\,p(W \text{ and } \overline{V}).$$

Hence the indifference between the two options implies the equality of the two expressions we have written. This equality implies – since the term containing $u(\alpha)$ cancels out –

$$u(\beta)\,p(W) = u(\beta')\,p(W \text{ and } V) + u(\beta'')\,p(W \text{ and } \overline{V}). \qquad (1.3)$$

Let us now give the two quantities

$$\frac{p(W \text{ and } V)}{p(W)} \quad \text{and} \quad \frac{p(W \text{ and } \overline{V})}{p(W)} ,$$

the names "conditional probability of V given W" and "conditional probability of $\overline{V}$ given W;" and denote these two quantities, respectively, by

$$p(V|W) \text{ and } p(\overline{V}|W).$$

Then our last equation becomes – dividing by $p(W)$ –

$$u(\beta) = u(\beta') \cdot p(V|W) + u(\beta'') \cdot p(\overline{V}|W). \qquad (1.4)$$

Now define "independence" as follows. Suppose the state x_2 is "irrelevant" to the state x_1 in the sense that the conditional probability of x_2 given x_1 is the same as the probability of x_1:

$$p(x_1|x_2) = p(x_1).$$

By the definition of conditional probability this means

$$\frac{p(x_1 \text{ and } x_2)}{p(x_2)} = p(x_1) ,$$

$$p(x_1 \text{ and } x_2) = p(x_1) \cdot p(x_2). \qquad (1.5)$$

Thus the "irrelevance" of x_2 for x_1 is equivalent to the relation
(1.3), which will define "independence" between x_1 and x_2. Since
(1.3) is symmetrical in x_1 and x_2 the following are equivalent:
independence between x_1 and x_2; irrelevance of x_2 for x_1; and
irrelevance of x_1 for x_2. One can extend the concept of independence to, say, N events and define it by

$$p(x_1 \text{ and } x_2 \text{ and } x_3 \ldots \text{ and } x_N) = p(x_1)p(x_2)p(x_3) \ldots p(x_N). \quad (1.6)$$

Thus if one tosses coins, one can compute the probability that the
independent events $x_1, \ldots, x_N$ will be all "heads"; or that the
first two are heads and the rest tails; or that some other preassigned proportion of tosses be heads. These computations are a
matter of arithmetic. As the result, one finds (one version of) the
law of large numbers: if the "probability of heads" equals p then
the "probability that the proportion of heads in a long sequence of
independent throws will converge to p" equals 1. Remember that
the probabilities in question (the numbers p and 1 in our last
sentence) are subjective degrees of belief, defined as guides in
choosing between actions.[10]
    We shall now sketch out the proof that any "preconceived"
(or "a priori") degrees of belief "should" be modified in the light
of experience, in a certain well-defined way, which is fundamentally
the one at the basis of sampling statistics. (Note the "should"! We
are talking of norms!).
    Suppose that my degree of belief in drawing a black ball from
an urn, on condition that the world is in state W, is π. This quantity is also called the "likelihood of the state W on the basis of an
observed drawing of a black ball." If the urn contains only black
and red balls, then clearly the likelihood of W on the basis of an
observed drawing of a red ball is $1 - \pi$. Similarly, let us denote by
$\bar{\pi}$ and $1 - \bar{\pi}$, respectively, the likelihoods of the alternative state,
$\overline{W}$, on the basis of an observed drawing of a black or of a red ball.
Let x_i be the i-th independent observation, and let "$x_i = b$" and
"$x_i = r$" mean that this observation is the drawing of a black or a
red ball, respectively. We can then rewrite our definitions as
follows:

$$\pi = p(x_i = b \mid W) \quad ; \quad 1 - \pi = p(x_i = r \mid W)$$

$$\bar{\pi} = p(x_i = b \mid \overline{W}) \quad ; \quad 1 - \bar{\pi} = p(x_i = r \mid \overline{W}).$$

Consider in particular, the first observation, x_1, and write the degree of belief that the world is in the state W *and* that the first drawing will be "black," thus:

$$p(W; \text{ and } x_1 = b).$$

On the other hand, denote separately the degrees of belief that the world is in state W (regardless of observations) and that the first drawing is black, by

$$p^0(W) \text{ and } p(x_1 = b),$$

respectively. If we now recall our definition of conditional probabilities, we have

$$p(W; \text{ and } x_1 = b) = p(x_1 = b|W) \cdot p^0(W)$$

and also

$$p(W; \text{ and } x_1 = b) = p(W|x_1 = b) \cdot p(x_1 = b).$$

The quantities $p^\circ(W)$ and $p(W|x_1 = b)$ are called, respectively, the *a priori* and the *a posteriori* degree of belief in W; while $p(x_1 = b|W)$ is, as we recall, the likelihood π. Comparing the last two equations, we obtain

$$p(W|x_1 = b) \cdot p(x_1 = b) = \pi \cdot p^0(W).$$

And similarly (replacing W by $\overline{W}$ and therefore π by $\overline{\pi}$)

$$p(\overline{W}|x_1 = b) \cdot p(x_1 = b) = \overline{\pi} \cdot p^0(\overline{W}).$$

Dividing the last equation into the preceding one, one obtains a simple form of the celebrated "Bayes Theorem":

$$\frac{p(W|x_1 = b)}{p(\overline{W}|x_1 = b)} = \frac{p^0(W) \cdot \pi}{p^0(\overline{W}) \cdot \overline{\pi}} \tag{1.7}$$

In words: the *a posteriori* degree of belief in a certain state of the world, given a certain observation, is proportional to the product of the *a priori* degree of belief in that state of the world *times* the likelihood of that state of the world given the observation. In this way, the observation leads to modifying the *a priori* degree of belief. The likelihoods, π and $\overline{\pi}$, operate as "correction factors." If the observation x_1 were "red" instead of "black," the correction factors would be $1 - \pi$ and $1 - \overline{\pi}$, respectively.

Suppose now the process is repeated: we take N independent observations $x_1, x_2, \ldots, x_N$, each time using the previously corrected degree of belief, correcting it further in the light of the new observation. Suppose we drew a black ball n times, (and therefore a red ball N-n times). Applying Bayes Theorem,

$$\frac{p(\overline{W}|x_1, \ldots, x_N)}{p(W|x_1, \ldots, x_N)} = \frac{p^0(\overline{W}) \cdot \overline{\pi}^n (1 - \overline{\pi})^{N-n}}{p^0(W) \cdot \pi^n (1 - \pi)^{N-n}}. \tag{1.8}$$

But, by the law of large numbers, as stated above, if the true state of the world is W, then the degree of belief is 1 that the proportion of black drawings, n/N will converge to π. Therefore, the number of black drawings, n, will converge to πN; and the ratio between the *a posteriori* degrees of belief into $\overline{W}$ and W, as given in our last equation, will approach

$$\frac{p^0(\overline{W})}{p^0(W)} \cdot \left(\frac{\overline{\pi}^\pi (1 - \overline{\pi})^{1-\pi}}{\pi^\pi (1 - \pi)^{1-\pi}} \right)^N$$

We see that as the number N of observations increases, the role of the *a priori* degrees of belief into the two alternative states of the world, $p^0(\overline{W})$ and $p^0(W)$, diminishes, overshadowed by the results of observations. Furthermore simple calculus shows that the expression

$$\overline{\pi}^\pi (1 - \overline{\pi})^{1-\pi},$$

considered as a function of a variable $\bar{\pi}$, has its maximum when $\bar{\pi} = \pi$. Hence, in (1.6), the quantity that is raised to the N-th power, is a ratio of a smaller positive number to a larger one; and its N-th power approaches 0 as N increases. Therefore, of the two *a posteriori* degrees of belief that form the fraction on the left side of (1.6), and that must add up to 1, the numerator converges to 0 and the denominator to 1. That is, the degree of belief that will be assigned to the true state of the world (W) will approach 1. Hence, the investigator who will repeatedly apply Bayes Theorem and choose his decisions on the basis of degrees of belief thus computed will in effect believe that he would obtain a better result than if he would not do so. Perhaps this is what writers on probability mean when they use the expression "practically certain" or "certain for all practical purposes,"[11] – an expression we shall also have the opportunity for using in the next two sections.

Section II. PROBABILITIES AND DESCRIPTIVE SOCIAL SCIENCE

We shall concern ourselves now with the uncertainties encountered by the social scientist when he tries to predict the behavior of people. Such prediction is rarely exact. It is usually
"probabilistic" or statistical, even when the sample used is very
large and even when the prediction is made, not about individuals,
but about large aggregates of people. After discussing the probabilistic character of descriptive social science, I shall give examples illustrating an important methodological problem that has
recently occupied statisticians as well as social scientists: that
of identifiability of structural characteristics. This will throw
some light on the following more general fact: whether statistical
data can yield the desired prediction depends not only on the size
of the sample and on the goodness of statistical formulae, but also
on the nature and validity of the assumptions which the investigator
had to make before processing a given set of data or, preferably,
even before collecting them. These assumptions (sometimes called "a model") are, of course, based on formerly acquired knowledge. In the case of a social scientist, this is often the knowledge
of "plausible" or of "meaningful" relations.

NORMS VERSUS HABITS.

We discussed in the first lecture some norms "recommended" to decision makers who face uncertainty. Those norms or behavior postulates were similar to the rules of logic or geometry.
It was not asserted that such norms were fully obeyed by all or
even a sizable proportion of men or women, in our own or any
other civilization, just as logicians and mathematicians do not assert that all or the majority of their countrymen or of members
of any other society are immune to errors of logic or arithmetic.
It is merely recommended that those errors be avoided. Recommended norms and actual habits are not the same thing.

As a matter of empirical psychology it may be interesting
to find in what manner a given individual deviates from such norms:
how often is he apt to fall victim to a particular sophism, or to have
trouble with his sums, or--nearer to our field--to be inconsistent
in his preferences. As a matter of social science in general, we

may be interested in the ethical and social conditions which affect the frequency of deviations from norms of reasonable thinking, counting and choosing. This knowledge of conditions affecting
people's behavior is, first, a matter of scientific curiosity. But
it has also its practical side. If we know what makes people more
or less illogical, or mathematically inept or poor decision makers,
we may also find how best to enable them to learn the "recommended" type of behavior--how, for example, they can get the
habit of "stopping to think." The normative and the descriptive
analysis complete each other.

In the previous section, we did not specify the source of the
uncertainty that faces the decision maker. It may be uncertainty
about nature. It may be uncertainty about the actions of other men.
In our initial example, the U.N. commander had to puzzle out
whether his Chinese adversary is or is not "aggressive" (in a
well defined sense of producing certain observable results under
specified circumstances). This is uncertainty about people. If
our commander estimates (or acts as if he had estimated) that the
odds for the Chinese command having "aggressive" designs are
such and such, he has done a bit of descriptive social science. It
may happen that, in my best judgment, my adversary behaves as
he "should" behave according to the norms of reasonableness
which I recommend to myself. Any application of the Theory of
Games (in its present form) is based on the assumption that this
symmetry of behavior norms is an actual fact. However, this need
not always be the case, nor need it be a useful approximation to
reality. It may be more useful to actually study my adversary, as
I would study weather or soil or any other uncertain natural pheno-
menon--provided such study of other people's behavior is feasible
and not too costly. A commander--or, for that matter, a diplomat,
or a labor union representative--will combine the theory of games
("What would I reasonably do if I were in the other fellow's position?") with as good an intelligence system as his resources can
afford, whether by sending spies or by employing anthropologists.
And, of course, what was said for a problem arising in fighting an
opponent is also true for problems arising in forming an alliance,
in building and operating within a social organization--in short in
making decisions whose outcome will depend on actions of my
fellow men about whom my knowledge is uncertain.

PREDICTION

Uncertain knowledge is not ignorance. Nineteenth-century
social scientists were fascinated by "iron laws of nature," when
they took eighteenth-century physics for their ideal. It was fash-
ionable, a hundred years ago, to speak of the iron law of demand
and supply or (with Karl Marx) to claim predictability for society's
future. We have learned today--possibly reflecting some trends
in physical sciences--to be quite happy when we can make a prediction only with some (specified) probability. For the "reasonable" man of our last lecture, a decision maker who weighs utilities with probabilities and maximizes the weighted sum, this kind
of knowledge is certainly not useless! At the same time, such
knowledge is usually the best that we can ever hope to have, in the
field of social sciences, where uncertainties of our physical en-
viroment are topped by the diversity and capriciousness of human
nature.

Briefly, empirical social science consists of statements
about probability distributions. As a trivial but useful example,
suppose a social statistician is hired to find what makes people
smoke much or little or not at all. Or he wants to find what makes
people communists. Let x denote the number of cigarettes smoked
by a certain man on a certain day (x may be 0, 1, 2, ... a many-
valued variable); or let x denote a certain man's being or not being a communist (here x = 0 or 1: a two-valued variable). What
is the probability that x will have a certain value? The tendency
to believe in smoking, or in communism, will depend on certain
individual characteristics among which one will expect to find the
age, sex, education, occupation of the subject; but also his income,
the characteristics of his parents and siblings . . . but possibly
also his past income and occupation . . . but then also his whole
past history and that of his ancestors, and, in fact, his whole genetic and cultural endowment. This is a long list of factors. Call
them $z^{(1)}$, $z^{(2)}$, . . . , $z^{(N)}$, with N very large. We could make the
desired prediction with certainty, for a subject whose $z^{(1)}$,...., $z^{(N)}$
are known, if we also knew which combinations of the values of
those variables make x = 0, which combinations make x = 1, etc.
That is, the social scientist can predict x from $z^{(1)}$,....,$z^{(N)}$ if
there exists a function

$$x = \phi (z^{(1)}, \ldots , z^{(N)})$$ (2.1)

(say) and if he has been able to find this function on the basis of his previous observations on x, $z^{(1)}, \ldots, z^{(N)}$ for each of a sufficient number and variety of persons. However, a complete list of factors that may influence the man's smoking habits or his political beliefs is hopelessly long! The social scientist picks out a smaller number of factors -- say $z^{(1)}, \ldots, z^{(n)}$ -- and replaces the assumption (2.1) of an "exact" relationship by a "probabilistic" assumption, as follows: The variable x is a random variable (also called a chance variable or a stochastic variable); and the probability with which it takes any given value is a function of the variables $z^{(1)}, \ldots, z^{(n)}$ only. In other words, there exists a "conditional probability of x, given $z^{(1)}, \ldots, z^{(n)}$,"

$$\pi \left(x \mid z^{(1)}, \ldots, z^{(n)} \right), \tag{2.2}$$

say. With the assumption thus changed, the predictor's task is to find, not the function ϕ in (2.1) but the function π in (2.2), from the values of x, $z^{(1)}, \ldots, z^{(n)}$ that he had observed on a sufficient number and variety of individuals. He can then state, for some new individual, with given $z^{(1)}, \ldots, z^{(n)}$ but an unknown x, the probability distribution of x: "the probability that Tom Smith, elevator boy at the State Department, middle-aged and unmarried, is a communist is 0.001%"; "the probability that Mrs. Brown, fashion editor, divorced, smokes 0, 1, ..., 30 cigarettes per day is, respectively, 1%, 5%, ..., 0%."

A very special, but convenient and familiar, form of this assumption will serve as illustration. One assumes that there exist n+2 numbers μ, σ, α_i, ..., α_n with the following property: the difference (called "disturbance")

$$x - \sum_{i=1}^{n} \alpha_i z^{(i)} \tag{2.3}$$

is independent of the $z^{(i)}$ and has normal distribution with expectation (mean) μ and standard deviation σ. In this case, the conditional distribution (2.2) of x, given $z^{(1)}, \ldots, z^{(n)}$, is also normal. Its expectation is

$$\mu + \sum_{i=1}^{n} \alpha_i z_i$$

and is called the "explained part of x." Its standard deviation, σ, is identical with that of the disturbance (2.3). The numbers α_i can be regarded as "weights" (not necessarily all positive) attached to the n explanatory variables; each of those variables contributes an additive component $\alpha_i z^{(i)}$ of x. If one could find, on the basis of past observations on the x and the $z^{(i)}$ of a sufficient number and variety of individuals, then, for any new individual, with known $z^{(i)}$ but unknown x, one would be able to make a "probabilistic" prediction such as, for example: the odds are 19:1 that this man's x lies in the interval

$$\mu + \Sigma \alpha_i z^{(i)} \pm 2\sigma \qquad (2.4)$$

The looks of this interval are familiar enough from textbooks and routines of research workers in social science. I am afraid its understanding is often confused by complications irrelevant from our point of view. One complication is that the constants μ, σ, and the α_i cannot be determined exactly from a finite number of observations. One can only determine their "estimates". These are suitably chosen functions of a finite number of observed values of the variables x, $z^{(1)}$, ..., $z^{(n)}$. Since these variables are [or at least x is -- according to (2.2)] random, the estimates are also random variables (they are "subject to sampling errors") so that the interval (2.4), computed from those estimates, it itself "wobbly." But this is beside the point. We are not interested in sampling theory today. We can assume today that the investigator has collected a very large sample indeed; and that he has used appropriate formulas to compute estimates that are practically certain to approach the estimated constants as the sample increases (such estimates are called "consistent"). Our point is that, even using an infinite sample and consistent estimates, he will not be able to predict x from a finite number (n) of explanatory variables except in a "probabilistic" fashion typified by the statement that "x will fall within the interval (2.4) with probability 0.05."

Another concept that we wish to disregard here is that of "errors of observation," a term originating in observatories and physical laboratories. There the number N of possible explanatory factors is supposed to be small enough to be manageable; and the fact that the exact, non-probabilistic assumption (2.1) is not satisfied is (or was till the advent of modern statistical physics) blamed upon the frailty of the observer's eye and of his other instruments. In social science, human frailty is shared between the observer

and his object. After repeatedly asking a blindfolded man which of
two weights is heavier, the psychologist may have to record a frequency distribution of contradictory statements: "The first weight
is heavier," "It is lighter," or "No difference." The psychologist
will have to formulate his conclusions and predictions in a probabilistic manner even if he is sure that his own errors of observation (confusing the weights or misunderstanding the subject's
responses) are negligible. A "random disturbance" originating in
the observed person not in the observer will always be present.
Furthermore, even if it should be possible to design laboratory
conditions so as to make both the errors of observation and the
random disturbance of the observed phenomenon negligible, this
cannot be achieved with data collected outside of laboratory walls
-- like the data on the smoking or the communist persuasion of
persons. The variables, immense in number (N-n), which the investigator of such a problem has decided to leave out of account,
are supposed by him to show their joint effect in the random disturbance (2.3). For example, each of the subject's ancestors has
contributed something to his make-up, but each only a little: just
like each of the innumerable causes that determine an honest card
deal contributes a little. Such joint effects of a large number of
separately insignificant causes are empirical phenomena that have
been idealized in the mathematical concept of a random variable
and a probability. An error of observation and a random disturbance, as defined, may both have their origin in those numerous,
separately insignificant causes. However, if you prefer to ascribe
the randomness of errors and disturbances to the free will of individuals, you may do so. This will not affect the choice of investigation methods.

The selection of the n explanatory variables, and the assumption that the difference (2.3) is independent of z_i and has a normal
probability distribution [or, more generally, that x has some probability distribution (2.2) for any fixed value of the n variables
selected as explanatory ones] may be false. If it is, it will lead to
probabilistic prediction statements that are false, even if they are
based on consistent estimates from very large samples. This suggests, of course, that one should test predictions like (2.4) against
new facts; and then revise the assumption (2.2) if necessary. For
example, one may change the list of explanatory variables or replace the linearity and normality assumptions by other ones. Thus
the selection of assumptions need not be entirely based on pre-
scientific knowledge but can be helped by progressive experience.

AGGREGATION

Large parts of social science deal, not with single individuals but with averages or aggregates. It has been occasionally
remarked that random variations of behavior from one individual
to another (or, for the same individual, from one day to another)
tend to "cancel out" when one deals with masses of man. Tsere-
telli, a political leader of the pro-Communist period of the Russian
revolution, even went so far as to say (in predicting the failure of
Communists to win the masses!), "Persons can err, masses
never"; and social scientists are apt to quote Boyle's law of gases,
which is exact enough, yet can be derived from the random behavior of billions of small particles. Do social scientists fool
themselves when they appeal to this analogy, thus trying to reduce
the prediction interval to a single point and to evade the incon-
veniences of probabilistic thinking?

As an example, let me refer to the economists' attempt at
explaining the aggregate investment, i.e., the total money outlay
on plant and equipment made in a year by all the firms of the
country.

This outlay is, of course, the sum of the outlays of individual
firms on *their* plant and equipment. One might try to explain the
decision of a manager or a management board of an individual
firm by those variables that are likely to influence the level of an-
ticipated profits, thus making the expansion of the firm's activities
in a given year a promising or a bad proposition. Thus, one would
think of explanatory variables like the following: the profits that
are already being made at the time of decision; the current demand
for the firm's product; the interest rate at which money can be
borrowed to expand the firm's plant and machinery; the cost of new
machinery and building. Clearly, many other variables will be
needed to describe the particular circumstances in which a given
firm finds itself, and which will affect the manager's anticipations
of the future of his particular market, and his decision to build a
new wing of the plant or, on the contrary, to sell parts of his machinery for scrap without replacing them by new ones. If the particular circumstances do not vary too strongly from one firm to
another, one might be able to explain the annual change in the aggregate plant and equipment of the American industry (so called
rate of aggregate investment) as a function of those general variables: the total profits of the past year; the total demand for all
products (represented by total national income); the average interest rate, the average cost of machinery and building, etc. To

do this, one would be able to utilize the published historical statistics, which gives for each year and even each quarter or month,
the aggregate outlays on plant and equipment, the total profits, the
interest rate, prices, etc. In this hope, various investigators have
looked for a statistical relationship between the aggregate annual
investment of the American industry and the several aggregate variables that we have mentioned. In particular, attempts have been
made to construct prediction intervals like (2.4), where μ and σ
are the mean and standard deviation of the estimate of annual
aggregate investment; while the $z^{(i)}$ are the various mentioned
explanatory variables, also of aggregative nature: total profits of
the preceding year, total national income, average interest rate,
etc. However, the standard error σ of the estimate, and hence
the prediction interval, proved to be very large; or, what is the
same thing, the "unexplained residual," the "disturbance" (2.3) —
with x interpreted as the annual rate of aggregate investment —
has a very large standard deviation. The meaning of the prediction interval being "very large" is simply this: it is so large as to
be useless for predictions.

For the social scientists, an interesting possible explanation
of the strong random variability of the unexplained residual of some
aggregative variables, is the phenomenon variously called "leadership," "imitation," "contagion," or "Zeitgeist" or "fashion." The
random disturbances in the response (e.g., in the decision to expand plant) of any pair of individual members of a human group to
a given set of circumstances may be positively correlated, both
disturbances being partly determined by unspecified common cause.
If this is the case, the response of the corresponding aggregative
variable to a given set of circumstances will be subject to more
unpredictable random fluctuations than if that correlation were
absent.

A mathematical illustration will help. Suppose p variables
$v_1, \ldots, v_p$ have a joint normal distribution with a common expectation $Ev_j = 0$ and a common variance $Ev_j^2 = \sigma^2$. Let them also
have a common correlation coefficient for any pair $j \neq k$,
$Ev_j v_k / \sigma^2 = \rho > 0$. Thus

$$Ev_j v_k = \begin{cases} \sigma^2 & \text{when } j = k \\ \sigma^2 \rho & \text{otherwise.} \end{cases}$$

What is the distribution of $\bar{v}$, the average of these variables? $\bar{v}$
has normal distribution. Its expectation = 0. And its variance

$$E(\bar{v})^2 = E\left(\frac{v_1 + \ldots + v_p}{p}\right)^2 = \frac{1}{p^2} E \sum_j \sum_k v_j v_k$$

$$= \frac{1}{p^2}\left[p\sigma^2 + p(p-1)\sigma^2\rho\right] = \sigma^2\left[\frac{1-\rho}{p}\right] + \rho$$

$$E(\bar{v})^2 \longrightarrow \sigma^2\rho \quad \text{as } p \longrightarrow \infty. \tag{2.5}$$

Thus, under our assumptions, the variance of the average tends to zero if and only if the correlation $\rho = 0$. Applying this to our problem of averaging the individual responses (e.g., the investment decisions of a number of firms), we can interpret v_j as follows:

$$v_j = x_j - \sum_{i=1}^{n} \alpha_i z_j^{(i)} - \mu \quad (j = 1, \ldots, p) \tag{2.6}$$

where the α_i and μ have the same meaning as in (2.3), (2.4), and the subscript j indicates the particular firm; its response (investment) x_j is explained by the variables $z_j^{(1)}, \ldots, z_j^{(n)}$, except for a random disturbance $\mu + v_j$, which has mean μ and variance σ^2. The variable x_j has then also variance σ^2, the same for all firms. If, for all pairs of firms, the random disturbances are not correlated ($\rho = 0$) then indeed the average of the responses of all firms tends to have zero variance as the number of firms increases. But this is not so if there is, pairwise, a positive correlation between the individual disturbances. In the extreme case, when all firms act in unison ($\rho = 1$), the average has the same variance as any individual response: an obvious result.[13] This mathematical illustration might be made more general – for example we might admit positive correlation coefficients of different sizes for different pairs of firms. But our result suffices, to show how "fashion" endangers predictability – a warning against the abuse of a misunderstood "law of averages." If the decision-makers, however numerous, follow a few leaders, then the personal circumstances, the ulcers or divorce proceedings of the leaders become important factors in predicting the average or aggregate of the decisions.

IDENTIFICATION

Suppose two random characteristics X_1 and X_2 are being measured on each person of a sample. For example, X_1 may be a person's consumption of cigarettes, and X_2 his consumption of cereals; or X_1 may be the person's answer to the question "Do you prefer blondes?" and X_2 his answer to the question "Do you feel comfortable with strangers?" Suppose that a parameter Z is known to exist which varies from person to person but is fixed for each person; and which influences X_1 and X_2 in a "probabilistic" fashion. That is, the probability that a person's X_1 and X_2 will take a given pair of values (or fall within given intervals) depends on the value of the person's Z. Thus the joint distribution of the numbers of cigarettes and bowls of cereals consumed by a person during a week may depend on the person's income, Z. In the case of the two questions – about blondes and about strangers – Z may stand for some characteristic, such as "ethnocentricity", of which the answers to the two questions are symptoms.[14] We shall denote the joint probability distributions of X_1, X_2, conditional upon Z, by

$$\pi (X_1, X_2 | Z), \qquad\qquad (2.7)$$

a function of three variables. It is quite analogous to (2.2), with the vector $(z^{(1)}, \ldots, z^{(n)})$ replaced by a single Z, and the number x replaced by the vector (X_1, X_2). [In a more general case, both the random variable to the left and the parameter to the right of the bar in (2.7) will be vectors.]

Suppose one has succeeded in estimating the function π from a sample. This knowledge could then be used in two opposite ways, to answer questions about a person not in the sample:

Question 1: given this person's Z, predict his X's.

Question 2: given his X's, make statements about his Z.

Why either of these applications of our knowledge of the conditional probability function π should ever arise in practice, will belong into our third lecture (on policies). For the time being, we shall regard both questions as legitimate expressions of scientific curiosity.

If the sampled persons had lent themselves to the measurement, not only of their X, but also of their Z, the problem of estimating the function π from the sample, and of subsequently answering Questions 1 or 2 about a person not in the sample, would be a familiar one. For example, the main use of computing a regression equation from a sample is to answer Question 1, in the manner of (2.4); using a sample to answer Question 2 is also a problem well known to statisticians, a discrimination problem.[15] However, a new twist is introduced by making Z a non-observable (at least not observable on the sampled individuals), a "latent" characteristic. It is natural to expect that this loss of information must be made up by some additional information if the problem is to remain solvable.

The following simple hypothesis (which is itself a bit of "additional information") will be used for the case of "cigarettes and cereals": X_1 and X_2 are proportional to Z, subject to random percentage deviations, denoted by U_1 and U_2, respectively. That is, there exist two constants, Λ_1 and Λ_2 such that

$$X_i = \Lambda_i \, Z(1 + U_i), \quad i = 1, \, 2.$$

Remember that X_1, X_2 have been measured on persons of the sample, but Z has not. (Collectors of family budget data are, in fact, able to ascertain single consumption items but have difficulty in finding the incomes!) It will be convenient to use logarithms. Write $\log Z = z$, $\log X_i = x_i$, $\log \Lambda_i = \lambda_i$, $\log(1 + U_i) = u_i$, $i = 1, 2$. Then

$$x_i = \lambda_i + z + u_i, \quad i = 1, \, 2. \tag{2.8}$$

We shall further assume that random deviations cancel out in a very large sample, in the sense that the expectations of u_1, u_2 vanish:

$$Eu_i = 0 \quad (i = 1, \, 2); \tag{2.9}$$

assume also that u_1, u_2 are jointly normally distributed. We shall write $Eu_i u_j = \sigma_{ij}(i, j = 1, 2)$. Our hypothesis involves thus 5 unknown parameters λ_1, λ_2, σ_{11}, σ_{22}, σ_{12}. Can we determine them and use them to make a probabilistic prediction of x_1 and x_2 for any given z?[16]

The answer depends on what information is in our possession *before* we collect the data. The main purpose of the present

example is to show how the character of this "*a priori* information" makes the problem determinate or indeterminate. With
insufficient *a priori* information, the problem is indeterminate,
however large the sample.

Assume, for example – in addition to the assumptions already made [(2.8), (2.9) and normality of the distribution of u_1,
u_2] – that we know the frequency distribution of z^{17}: viz., normal with known mean and variance (ζ and ω, say), and independent of the disturbances u_1 and u_2; hence, $Ezu_1 = 0 = Ezu_2$. As
before, we shall neglect sampling errors (by assuming our sample
very large), so that the sample averages $\bar{x}_1$, $\bar{x}_2$ are almost equal
to the corresponding expectations; then by (2.8), (2.9), approximately

$$\bar{x}_i = Ex_i = \lambda_i + \zeta \; ;$$

hence   (2.10)

$$\lambda_i = \bar{x}_i - \zeta \; (i = 1, 2),$$

thus determining the two unknowns λ_1, λ_2 [18]. Moreover, the
sample moments (sample averages of squares and products) computed from the observed values of x_i in the (very large) sample,
serve to determine σ_{11}, σ_{22}, σ_{12}, the parameters of the distribution of u_1, u_2. For, by (2.8), (2.9),

$$x_i - \bar{x}_i = z - \zeta + u_i \; ;$$

therefore

$$E(x_i - \bar{x}_i)(x_k - \bar{x}_k) = E(z-\zeta)^2 + Eu_iu_k + (z - \zeta)(Eu_i + Eu_k)$$

$$= \omega + \sigma_{ik} \; ; \quad i, k = 1, 2.$$

Hence, in a very sample, approximately

$$\left. \begin{array}{l} \text{sample average of } (x_1 - \bar{x}_1)^2 = \omega + \sigma_{11} \\[2mm] \text{sample average of } (x_2 - \bar{x}_2)^2 = \omega + \sigma_{22} \\[2mm] \text{sample average of } (x_1 - \bar{x}_1)(x_2 - \bar{x}_2) = \omega + \sigma_{12} , \end{array} \right\} (2.11)$$

where ω and the sample moments are known. The parameters

σ_{11}, σ_{22}, σ_{12} thus estimated serve to determine (using the tables for bivariate normal distribution), the probability with which u_1 will fall into some given interval, and u_2 will fall, at the same time, into some given interval.

This would answer our Question 1. As to Question 2, I shall not go into details here. Suffice it to say that, once we know the conditional distribution of x_1, x_2 given z, we can also estimate the parameter z characterizing an individual, from values x_1, x_2 observed (once or in repeated observations) on an individual.

But suppose our *a priori* knowledge is less complete than in the example studied so far. For example, suppose we know the mean (ζ) of z (i.e., the geometric mean of average incomes of the U. S. population) but do not know its variance ω. We see from (2.10), (2.11) that we can then determine λ_1, λ_2 but not σ_{11}, σ_{22}, σ_{12}. Consequently we can predict x_i for a given z only in the sense of providing the conditional expectation of x_i ($= \lambda_i + z$) but not of stating an interval into which the x_i should fall with preassigned probability. Nor shall we be able to estimate an individual's z from an observation on his x_1, x_2.

Or suppose we have the knowledge of both μ and ω, but have also a larger list of unknowns, because we are convinced that the assumption (2.8) is too special and should be replaced by a more general one:

$$x_i = \lambda_i + \beta_i z + u_i \quad [19] \quad i = 1, 2, \quad (2.12)$$

with β_1, β_2 unknown. Using this equation, we can again express – similarly to (2.10), (2.11) – the two sample means of x_1 and x_2 and their three sample moments in terms of the 7 unknowns. We shall be 2 equations short. The problem is indeterminate.

Consider, on the other hand, the case when we have fewer unknown constants than we have equations to determine them. Suppose again that we know both ζ and ω and let our hypothesis again be expressed by (2.8), (2.9). But, suppose, in addition, we know from other sources that $\sigma_{12} = 0$, i.e., there can be, at any fixed income, no correlation between eating of cereals and smoking. We have then only four constants to determine (λ_1, λ_2, σ_{11}, σ_{22}), yet can derive from the observations the same five equations (2.10), (2.11) as in our first example, in which σ_{12} was unknown. If the hypothesis now used is correct, i.e., if (2.8), (2.9), as well as the assumed frequency distribution of z and the assertion $\sigma_{12} = 0$, are all valid, then one of those equations derived from observations is redundant for the purpose of determining unknown parameters. But then it can be used to test the hypothesis. Indeed, the assertion $\sigma_{12} = 0$ makes the last of the equations (2.11) into a relation between two known quantities, viz., between the observed cross-moment of x_1 and x_2 and the known variance ω of z. If this relation is not, in fact, satisfied, our hypothesis is wrong: e.g., (2.8) may be false, or z or u_1, u_2 are not distributed normally, or $\omega \neq$ variance of z, or $\sigma_{12} \neq 0$, etc.[20]

To sum up our examples: We started with a case in which all unknown constants could be determined from an equal number of (independent) equations obtained from observations – all constants were "*identifiable*." By modifying the assumptions used or the kind of data available we obtained a case in which some of the constants, and another in which all of the constants were (however large the number of observations!) not determinable, "*nonidentifiable*." Finally, we have had an example of "*over-identification*": observations yielded more (independent) equations than there are unknown constants; if these equations are inconsistent,[21] the hypothesis used must be rejected.

The term identifiability was suggested by T. C. Koopmans and the relevant mathematics were studied by the staff of the Cowles Commission for Research in Economics in considerable detail(see, e.g., the Commission's Monographs No. 10 and 14) because of the importance of the identification problem in economics.[22] However, the problem seems to be present in other social sciences as well, e.g., in the Lazarfeld theory of latent structures and in Thurstone's factor analysis.) In fact, my examples were chosen with the very purpose of providing a link between problems encountered in economics and those more familiar to a sociologist or psychologist, but, alas, less familiar to me. Let me, then, venture again to interpret x_1 and x_2 as answers to two questions asked of a person possessing an unknown degree z of some measurable characteristic. Z is a parameter, changing from person to person. It is not a random variable.[23] The variables x_1 and x_2 can each take values 1 (for "yes") or 0 (for "no"). Assuming that a very large number of persons have been questioned, we want to determine the conditional joint probability

$$\pi = \pi(x_1, x_2 \mid z). \tag{2.13}$$

This is the same as (2.2), with n = 1 and with x interpreted as a vector consisting of two components. Since x_1, x_2 can have only

two values each, it is inappropriate to state an assumption about
the distribution of a random "unexplained residual," a continuous
quantity such as (2.3), or the u_i in (2.8). Instead, we specify
directly the function (2.13) of z, i.e., assume that the respective
probabilities of the four possible alternatives [1) $x_1 = x_2 = 0$;
2) $x_1 = x_2 = 1$; 3) $x_1 = 0$, $x_2 = 1$; 4) $x_1 = 1$, $x_2 = 0$] are determined by z in a specified fashion (Lazarfeld's "trace lines").
Suppose, for example that the function π can be tabulated as follows (each cell corresponding to the probability of one combination of answers)

x_1	$x_2 = 0$		
0	$\alpha_{00} + \beta_{00}\ z$	$\alpha_{01} + \beta_{01}\ z$	(2.14)
1	$\alpha_{10} + \beta_{10}\ z$	$\alpha_{11} + \beta_{11}\ z$	

(This presupposes of course that z has an upper and a lower
limit). The α's and β's are unknown. Since the four probabilities
must add up to 1 for any z, the α's must add to 1, and the β's to
0. We have thus 6 (not 8) unknown constants. Can we determine
them from the sample? Call p_{ij} the proportion of people, in a
very large sample, whose pair of answers is: $x_1 = i$, $x_2 = j$. Denote by ζ the mean of z in the sample. Then

$$p_{ij} = \alpha_{ij} + \beta_{ij}\ \zeta \qquad i, j = 0, 1. \qquad (2.15)$$

ζ can be chosen as a unit of measurement of the z. The four proportions p_{ij} are all observable, but since they must add up to 1,
only three of the four equations (2.15) are independent. This is not
enough to determine the 6 unknowns. They are not identifiable.

But suppose we know with certainty the following property of
our questionnaire: for any given person, the probability of answering the first question by yes is independent of whether he answers
the second question by a yes or a no (though, of course, both probabilities vary from person to person, depending on z). Obviously,
not every questionnaire satisfies this condition. This is a case of
a "pure test," in Lazarsfeld's terminology. The probability that a
person answers with "yes" the question "Is your name John?" depends on how the same person answers the question "Are you a

woman?" If the probability of a person's being a man is 0.5, and
the probability of a person's being called John is 0.1 (the average
between the probability 0.2 of a man's being called John and the
probability 0.0 of a woman's being called John), then the probability of a person's both being a man and being called John is not
0.5 x 0.1 (as it would be if these two events were independent) but
0.5 x 0.2.

Or consider two questions that are almost identical in content. Suppose the probability for the first question to be answered
affirmatively by any person with z degrees of "ethnocentricity" is
q; the corresponding probability for the second question will then
be near q; and the probability that a person with z degrees of
ethnocentricity will answer both questions in the affirmative will
be, not near q^2 but near q.

It may also be that the degree of dependence between the
answers depends itself on z. An extreme ethnocentric may strongly associate dark hair with fast talk (and perhaps dislike both)
while a man on the other end of the ethnocentricity scale will not
have this ready image in his mind: thus a test may be "pure" for
some persons, not "pure" for others.

Suppose, however, the investigator is sure to have formulated
his questions so that, for a fixed z, the answers are completely
independent; he is sure that all traces of possible associations,
logical or otherwise, between the questions, have been weeded out.
This *a priori* knowledge permits him to specify the function π
more narrowly. For example, in the case (2.14) the assumption
of independence will be expressed by the condition

$$\frac{\alpha_{00} + \beta_{00}\, z}{\alpha_{10} + \beta_{10}\, z} = \frac{\alpha_{01} + \beta_{01}\, z}{\alpha_{11} + \beta_{11}\, z} .\qquad (2.16)$$

Multiplying out and transferring all terms to one side, we obtain a
quadratic expression in z which must vanish for any z. Hence
each of its three terms vanishes, thus providing us with the three
missing equations. Our 6 constants have now become identifiable.

In this example, the assumption of independence between
answers (in the sense defined) has proved powerful enough to
make an otherwise unidentifiable set of unknowns identifiable. The
result can be used to estimate the latent characteristic z of a
person outside the sample (the discrimination problem mentioned
above): e.g., if his answer is "no" to both questions, the maximum

likelihood estimate of his z is obtained by maximizing with respect to z the probability π $(0, 0 | z)$. We therefore put $\alpha_{00} + \beta_{00} z$ = 1. One can also estimate an appropriate confidence interval for z. If all the unknown constants α_{00}, β_{00}, etc. had been unidentifiable it would have been impossible to estimate z. We can say that non-identifiability would make the confidence interval for z infinite. It can be conjectured that if z is identifiable both with and without the assumption of independence, the appropriate confidence interval for z is shorter when this assumption is made than when it is not made.

Since the assumption of independence between questions can have such powerful implications, the investigator, in using or designing the questionnaire, will have to be very critical.[24] As in many other cases, the soundness of statistical results will much depend on the soundness of pre-statistical assumptions which prove inaccessible to statistical test.

Section III. PROBABILITY AND POLICY

In the first lecture we discussed the following rule of conduct: choose that decision which makes the "moral expectation" (= the mathematical expectation of utility) as large as possible. This presupposes consistency in the decision-maker's system of preferences. A rational policy maker must "know what he wants." In addition (at least in the approaches of Bayes and Ramsey), he must "know what he believes" – his system of subjective probabilities, too, must be consistent. To require these consistencies is on the same plane as to require that the policy maker do not make errors of logic and arithmetic: that he avoid contradictions. Logic is self-control, and this includes logic of decision. In Ramsey's words, one should be able to "stop to think it out," rather than to act on the temporarily uppermost desire and belief. This is an ideal, a skill which good decision-makers possess in a higher degree than poor ones. A bad decision-maker tosses in bed and decides in a half-dream. A good decision-maker dresses up a payoff matrix (though not necessarily with pen on paper). I suspect this skill is not entirely inborn and can be acquired by training: a fruitful field for applied psychology.

We also found in our first lecture that the rule of maximizing moral expectation leads to the proposition that degrees of belief (which we needed to know in order to compute moral expectations) are, in the limit, equal to relative frequencies obtained from samples. Accordingly, we devoted our second lecture to showing how certain probability distributions that interest a social scientist are obtained from observations. The probability distributions that interest the social scientist must be usable for prediction of the behavior of people. In the concluding part of the second lecture, we found that certain probability distributions needed for such prediction may be inaccessible to estimation, no matter how large the sample. Certain parameters are "non-identifiable." Yet these parameters are often just the ones the social scientist is particularly curious about: he feels they constitute his "theory," as distinct from "mere description." He is interested in "structures," "latent parameters," and not in mere "empirical regularities" and must be disappointed whenever he finds that the goal cannot be attained with the available kind of data.

What are those "latent" properties, those "theories" behind the manifest data? Why are they interesting? And what makes them so elusive? My tentative answer will be: that "theories" are sought for the sake of decision-making; and that the difficulty in getting at them is due to the difficulty of performing experiments.

To take up one of the examples of our second lecture: Why is a market research organization not interested in merely estimating from its data the bivariate distribution of the consumption of cigarettes and the consumption of cereals? That would permit them to predict the one from the other. But this is not interesting. Instead, there is lurking a theory that both smoking and the expenditure on cereals depend on the third variable, income, which happens to be difficult to ascertain and is thus "latent" rather than "manifest." We have shown that under certain hypotheses it is possible, and under other hypotheses impossible, to obtain from data on cereals and cigarettes consumed by a sample of people, a relationship that will predict cereals consumption from income and that is presumably more "theoretical," more of a "structure," than the relationship between the consumption of cereals and that of cigarettes. The relationship involves two kinds of knowledge: the "prestatistical" hypotheses just mentioned and the numerical parameters estimated from the sample. E.g., the hypothesis may be: cigarettes and cereals are consumed in proportion to incomes, apart from a random percentage deviation for each of the two items, these deviations being distributed normally, with zero correlation. The numerical parameters to be estimated may have been, in this case, the unknown (geometric) mean of the ratios of each of the two expenditure items to the individual's income, and the variances of each of the two deviations. We have seen that if we know the correlation (e.g., zero) between the two deviations, and know the income distribution (though not the individual incomes) in the population from which the sample was taken, the set of parameters is identifiable. But some or all of them become non-identifiable if our *a priori* knowledge is less complete — for example, if we do not have grounds to assume that the average relation between income and smoking or cereal-eating is one of proportionality, or that the two deviations from proportionality are non-correlated (i.e., that a man's smoking beyond his means is compatible with over-eating as well as with under-eating cereals, compared with the average breakfast of his income group). In these cases, knowledge of the "latent" relation between income and the consumption items becomes inaccessible, with the type of data we have assumed in our example.

Why hanker after this inaccessible knowledge? Why not be content — to continue with our example — with predicting cereal consumption from cigarette consumption or vice versa, which is perfectly possible on the basis of our data? Presumably because the

market research organization does not expect the latter kind of prediction to be of much use in future practical situations. It does find
it useful to predict consumption from income. Why? Because it
visualizes the following situation: given a new market, with customers' income distribution known and different from that of the
population previously studied, predict the demand for cereals or
cigarettes. If the decision to face new markets would never have to
be taken, research about the influence of income (or other such factors) on consumption would be unnecessary: it would suffice to
know past consumption.

Similarly, if – in line with the last example of our previous
lecture – the manifest data are answers to a questionnaire and the
latent parameter deemed to underly those answers is the "degree
of ethnocentricity," the reason why we are interested in measuring
the latter is, presumably, its potential usefulness. It is not useful
to predict that a "yes" answer to a certain question entails, with a
certain probability, a "no" answer to another question (with population the same as the sampled one). I presume that what is really
wanted is to predict the action of some new individual or group. It
is assumed *a priori* that, for example, the discourteous treatment
of immigrants by an official is determined by his degree of ethnocentricity which also influences his answers to questionnaires and
which (if "identifiable") is revealed by those answers. One wants
to use those answers of the aspirant to an office to predict the
behavior of the future official. A convenient way to state the relation between the observable answers to the questionnaire and the
virtually observable action of the official is *via* the "degree of ethnocentricity" which influences both. It is assumed to be "behind"
those observables, just like the genetic make-up of an individual is
"behind" observable data on his and his ancestors' hereditary features, even though genes might never become observable through
the strongest ultra microscope. The study both of genotype and of
"ethnocentricities" would not be called for if predictions of the
effects of changed genotype and changed ethnocentricity (or their
changed distribution within a population), as in problems of animal
breeding or the administration of policies towards ethnical minori-
ties, were never to be made.

Permit me to use an example from economics: a severely
simplified variant of a "Keynesian" model designed to discuss fis-
cal policy as an instrument for maintaining employment and stable
prices.

Consider the dollar value of all goods and services produced
during a year (not counting those used for repair or renewal of the

existing stock). This dollar amount can be called the (net) national product. It is composed of the dollar amounts – called incomes – paid out, in the course of production, to workers, factory-owners, capital-lenders. Thus net national product is identical with national income. Denote this quantity by y. Consider now another quantity: the dollar value of all goods and services demanded during a year (again not counting repair and renewal). This national demand is composed of three parts: 1) the demand of consumers for food, shelter, etc. – denote it by c; 2) the demand of businessmen for machines and other goods to increase their plants and inventories (a matter I had occasion to mention in the previous lecture) – denote it by b; 3) the demand of the government for the services of its employees and for public buildings, armament goods, etc. – we shall denote it (for reasons that will appear presently) by a Greek letter, ρ (for Roosevelt). In general the national demand $c + b + \rho$ is not identical with the national product (income) y. People who decide about production (and hence about the incomes disbursed) may or may not be able to quickly adjust production to demand. However in our context we need not discuss this adjustment process, its motives and form, except in a footnote later.[25] We shall assume that production is adjusted to demand instantaneously, so that always

$$y = c + b + \rho. \qquad (3.1)$$

Of these quantities, only ρ is directly controlled by the policy-maker, the government. What determines the rest, namely b and c?

As to b, let us assume that businessmen feel encouraged to expand their plant when the current national income, y, is high; at least they feel so "on the whole," i.e., apart from some random deviation. To fix the ideas, let us use a linear approximation:

$$b = \beta y + v_b, \quad \beta > 0; \qquad (3.2)$$

where β is a parameter characterizing businessmen's behavior and v_b is a normally distributed random variable; denote its mean and variance by the Greek letters μ_b and σ_{bb} respectively.

As to c, let us assume that people's consumption depends, apart from a random deviation v_c, only on the amount of income that remains in their hands after payment of taxes, and on nothing else. Using again a linear approximation,

$$c = \gamma (y - \tau) + v_c, \quad \gamma > 0; \tag{3.3}$$

where γ is a parameter descriptive of consumers' behavior and τ denotes the tax collected. The mean and variance of v_c (assumed normal) will be denoted by μ_c and σ_{cc}, respectively. Since the random deviations in the behavior of consumers may or may not be correlated with those in the behavior of businessmen we need also a symbol σ_{bc} to denote their covariance.

Let us now marshall all our symbols:

government-controlled parameters: ρ, τ;

non-controlled parameters: β, γ, μ_b, μ_c, σ_{bb}, σ_{cc}, σ_{bc};

other variables: b, c, x.

Finally, we assume for simplicity that the government determines directly the tax collected, τ (and not, as is actually the case, the tax rates only).

Let us now marshall all our quantities:

government-controlled parameters: ρ, τ;

non-controlled parameters: β, γ, μ_b, μ_c, σ_{bb}, σ_{cc}, σ_{bc};

dependent variables: b, c, y;

random deviations: v_b, v_c.

We have three dependent variables and a system of three equations. We can solve for b, c, y. For example, equation (3.4) below gives the solution for y. Since the system involves random deviations v_b, v_c, the dependent variables b, c, y are also random: they fluctuate with v_b, v_c. If the deviations v_b, v_c were observable, one could determine, for every pair v_b, v_c, the values that the dependent variables b, c, y would take, provided one knows the parameters ρ, τ, β, γ. Actually v_b, v_c are not observable but their probability distribution is fully determined by the parameters μ_b, μ_c, σ_{bb}, σ_{cc}, σ_{bc}. If one knows these parameters, one can find the probability distribution of b, c, y for any given set of values of the controlled parameters ρ, τ and of β, γ.

We are not concerned here with whether the model is economically sound. It is too crude. We merely use it as an example for our methodological discussion. The model's three equations, together with the probability distribution of the random deviations

v_b, v_c, purport to "explain" the observed distribution of the three dependent variables b, c, y. The model expresses a hypothesis about the behavior of consumers and businessmen, summarized by the non-controlled parameters – the Greek letters excluding ρ and τ. The policy problem is for the government to choose the best values of the controlled parameters ρ, τ, – the values that will maximize the government's "expected utility," a term defined in our first lecture. If the government were concerned simply with the national income y (a dollar amount, as you remember) it would choose ρ and τ so as to maximize the expected value (the mean) of y – call it μ_y, one of the parameters of the distribution of y. How is the distribution of y determined by ρ and τ? The random variable y is related to ρ, τ in a linear fashion, as is seen by solving our three equations:

$$y = \lambda (\rho - \gamma \tau) + \lambda (v_b + v_c), \qquad (3.4)$$

where $\lambda = 1/1 - \beta - \gamma$. Since $v_b + v_c$ is distributed normally, so is y. The mean of y is

$$\mu_y = \lambda (\rho - \gamma \tau) + \lambda (\mu_b + \mu_c); \qquad (3.5)$$

this is how μ_y is affected by the government's choice of public expenditure ρ and tax revenue τ.

Note in passing that the policy-maker might be concerned, not only with a high mean national income but also with a high predictability of national income, as expressed by its variance, σ_{yy}. As the late Senator Arthur Vandenberg said in criticizing the New Deal: "We don't want to live on a flying trapeze." It is worthwhile to remark, as an exercise in the logic of these matters, that in our particular model the policy-maker is unable to affect σ_{yy}. The variance of y is not affected by adding to y a constant; it is, by (3.4), simply proportional to the variance of $(v_b + v_c)$ and is equal to

$$\sigma_{yy} = \lambda^2 (\sigma_{bb} + \sigma_{cc} + 2\sigma_{bc}). \qquad (3.6)$$

Thus, the knowledge of the last three of the non-controlled parameters of our list above, is irrelevant for policy purposes if the policy goal depends on μ_y and/or σ_{yy}. If our model were non-linear, the result might be different, and the knowledge of σ_{bb}, σ_{cc},

σ_{bc} important to the policy-maker concerned with high and/or reasonably predictable national income. In any case, this knowledge is
necessary if one wants to "predict", in the sense of our Lecture II,
the random variable, income: i.e., if one wants to estimate the distribution of y. This is, in our example, described by μ_y and σ_{yy},
and to know σ_{yy} one has to know σ_{bb}, σ_{cc}, σ_{bc} . But such prediction may be of no concern to a practical policy-maker.

Continuing with a government bent on maximizing the expected value μ_y of national money income, return to our equation
(3.5). We shall assume $\lambda > 0$, that is $\beta + \gamma < 1$. This assumption is not based on systematic statistical studies but on a general
estimate of plausible behavior of consumers and businessmen and
also on the observed "stability" of a system, a consideration which
we cannot discuss here in any detail.[26] If, then, $\lambda = \beta + \gamma -1 < 0$,
the expected money incomes μ_y as determined in (3.5) is increased by raising ρ and cutting down τ. If there is an upper
limit on government expenditure – say, ρ_{max} – and a lower limit
on tax revenue – say, τ_{min} – then money income is highest with
$\rho = \rho_{max}$ and $\tau = \tau_{min}$ (possibly zero). Now knowledge about the
behavior parameters β, γ is necessary to find these optimal
values of the government-controlled parameters, except the validity of the assumption $\beta + \gamma -1 < 0$.

This result is due to the fact that, under our assumptions, –
as summarized in (3.5) – the expected money income μ_y changes
monotonically(has no turning points) in response to changes in ρ
and τ. Therefore y can achieve a maximum only at some boundary values of ρ and τ. If we introduced, for realism's sake, an
upper limit on the deficit $\rho - \tau$, the same general result would
remain true: no knowledge of the non-controlled parameters
would be necessary to determine the policy (ρ, τ) that maximizes
expected income (μ_y).

Let us now change our example so as to make it more up-to-
date. To think of a government that tries to maximize the expected national income measured in dollars (the money income y) was
possible in times of depression when prices were relatively stable,
and a rise in money income was about equivalent to a rise in physical production and employment. In present inflationary times one
has to think not only of the money income y but also of the price
level, call it p. The physical production is $Y = y/p$; and the government is concerned with both Y and p. This is how we modify
the previously assumed utility function of the policy maker. We
have also to modify the model (3.1), (3.2), (3.3), by adding statements about what determines the dependent variables we have just
added to our list, viz., Y and p.

One simple hypothesis is to assume that physical production
Y cannot rise above a maximum, η (the "full employment output"); and that the price level p is constant (p = π, say), as long
as this maximum output is not reached. That is, our two additional depedent variables, Y and p, are determined as follows, in
terms of our old dependent variable y and the parameters π and
η :

$$
\begin{cases}
\mathbf{Y} = \mathrm{y}/\pi, \ \ \mathrm{p} = \pi & \text{when } \mathrm{y} \leq \eta \\
\\
\mathbf{Y} = \eta \ \ , \ \ \mathrm{p} = \mathrm{y}/\eta & \text{when } \mathrm{y} > \eta\pi.
\end{cases}
\tag{3.9}
$$

Roughly, the first line corresponds to an unemployment situation
and the second line to a full employment situation. In the former,
money income y changes because of changes in physical output Y;
in the latter, y changes because of changes in price level p. If
we retain, in addition, our old equations (3.1), (3.2), (3.3) and
therefore also their implication (3.4) we see from (3.9) that the
new dependent variables Y and p are random variables whose
distribution depends on the same parameters as does the distribution of y, and, in addition, on the parameters η (maximum output) and π (constant price level during depression).

We can assume that the policy maker regards high physical
output as desirable, and a strong rise in prices over their depression level as undesirable – e.g., because of the injustice that such
a rise would inflict on certain people. Thus his utility function –
Y(Y,p), say – is increasing in Y and decreasing in p, with
p $\geq \pi$. As a simple example, we may have, as his utility

$$
u = Y(\mathrm{Y},\mathrm{p}) = \mathbf{Y} - A\mathrm{p}, \ \ A > 0, \ \mathrm{p} \geq \pi.
\tag{3.10}
$$

The reader will notice that we use italicized capitals to indicate a
new class of properties – not the parameters (controlled or non-
controlled) of the model but the characteristics of the decision-
maker's valuations, his "tastes." In particular, A is the number
of units of real income (e.g., billions of dollars) with the purchas-
ing power of the year (1940) that he thinks it worthwhile to sacri-
fice in order to avoid the rise of price level by one point. In assigning any pair of values to the controlled parameters ρ and τ,
he will affect the distribution of Y and p, and hence the expected
value of u, that is, his "moral expectation," in the sense of
our Lecture 1. Our assumptions (3.9), (3.10) will help as an

illustration. Under these assumptions, the utility u is the following function of money income y:

$$
u = \begin{cases}
\dfrac{y}{\pi} - A\,\pi & \text{when } y \leq \eta\,\pi \\[3mm]
\eta - \dfrac{Ay}{\eta} & \text{when } y \geq \eta\,\pi.
\end{cases}
\tag{3.11}
$$

This function is represented on **Figure III.1** by a broken line consisting of two straight line segments: utility u rises with money
income till the latter reaches $\eta\,\pi$; then u falls. Each bell-shaped
curve (of which only two are drawn) indicates one of the possible
normal distribution density functions of y, with a fixed variance
[which, by (3.6), does not depend on policies] and a varying mean
[which, by (3.5) does depend on ρ and τ]. (The two drawn curves
have respective means μ_y and μ'_y.) Thus the policy (ρ, τ) determines the position of the bell-shaped curve, i.e., gives the probability that money income y will fall into any given (small) interval.
If this probability is multiplied by the utility that corresponds to

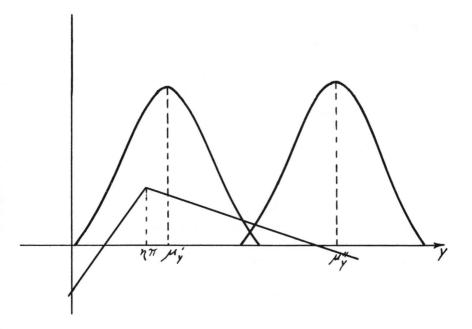

Figure III.1

the value of y in this (small) interval and that is determined by
(3.11), and if all such products are added, one obtains the expected
(mean) utility that corresponds to a given policy (ρ, τ). Using our
diagram, multiply in your mind each ordinate of the bell-shaped
curve by each corresponding ordinate of the broken line, and add
all such products. Their sum is the expected utility. Clearly, as
the bell-shaped curve moves too far to the right or to the left, the
higher utilities (i.e., the ordinates of the broken line taken in the
proximity of the full-employment point, η π) are multiplied with the
lower probabilities (ie., with the ordinates at the left or right "tail"
of the bell-shaped curve). Hence there exists some intermediate
position of the bell-shaped curve – and hence some value of μ_y
– that results in the highest expected utility.

    To this optimal value of μ_y will correspond, by (3.5), an
optimal value of $\rho - \gamma \tau$, given the non-controlled parameters.
Hence the knowledge of those parameters (β, γ, μ_b, μ_c) is needed
to find those pairs of value of the policy-parameters ρ and τ, that
will maximize expected utility, given the "taste-parameter" A of
the policy-maker. Of course, the knowledge of the feasible limits
such as τ_{min}, ρ_{max} will also have to be used, to sift out the non-
feasible combinations of taxes and expenditures. But, unlike in
our previous example, this knowledge will not suffice. It becomes
necessary to estimate the parameters that characterize the behavior of consumers and businessmen.

    We see thus that the need for the knowledge of certain pa-
rameters, and therefore for their identifiability (in the sense of
Lecture 2), depends, in general, on the whole model in which these
parameters occur; and on the utility function of the decision-
maker.

    Does not this land us in a rather cross pragmatism? What
about theory for its own sake, a theory that is not used to give
advice, to choose, to act? A pragmatist will say that theory provides us with solutions which are potentially useful for a large
class of decisions. It is welcome because we cannot foresee
which particular decisions we shall have to take. Our decisions
may or may not be such as to leave certain properties of the system unchanged. Hence, the more we know about its properties
the better. If we merely want to know how long it takes to boil an
egg, the best is to boil one or two without going into the chemistry
of protein molecules. The need for chemistry is due to our want
to do other and new things!

    The word "value" is more respectable than "utility," yet
means essentially the same. If the satisfaction of scientific

curiosity is recognized by our culture as one of the major values, the search for facts as well as theories is justified even if no predictive uses can be seen for the results. Yet, an additional scrutiny in terms of other social values remains important. Especially in social science there has been a temptation to use statistical tools for laborious rediscovery of the trivial, or the recording of the useless. One should not brush away as "utilitarian" or "pragmatic" the reminder that we ought to help in the making of socially important decisions.[27]

5. The Principal Components of Scalable Attitudes*

By **LOUIS GUTTMAN**

The Israel Institute of Applied Social Research

The idea of components is becoming of increasing importance in sociology and psychology for analyzing the interrelationships of data. In the three lectures of which this is the first,[1] I shall propose that it is helpful to distinguish between three general types of systems of components. Each type may be regarded as belonging to or constituting a different level of analysis. The first kind of system I shall term *semantic* components; the second, *elementary* components; and the third--following an existing concept and terminology--*principal* components.

Each lecture will provide an example of one of these three systems. Logically, we should arrange the lectures in the order in which we have just listed the three varieties of components, for that is the natural order of occurrence in the design and analysis of observations. Semantic components refer to the definition of the content to be observed. Elementary components represent a hypothesis as to why the observations are interrelated the way they are. And principal components provide a subsequent new frame of reference for the same data.

Although principal components are but a secondary concept compared to the other two, and are arrived at last in a given structural analysis, we shall discuss them first and indeed reverse completely the logical order of these lectures. There are at least two reasons for doing this. It is known in the teaching of logic or of mathematics, for example, that the most "primitive" notions are often the hardest for beginners to assimilate; more complex notions may be partially absorbed more easily at the outset because they afford more toeholds. A second reason is that our particular

* In preparing this lecture for publication, I was immeasurably aided by a transcription of another version delivered later at the University of Chicago. The recording was made by the National Opinion Research Center, and the typescript prepared by the Laboratory of Social Relations of Harvard University. To Professors Clyde Hart and Samuel A. Stouffer my many thanks. Data which became available after my return to Israel, notably on the fourth principal component, have been added to the present written version.

example of a theory of principal components is actually quite simple, and can be followed relatively easily without any previous
acquaintance with the subject.

The example by which we shall illustrate the possible role
of principal components in analyzing the structure of observations
is taken from the theory of scale analysis. This happens also to be
a striking example of the creative role that mathematics can play
in psychological theory, a point which will constitute one of our
main emphases throughout. The story we have to tell in this regard seems to be quite without precedent in social psychology.

Depth interviewers have constantly objected to "oversimplified" scale approaches to attitude research. One of the pioneers
in item analysis--Rensis Likert--whose techniques are today still
among the most widely accepted, has himself virtually abandoned
his former approach in favor of more open-ended and probing
methods.

In our newer theory of scale analysis (as opposed to scale
construction), the mathematics reveals a justification for the probing methods. We shall see that a perfect scale--while a function
of but a single variable--nevertheless has infinitely many principal
components. The latter can have psychological interpretations
similar to those often sought for in depth interviews. A complete
analysis of a scale--mathematically and psychologically--shows an
implicit depth aspect which has hitherto been overlooked for scales;
and conversely, it shows a scaling aspect which has hitherto been
overlooked in depth interviews. Both aspects are part and parcel
of the same scalable phenomena, and cannot be separated in the approach to be described in the present lecture.

It is not our intention to discuss here the mathematical theory
of the principal components of perfect scales; that will be found in
the volume *Measurement and Prediction*.[2] This book also contains
the most extensive discussion available of scale (and intensity)
analysis in general.

It is a *psychological* theory which concerns us here, as well
as the extraordinary interplay between the mathematics and the
psychology. This interplay has taken place thus far only for the
case of social attitudes, and it is to such attitudes that we restrict
our discussion.

Scale analysis is applicable much more widely than to attitudes. For example, it is useful for mental tests and examinations.
It has been found to rank the States of the Union with respect to
their laws concerning Negroes.[3] Many other kinds of phenomena
are occasionally found to be scalable. For such phenomena, we
know virtually nothing as yet as to the interpretation of their

principal components, apart from the scale ranks themselves--
which are related to the *first* principal component.

It may be that non-attitudinal data that are scalable may require different kinds of interpretations of their respective principal components from that which we are now going to present for
social attitudes. This is common in science, that phenomena may
have the same *type* of mathematical equations, but different physical interpretations.

THE PERFECT SCALE

First we review what is meant by a scale for qualitative
data. The idea of a *perfect* scale is quite simple. It is called
"perfect" to distinguish it from other concepts of a scale, because
it has the property of perfect internal consistency.

One way of arriving at the concept is as follows. Suppose we
pose an attitude question like:

"Is war good?"

and require respondents to answer either "Yes" or "No". We
might find, for example (this is purely hypothetical as people may
refuse to answer without qualification), that 40% say "Yes" and
60% say "No". Now we could ask the same question in another way:

"Is war bad?"

This time we might find that 80% say "Yes" and 20% say "No".
This conforms to the kind of thing that happens empirically.

Can there be any consistency between the parts of this picture? Do the people have a definite attitude toward war? Our answer is that these data *can* be regarded as perfectly consistent and
conforming to a one-dimensional attitude, *provided* there is a certain pattern of consistency between the responses. To study consistency, we need the fourfold table of the joint occurrences of the
replies to the two questions. So far, all we are told is the marginals of the two questions, so we prepare a blank table with these
marginals as shown in Table 1. The question on war being "good"
has marginals of 40 and 60, while the question on war being "bad"
has marginals of 80 and 20.

If these people are really aligned on a single attitude continuum, so that the differential responses are slices of the same continuum but at different places, then the 20% saying "No" to the
"War is bad" question should surely be included in the 40% people
saying "Yes" to the "War is good" question. They would be the
people who are most favorable to war. So we enter "20" into the

Table 1

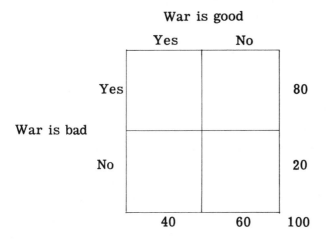

War is good

	Yes	No	
Yes			80
No			20
	40	60	100

empty cell in the lower left hand corner of Table 1 above. But then all the remaining missing entries can be computed exactly, for they must add up to the given marginals. The completed table thus is:

Table 2

War is good

	Yes	No	
Yes	20	60	80
No	20	0	20
	40	60	100

An important feature of Table 2 is the zero cell, showing that one of the possible combinations of responses does not actually occur. Out of four possible combinations, only three occur. One consequence is that the three occurring types can be arranged in an unambiguous rank order, from those most favorable to war to those least favorable, as in the following Table 3:

Table 3

Rank	Combination of Responses	Frequency
Highest	Yes, war is good; No, war is not bad	20
Intermediate	Yes, war is good; Yes, war is bad	20
Lowest	No, war is not good; Yes, war is bad	60
	Total	100

Had also the fourth type occurred: "No, war is not good; No, war is not bad", there could be all kinds of debates as to where to place it in the table. But if it is absent, then clearly there is little room for argument as to the meaningfulness of the ranking of the remaining three types.

But more than just these two questions could be asked about attitude toward war. Indefinitely many more could be phrased containing essentially the same content. The totality of such questions is called the *universe of content* for the attitude being studied. Each additional question may yield responses with a different set of marginals. If the entire universe forms a perfect scale, then the fourfold table between any two dichotomous items from the universe must have a zero cell like for our first two questions in Table 2. But more than this, we have to consider higher order joint occurrences than just two questions at a time.

If n dichotomous items are asked, then there is a total of 2^n combinations of responses possible. How many of these must have a zero frequency if a perfect scale holds? We shall now see that at most n+1 combinations can occur, or have nonzero frequencies. These will be called *scale types*. Furthermore, there is always an unambiguous order among the scale types, so that they can be ranked from highest to lowest without any debate.

If there is an underlying continuum for the universe of attitude toward war, let us represent it as a straight line in the following "percentile" metric:

Figure 1

The more a person is favorable to war, the higher the percentile he occupies compared to the rest of the respondents. For example, the percentile of 60 means that 60% of the respondents have a lower position than this one, while 40% have a higher position.[4]

Returning to the item "Is war good?", it can now be repre-sented as a function of the percentile metric in Figure 1 by merely inserting a cutting point at the 60th percentile. Denote this cutting point by a. Then the 60% of respondents who answer "No" are in the interval to the *left* of cutting point a, and those who answer "Yes" are to the *right* of point a, as in Figure 2:

Figure 2

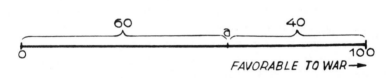

If the second item, "Is war bad", belongs to the same con-tinuum, it can be represented by a cutting point b on the same dia-gram, at the 80th percentile, yielding Figure 3:

Figure 3

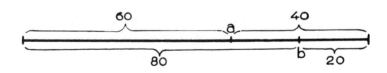

Figure 3 gives exactly the same results[5] as does the fourfold Table 2, if one interprets *discernible segments of the continuum* as *scale types*. The first discernible segment is from percentile 0 to a,

containing 60% of the people, namely those in the lowest rank of
Table 3. The next discernible interval is from a to b--the 60th to
80th percentiles--and hence contains 20% of the people, the intermediate rank of Table 3. And the third interval is from b to 100,
containing the 20% of the respondents who comprise the highest of
the three ranks of Table 3. There is a one-to-one correspondence
between the intervals and the scale types.

    Any further dichotomous item which is perfectly consistent
with the same continuum can similarly be represented by a cutting
point in the same diagram as Figure 3. Clearly, an additional cutting point c must fall within one, of the three already discerned intervals, or at worst[6] coincide with a or b. If c falls within one of
the intervals, then it will separate it into two discernible subinter-
vals, and will leave the other intervals intact. Thus, there will now
be four discernible intervals all told from the three dichotomies.
By induction, it is clear that each further item with a distinct cutting point will increase the previous number of discernible
intervals by one.

    If a cutting point c happens to coincide with a previous cut-
ting point a or b, then the new item contributes no new differen-
tiation; it is indeed *perfectly dependent* on the item which has the
same cutting point; all people in one category of one item are in the
corresponding category of the other.

    Therefore, if all n dichotomies belong to the same continuum,
they will yield at most n+1 discernible intervals. Each of these
intervals corresponds to a unique combination of n responses, so
at most n+1 types of people can have nonzero frequencies.
Furthermore, it is now easily seen that these n+1 types can be
arranged unambiguously according to *their content* in a rank order,
and that this rank order is the same as that of their corresponding
discernible intervals. Consider two adjacent intervals; then their
response patterns are identical on n-1 of the items, but differ on
only one item. On the item on which they differ, the *higher interval
has the more favorable response*. Hence the n+1 types can be
called *scale* types; they can be assigned ranks which have undebat-
able meaning with respect to the content being studied. A higher
rank is in a real sense "more favorable" than a lower rank.

    The argument just presented is not limited to dichotomies.
On the same continuum, a trichotomous item would be represented
by *two* cutting points, etc. The theory is perfectly general for any
number of categories per item, and the number of categories may
vary from item to item in the same universe.

    This is as far as we pursue the basis of scale analysis here.

To summarize, by a perfect scale we mean a set of items such that each item separately can have its categories put into a one-to-one correspondence with intervals of the same continuum.

The practical techniques of scale analysis are devoted to testing with empirical data the hypothesis that such a correspondence is approximately possible, by studying the interrelations among the items. The Cornell technique is at present among the most suitable.[7] If the hypothesis is sustained, then there ensues an empirical approximation to ranks along this continuum. The empirical ranks might be called an empirical scale variable, while the continuum represents an "underlying" scale variable.

Since only a finite number of items can be used in practice, only discrete empirical ranks can be computed. But it can be hypothesized that, if the number of items is increased indefinitely, a continuous ranking will be arrived at, namely, the underlying percentile metric.

THE PROBLEM OF METRIC

An immediate psychological problem arises out of considering what happens if questions are rephrased. For example, assuming a scale exists, is there meaning to saying that some people are "favorable" to war and other people "unfavorable"; that is, that some have *positive* attitude and others have a *negative* attitude towards war? All that a rank order tells us is that some people are *more* favorable and others are *less* favorable. But how favorable must a person be to have a *positive* attitude, and how much less favorable must another be to have a *negative* attitude? In other words, does there exist a point on the percentile continuum such that all ranks to the right of it can be said to represent a positive attitude, and all ranks to the left a negative attitude?

To attempt to define such a zero point by an observed item from the universe of content is obviously a precarious procedure. For example, suppose we were to assume that all people who say "No" to our first question on war are actually negative to war. This would make 40% of the population positive, and 60% negative. Somebody else could come along and protest that for some reason our question was "biased", and instead we should use the second item, "Is war bad?", which would give us only 20% positive and 80% negative. A third person could come along and claim that for some reason both these questions are "biased" and propose another

one of his own from the universe, with still a different cutting
point. Who is right?

In the past, many attempts have been made to give instructions on how to word a question so that it be unbiased, but there is
little agreement among social scientists as to which of the alternative sets of instructions to use. The reason for this is now clear,
for the rules remain on an intuitive basis that is no sounder than
not having rules and trying to decide by a separate intuitive
procedure for each research project individually.

To argue that perhaps one should not use a single question
after all, but should use several questions together, does not make
the problem any better. Instead of having one cutting point, we
would have several; and we would be no closer to a solution. For
example, consider the intermediate type "Yes, war is good; Yes,
war is bad". Is this positive, negative, or straddling the zero
point? Some can argue that "those who are not for us are against
us" and call such a type positive or negative, as the case may be;
others can argue that such an apparent straddling represents a
neutral position.

It is clear that there can be no removing of disagreements
about "bias" unless one can formulate an objective procedure for
determining a zero point on the attitude continuum. One of the surprising and fundamental features of the mathematical theory of
scales is that it provides the basis for such a procedure. The
second principal component, which can often be called the *intensity
function* for certain attitudes, defines an objective and meaningful
zero point that belongs intrinsically to the universe of content.

The problem of a zero point is but one special problem concerning the underlying metric. More generally, it is of interest to
inquire whether or not there exists some psychologically meaningful metric for the underlying continuum apart from mere rank
order. Does the difference between two adjacent ranks in one
region mean the same as the difference in another region of the
percentile? The higher order principal components turn out to be
involved in the answer to this question.

THE FIRST PRINCIPAL COMPONENT:
THE UNDERLYING LEAST-SQUARES METRIC

Before plunging into the psychological aspects of the solution
to the problem of metric, let us review briefly the mathematical

meaning and properties of the principal components of perfect scales.

If we seek a metric apart from rank order, what properties should such a metric have? By another metric, we mean a stretching and contracting of the various differences between the scale ranks. What should our criterion be for the "best" way of doing such stretchings and contractions?

The criterion we shall adopt is that of *maximizing the internal consistency in the sense of least-squares*.

This means the following. Each respondent, instead of getting just a rank, is now going to get a numerical value, say x, on the new metric. Thus, the respondents will have a frequency distribution of x values. Let the variance of the distribution be σ_x^2. Now let us consider again the first item: "Is war good?" The 40% who say "Yes" will have a subdistribution of x values; let us say its mean is $\bar{x}_1$. The 60% who say "No" will also have a subdistribution with a mean value of, say, $\bar{x}_2$. We would like these two subgroups who say "Yes" and "No" respectively to be as different as possible on the new metric. Thus, we would like the difference between $\bar{x}_1$ and $\bar{x}_2$ to be as large as possible compared to σ_x^2. In the same way, for the second item, "Is war bad", we would like the mean scores for the two subgroups of respondents to be as different as possible. And so on for all items in the universe being studied.

But if we maximize the difference for one item, we will *not* at the same time be maximizing it for another. What we have to do is to consider the totality of differences over all items simultaneously. The mean of the squares of these differences[8] over all items, then, is to be maximized compared to σ_x^2. The x values that do this will be our new metric.

It turns out that *maximizing* differences *between* subgroups is equivalent to *minimizing* differences *within* subgroups. Hence the term "least-squares" is used for a process like ours, referring to the minimizing of subvariances.

The equations for solving for the new metric were known[9] before the general concept of perfect scales was developed. These equations can be applied automatically to any set of data, scalable or not. The procedure, however, has particular meaning for the case of perfect scales, and leads to some quite unexpected properties for this special case that hold for no other kind of response structure.

It turns out that, for perfect scales, *there always is a best solution or metric* in the sense defined. Furthermore, these new

values or scores have a monotone relationship to the original rank
order metric. As the rank goes up, so do the scores, as in Figure
4. That was to be expected if we were really getting a consistent
metric; it should merely expand and contract differences between
ranks, but not *reverse* any rank relationships. A person who has
a higher scale rank than another should also have a higher x score;
and so he does in the newly derived least-squares metric.

THE GEOMETRY OF THE PRINCIPAL COMPONENTS

The very same mathematical equations that yield the most
internally consistent metric yield a lot more than this. They tell
us that, after the *most* consistent solution--say Solution I--there
is a next best solution, say Solution II. The x values provided by
Solution II don't separate the means $\bar{x}_1$ and $\bar{x}_2$ as much, relatively, as do those from Solution I; but after Solution I, they are *next
best*. Furthermore, they also have a definite kind of relation to the
underlying rank order. This time it is not a monotone relationship,
but U- or J-shaped, as in Figure 5. The x values are higher toward the 0 and 100 percentiles and descend towards the middle.

Figure 4   Figure 5

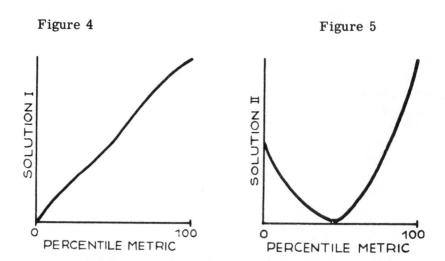

After Solution II, the equations say there is a *third best* solution, say Solution III. When Solution III is plotted against the rank
order, it must always yield a curve with *two* bends in it, or one
more bend than does Solution II, as in Figure 6. (Solution II

correspondingly has one more bend than Solution I, since Solution I has no bends at all, being a monotone function of the rank order.)

After Solution III, there is a fourth best solution, which yields a graph with *three* bends in it, as in Figure 7. In general, if there are n dichotomous items, then there are n solutions to the equations of internal consistency, each being next best to the preceding one, and each with one more bend in its graph than the preceding one. Also, interestingly, the nth solution, is also the *worst* possible, or *least* internally consistent of any possible metric.

Figure 6   Figure 7

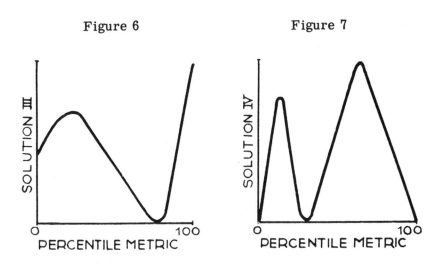

Since the universe is thought of as containing infinitely many items, there are infinitely many solutions to our equations, with the properties of succession just described.

Such solutions to the type of equations which emerged from our quest are called in mathematics the *principal components*[10] of the system of equations. Solution I is the first principal component. Solution II is the second principal component, etc.

Thus, principal components are in the first instance a mathematical concept or phenomenon. Any set of data, when analyzed by our equations of internal consistency, will be found to have mathematical principal components. However, only perfect scales will have the *law of formation* that we have described, with each component having one more bend in it than the preceding component. (The absence of a law for non-scales could perhaps be surmised by considering that if we didn't have scale ranks before we began, we would have nothing to plot the components against in the first

place.)   The equations give even further details about the law of
formation of scale components; and these--when interpreted
psychologically--turn out to be of fundamental importance for
attitude research.

A last word here, largely for the mathematical reader, and
then we get back to psychology in the next section. The maximizing problem described above leads, for finite n, directly to a
certain matrix of the joint occurrences of the items, of which our
principal components are the latent vectors. Most interestingly,
by differencing the matric equation, we arrive at a second-order
difference equation[11] of the form:

$$\Delta(c_i \Delta X_i) + \phi f_{i+1} X_{i+1} = 0,$$

with certain boundary conditions, where the x_i are the $n+1$ unknowns to be solved for, c_i and f_i are certain positive parameters
belonging to the universe of content and the population of respondents, and ϕ is essentially the inverse of the latent root of the
original matrix associated with the vector of the x_i. It is by
studying the difference equation that the properties of the scale's
principal components are learned.

For finite n, the solutions x_i of course yield only $n+1$
values, to be plotted against the $n+1$ ranks; a discrete, rather
than a continuous, graph results. But as n increases, the number
of points in the graph increases and the points come closer and
closer; in the limit they are continuous curves such as we have
drawn above. Correspondingly, the difference equation is in a
limit a *differential* equation, indeed exactly of the type studied in
the Sturm-Liouville boundary-value theory. The latter has as
solutions the classical orthogonal polynomials like those of
Legendre, Hermite, etc., and these indeed are examples of principal
components of continuous scales.

The solutions for finite n are the discrete analogues of the
continuous case. In a sense, the difference equation is more general than the differential equation which is its limit, since the
latter can be derived from the former, but not vice-versa. The
general difference equation above seems to have been discovered
first by scale theory. This seems to be one instance where the
social sciences have arrived at a formula which contains classical
equations of physics and mathematics as special cases.

THE SECOND PRINCIPAL COMPONENT:
INTENSITY

The difference equations for the principal components of perfect scales were known as long as seven or eight years ago, along with the properties of their solutions. But some time elapsed before any psychological meaning could be attached to them or use made of them in practice.

An interpretation--for the case of certain attitudes--was first found for the second principal component, as the *intensity* of the attitude. If scalable attitude has a meaningful zero point, then as people have ranks farther and farther to the right of it, they should become more and more positive, and hence more and more intense. Similarly, as ranks get farther and farther to the left of the zero point, they should become more and more negative, and hence also indicate more intensity. Intensity accordingly should have a U- or J-shaped relation with the underlying rank order. Thus, intensity could possibly be the second principal component.

Suchman and I worked out two different ways for studying intensity in practice and relating it to the observed rank order: the foldover technique and the two-part technique.[12] Experiments verified that the relationship was just about as predicted. The study of the intensity function is becoming more and more accepted in attitude and opinion research, and indeed is routine procedure in all projects of the Israel Institute of Applied Social Research (which uses the foldover technique primarily). A major reason-- but not the only one--is the solution it gives to the problem of bias.

The zero point is located in practice by *internal* intensity methods such as the foldover or two-part technique.[12] Evidence is growing that it has psychological meaning also with respect to *external* variables.

Two different kinds of research projects have shown that the zero point actually tends to be a *point of indifference*. One of these researches has already been published.[13] It showed that the intensity of the public's attitude toward civil servants in Israel decreases as the amount of contact with government offices decreases, so that those at the lowest intensity--or at the zero point of content--had the least amount of contact. Furthermore, the proportion of "No reply" on the attitude was inversely related to amount of contact with government offices, the proportion increasing as contact decreased. Thus people with the least amount of contact tended either not to reply or to express a neutral attitude, implying (indirectly) that an excess of "No reply" relates to an attitude in the neighborhood of the zero point.

A second research project carries this finding much further, and shows how the problem of the "filter" question of public opinion polls can be solved by intensity analysis. In a study of radio listening habits in Israel, it was desired to ask the general public their attitude on various regularly scheduled programs. The attitudes were desired only of people to whom radio listening was relevant. Such people could not be selected in advance of the interview. A filtering system had to be designed objectively to separate listeners from non-listeners at the outset of the interview, so that the interview could economically be terminated for non-listeners before specific questions on programs were asked. It would not do merely to pose a filter question like "Do you habitually listen to radio?"; as for all such single questions., the response would depend on the wording and on the interviewer. Instead, we asked a series of questions on the relevance of radio listening to the respondent. These formed a scale, and the scale had an objective zero point which separated those with positive listening habits from those with negative (!) listening habits (the content type at the zero point listened just a bit, but unsystematically: less listening than this is hence psychologically negative). In the pretest, everybody-- whether with a positive or a negative listening habit--was asked the specific program questions. Each program, when related to the filter scale of general relevance, had few "No reply" cases on the positive side of the filter zero point, but had a tremendous jump to virtually 100% "No reply" when one crossed the zero point to negative listening habits.[14]   These data are being prepared for publication.

Further examples are available from various projects of the Israel Institute, showing how the zero point of an attitude acts as a pivot in U-shaped relations with other outside variables[15].

THE EMPIRICAL INVARIANCE OF BENDING POINTS

Once we have arrived at the concept of intensity and have techniques for studying it directly, we can forget for the while that it was the *mathematical* second principal component that gave us the idea of looking for such a psychological thing in the first place. The concept and techniques now stand on their own feet without regard to ideas of principal components, for we can use them directly without an intermediary.

Given a set of scalable attitude items, we now know how to assign each respondent two ranks in practice, one on content and one on intensity. For our purposes, both of these kinds of ranks are expressed in terms of empirical percentiles, and can be plotted against each other. The empirical scattergram looks typically (schematically) as in Figure 8.

Figure 8

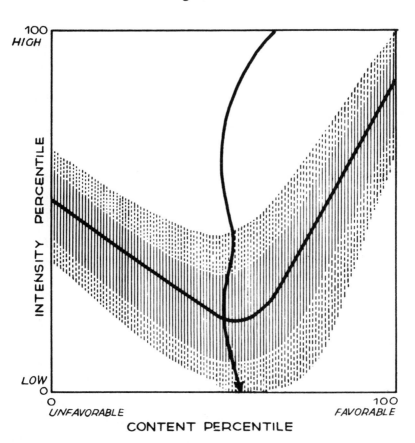

The solid curved lines indicate the two regressions: the "bow" is the (median) regression of intensity on content, and the "arrow" is the (median) regression of content on intensity.

If we were measuring the pure, intrinsic intensity that we seek, then there would be no scatter around the bow. In that case, the bow would actually begin and/or end at the top intensity percentile, and actually reach the zero intensity percentile at some point

on the content scale, which would be its bending point. Furthermore, the arrow would have its head exactly at this same bending
point. This bending point, then, would be the *zero point* of content,
since intensity rises as one departs from it in either direction.

When there is empirical error, as in the diagram, the bow
is but a regression curve, and is pulled away both from the top and
bottom of the diagram, so its bending point is in midair and possibly biased. In practice, then, we use the estimation of the arrowhead as the estimated zero point. This can be unbiased since error
can balance around it (unless it is too close to one end or the other
of the continuum). The estimate used is the median content percentile of the subgroup with the lowest intensity rank (choosing,
say, not less than 100 people for this lowest intensity group, to
maintain sampling reliability).

Now, an important feature of this method of analysis--for
empirical as well as for ideal data--is that we obtain a zero point
for content *with no other knowledge of the rest of the new metric*.
We need only crude empirical ranks on both content and intensity.
Furthermore, since we use *medians* in our regressions, our estimate of the zero point *will not vary essentially with the sampling
of items*. A different set of items from the same scalable universe
could give a different set of cutting points for the observed ranks,
but not in any essential way change the percentile estimates if
made in the manner prescribed.

The zero point determined by these empirical techniques is
thus objective in that *it is not dependent on the sample of items
used,* provided the universe is a scale. And it is meaningful in the
sense desired for a zero point, differentiating between rising intensities on either side.

The invariance of the zero point with respect to the sampling
of items was illustrated by two striking experiments. In each experiment, one set of items was chosen with marginals all above
50% for the "more favorable" category, and the other set from the
same scalable universe was chosen to have the marginals all below 50%. Yet both of the oppositely biased sets of data yielded the
same empirical intensity curve (see *Measurement and Prediction,*
pp. 266-275).

The reason rank order is sufficient here to give information
about the underlying metric is that we are dealing with a *bending*
point. *The property of bending does not depend upon metric.* One
can stretch and contract the content metric all one pleases, and
one can stretch and contract the intensity metric all one pleases.
But a U- or J-shaped curve will remain U- or J-shaped through

all these proceedings, and the bending point will remain at the same percentile as ever. Hence rank order is as good a metric as any for aid in determining the zero point.

But couldn't all this trouble about measuring intensity directly be avoided in the first place? Why not simply *solve the mathematical equations* for the second component, plot it against the rank order, and in this way determine the zero point? The answer is, that this mathematical procedure will yield a "zero point" that *depends on the sample of questions used*. The true zero point refers to the entire universe of content. If we knew the *universe parameters* needed for the equations, then we could solve and get the correct answer. But if we use parameters from but a sample of items, these can be entirely different from the universe parameters. In the example cited of oppositely biased sets of items, each set has entirely different sample parameters, and would yield an entirely different "zero point" from the other. We cannot depend on any notion of "random sampling" of items; there is reason to believe that there is no such thing for ordinary research problems. We need a technique in which results are invariant with respect to item selection.

The bow-and-arrow technique we have described is the only kind known that does not depend on the sampling of items. Because we don't know the universe parameters, we have to measure intensity directly as an independent variable; the observed relationship to content is then invariant. That it has produced such a technique that transcends the particular wording of the items used is one of scale analysis' most important achievements. Here is apparently the first instance of this kind of invariance in attitude research.

THE THIRD PRINCIPAL COMPONENT: CLOSURE

The mathematics suggested that one should look for a psychological meaning for the second principal componet. After a while, a meaning--intensity--was hypothesized; experiments were then designed which proved that the data behaved as predicted.

The same mathematics suggested that one should look for a psychological meaning for the third principal component. Quite a while elapsed, but none could be hypothesized.

A couple of years ago in Israel, by Merton's famous process of serendipity, [16] we discovered a meaning for the third component.

I say "discovered", for it was unpremeditated and not previously hypothesized as in the case of intensity.

What is known mathematically about the third principal component of perfect scales is that its graph is a curve with two bends in it when related to the content ranks. It is known further *that these two bends must take place on opposite sides of the zero point.* A typical example is as in Figure 9:

Figure 9

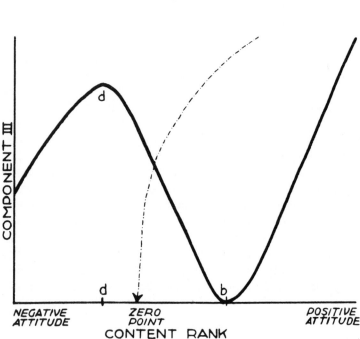

CONTENT RANK

The two bends of component III are labelled b and d. The content ranks at which the bends take place are designated by the same letters as the respective bends. The zero point is as defined by the second component, were the latter plotted on the same chart. To avoid cluttering up the diagram, we have drawn in the arrow instead of the bow of the intensity function, so that the arrowhead indicates the zero point precisely. Then the mathematics say that b must be on one side of the arrowhead, and d must be on the opposite side. Thus b divides the positive segment of the content ranks into two parts, the *more positive* and the *less positive*; and

d divides the negative segment into two parts, the *less negative*
and the *more negative*.

The discovery of a psychological theory for these new sub-
divisons took place in connection with a project conducted by the
Israel Institute of Applied Social Research on the post-war plans
of the Israeli soldiers. This research was completed about a year
before large-scale demobilization took place.

The Research Branch of Information and Education Division
in the American Army, under Professor Samuel A. Stouffer's
scientific direction, faced the same problem during World War II.
As John E. Clausen pointed out clearly [17], it was not sufficient for
prediction purposes merely to have rank orders on a scale, even
with an objective zero point from intensity. A person may have a
positive attitude toward something but not be positive enough to do
anything about it.

A cross-section of the Israel army was administered a
questionnaire which contained a series of scalable areas, one for
each type of postwar plan. There was a scale on remaining in the
professional army; a scale on starting a small business of one's
own; a scale on joining an agricultural cooperative; and scales on
going to school, joining an urban cooperative, etc.

Each of these universes was studied separately by a series
of questions, and--using the Cornell Technique--the hypothesis of
scalability was sustained in each case.

Furthermore, the empirical intensity diagram was plotted
for each area separately, and the zero points approximated by the
arrowhead technique. So we knew how many had a positive attitude
on each postwar plan separately. Adding up all the separate percentages of positives showed the total to be about 150%!

This, of course, is really no contradiction. A person can be
positive simultaneously on two or more alternative plans. If he
wants to go into business, that doesn't mean he would not like to go
to school, or possibly go into agriculture. Our problem really is:
given that a person is positive simultaneously to different things,
which will he actually choose if he can ultimately make but one
choice?

Fortunately, we had asked a series of questions from another
universe--which also proved to be scalable--with the following kind
of content: "Have you made up your mind as to your postwar plans?"
"How sure are you about what you want to do when you get out of the
army?" "If economic conditions are worse than now, will you change
whatever plans you now have in mind?" The check list of answers
contained typically five choices like: "I have definitely made up my

mind" down to "I have definitely not yet decided". Notice that
such questions do not ask what the *particular* plan is.

This scale also had its intensity component studied, and a
zero point established. Thus the scale ranked soldiers from most
positive to most negative on the definiteness of their postwar plans.
The most positive person was most set on whatever he planned to
do. The most negative person was most definite that he did not
know what he wanted to do. And men around the zero point did not
know whether they had any definite plans or not!

It was thought that such an area might help in the prediction
problem, and it was tabulated against each plan separately. To our
surprise, each regression showed an essentially two-bended curve.
Furthermore, in each case the bends took place on *opposite sides
of the respective zero point*, just as required by the mathematics
of the third component. The positives were divided into *more
positive* and *less positive*, and the negatives into *less negative* and
more negative.

This study was based originally on 600 cases. There was
considerably more regression error than in the case of empirical
intensity, so that each regression curve was pulled even more
away from both the bottom and top of the graph, occupying a nar-
rower band in midair. Thus, the observed oscillation might be due
to a sampling error. The study was fortunately able to be repeated
three months later on 2,000 cases. The regression errors remained just as widespread as before; but the regression curves
were essentially the same in both studies, despite the narrowness
of the band created by the errors. The existence of the bending
points on each side of the zero point was substantiated.

This encouraged the development of a general psychological
theory for this type of attitude problem, in which the third component is called *closure*. Closure for the present example refers to
a *universe of universes*. Each postwar plan yields a subuniverse.
Assuming each subuniverse is a scale, each has its own intensity
function (and zero point) which varies from scale to scale within
the superuniverse. But all these scales have the same third principal component--their mutual closure--which expresses the
totality of comparisons among the subuniverses.

This can be made clearer by the typology made possible by
the closure for each scale separately, as will be illustrated for the
postwar plan problem. Closure is observed as a scalable area in
its own right. So it has its own intensity function and zero point.
It is helpful to indicate the zero point of closure in the usual
diagram by drawing a horizontal line at the closure rank which

corresponds to it, as in **Figure 10.** Figure 10 shows an idealized curve (with no scatter) corresponding roughly to the data about the particular plan of remaining in the army:

Figure 10

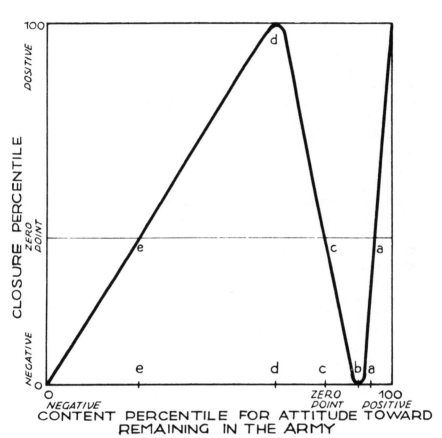

The symbols b and d again indicate the two bending points, as well as their respective content percentiles. Three further points-- *crossing*-points--are indicated as a, c, and e, where the closure changes sign from positive to negative, or vice-versa. We assume for the moment that c occurs at the same content percentile as the zero point. All told, there are now five cutting points along the content percentile, yielding six discernible intervals.

Now these cutting points have been arrived at by an entirely different method from that of selecting items from the universe and using their observed marginals. The latter method, as we have seen, yields nothing intrinsic to the universe beyond an aid in establishing content ranks; its results depend entirely on the particular items selected.

Our new type of cutting points comes from curves which are intrinsic to the universe and whose bending points can be approximated in practice by methods which do not depend on the particular sample of items used (always provided a scale exists in the first place). Each of the new cutting points have the same invariant property [18] we found with respect to the zero point.

The six resulting discernible intervals are then invariant with respect to the selection of items, and represent invariant or absolute *psychological types*. The meaning of these absolute types must come from the *psychological meaning of the principal components involved*--intensity and closure--just as the characterization of the original empirical scale types we opened with comes from the content of the observed items whose cutting points determined them.

Let us denote these six absolute types by the same letters a, b, c, d, e, and add the sixth letter f. The most positive of the six types will be denoted by a; it includes the ranks from point a to the 100th percentile. The next most positive type is b, including the ranks from point b to point a, etc., the most negative type being f, including the ranks from the 0th content percentile to point e. By referring to Figure 10, these six discernible types can be classified according to whether they are positive or negative on the first and third components, as in the following Table 4:

Table 4

Psychological Type	Content Sign	Closure Sign
a	Positive	Positive
b	Positive	Negative
c	Positive	Negative
d	Negative	Positive
e	Negative	Positive
f	Negative	Negative

The meanings of the signs come from the respective intensity functions of content and closure.

The most positive with respect to attitude toward remaining in the army is type a. Soldiers of this type not only have a positive attitude toward remaining, but they also have made up their minds as to what plan they prefer--they are positive on closure. The plan they have decided on is evidently to remain in the army.

Type b occupies a less positive interval of content. It is still positive to remaining in the army, but hasn't decided finally on its plans. But so is type c positive on content and negative on closure. What is the difference between types b and c? This can be seen by going on to type d. Here the men are slightly negative to remaining in the army, but they are positive on having decided their postwar plans. It must be that they have largely decided on some other plan than remaining in the army [19]. Returning to types b and c, then--following Figure 10--b is closer to a because, although its closure is negative and it is undecided on all plans, yet amidst all its indecision, it tends to prefer remaining in the army over the other alternatives. Conversely, since type c leads into d--although it represents the same amount of indecision as b--it tends to prefer something else to staying in the army. Hence b is more positive to the army plan than c.

THE "PREJUDICE" PRINCIPLE

Type d and e also have the same combination of signs on content and closure. Why is e more negative then d? To see this, let us go on to compare them with type f. *And here we are led to propose what seems to be a new psychological principle that our empirical data support.*

Type f is negative on closure--its most extreme respondents say that *they know they have no plans*--and yet it is also negative to the army. Types d and e, while being negative to the army, have a positive program of action.

If two people are negative to the same plan, and one has an alternative while the other has not, who is the more negative? The theory of closure says that the *one without an alternative is the more negative.*

Why this is plausible can be seen in another way. If a person has no plan at all, he should have an open mind to any plan. Being ready to listen to any plan should indicate a mild positiveness to any plan; a planless but open-minded person should be at a bending point b in Figure 10 for each of the alternatives. But if there is a particular plan he objects to, even though he *knows* he has no alternative he prefers, then he is strongly prejudiced against this particular plan. He will have the most negative attitude of anybody.

Our empirical data, of course, support this principle, because they have regressions of just this type. The people most set against staying in the army were among those who had no preferred plan.

Being negative to a particular choice, then, even though an alternative preference is absent, is the most extreme antipathy.

The difference between d and e can now be interpreted. Both types do have alternative plans; but the negativeness of e to the army tends toward prejudice--in the direction of f--while the negativeness of d is of a milder unprejudiced sort, tending toward indifference or the zero point.

According to this interpretation, a large proportion of the men was strongly prejudiced against remaining as professional soldiers. On the other hand, prejudice against the other plans was usually hardly noticeable. For example, the (idealized) curve of the findings on attitude toward returning to school is as in Figure 11. The same closure scale is used as for the previous attitude about remaining in the army, with its same zero point. But it now has a different relation to the new content. The proportion of cases in the six psychological types has changed. Very few are in type f, or are strongly antipathetical to going to school.

This illustrates another important sense in which we have arrived at absolute psychological types. *Our six types can be compared from scale to scale.* Just as we can compare the proportion *positive* from scale to scale, just so can we now make more refined comparisons with respect to each type separately. We have arrived at a purely psychological metric that is comparable from universe to universe.

For the actual predictions of post-war plans, types a and b were used from each scale. The proportion of men in type a was taken as the minimum who would carry out the given plan, and the proportions in types a and b combined as a maximum. The optimum prediction was given as halfway between these two proportions. A year later, it was possible to check two of the overall predictions, with respect to staying in the army and going into agriculture. The predictions were accurate within less than one percent. The Defence Ministry had only fragmentary data on a third plan, on those who returned to school (there was no GI bill for the most part), but the new enrollment at the Hebrew University

Figure 11

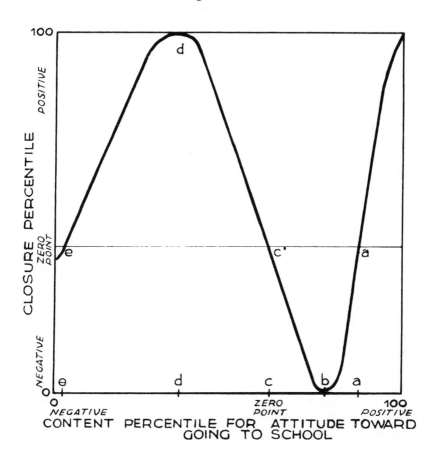

CLOSURE PERCENTILE

POSITIVE

ZERO POINT

NEGATIVE

CONTENT PERCENTILE FOR ATTITUDE TOWARD GOING TO SCHOOL

NEGATIVE   ZERO POINT   POSITIVE

was close to the overall prediction. On the other plans, there were no data for checking. It appears, then, that in the course of the year after the research, whatever changes in attitude occurred tended to cancel themselves over all the men.

We do not take space here to go into the practical computational problems involved in the third component, which are more difficult than in the case of intensity, because of the nature of the bends involved and the larger error scatter found in practice.

THE FOURTH PRINCIPAL COMPONENT: INVOLUTION[20]

On the basis of the closure interpretation of the third principal component, a psychological hypothesis was made possible for the fourth component. In particular, it was suggested by the principle concerning "prejudice" among the negative types. Here, "prejudiced" people were the most negative. But why can't people also be "predjudiced" positively and have the same principle work on the other side of the zero point as well? If we could find a variable which would be symmetric this way with respect to "prejudice", it could well take on the shape of the fourth component. What we need is something that can be unreasoning and positive, unreasoning and negative, or unreasoning and neutral.

A hypothesis was made as to the substance of such a variable, an experiment was carried out, and the hypothesis was sustained: a curve with three bends ensued.

The progress here is now of entirely different nature than with closure. There, some lucky data were examined, and led to the theory of closure. But now, knowing that mathematically there exists a component with three bends, and having a psychology for closure, we develop a further psychological theory for the fourth component; and then we deliberately design the experiment and examine data.

The research project was on radio listening in Israel. The content scale in which we are interested is general attitude to the Voice of Israel. A cross-section of 2,000 adults was studied, and a series of questions from this universe was asked like "Do you think the broadcasts are good in general?" This area was found to be scalable.

The area that was hypothesized to act like the fourth component of the content just described might be called *involvement* in the broadcasts of VOI[21]. Sample questions were: "How often do you listen to the Voice of Israel?" "Do you make it a point to open the radio at certain hours for certain programs?" This area also was found to be scalable. Its intensity function yielded a zero point as usual, and the division into positives and negatives has a most interesting interpretation. Those who are most involved will be called *most positive;* of course, they are the ones who listen most, have most definite listening habits, etc. Those who are least involved tend not to listen. Thus, the extreme *not listening at all* means *negative* involvement, for it is on the opposite side of the zero point from positive involvement. The zero point is at a scale type which listens a little to the Voice of Israel, but not systematically. We can say that some people tend to listen to VOI, and others tend not to listen, according to the side of the zero point they are on.

When the involvement ranks were plotted against the ranks on the attitude of approval of the Voice of Israel, the regression was found to bend as predicted, as shown in the idealized graph of Figure 12.

Figure 12

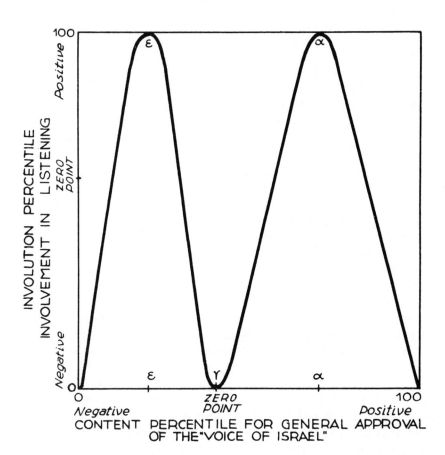

The three bending points, and their corresponding cutting points on content, are labelled α, γ, and ϵ respectively.

What had been predicted was that--furthering the psychology of the third component--of those *least involved* in listening to VOI, some would be the *most favorable* of all to the Voice, some would be the *least favorable*, and the others would be *neutral*. It was further predicted that those *most involved* would be in the two intermediate regions; some would be positive, but not the most positive of all; some would be negative, but not the most negative of all; none would be neutral. The psychology behind the prediction was this. If a person is not involved, he should ordinarily be neutral; but, if he should venture an opinion one way or the other, even though he is not involved, this will be unreasoned or "prejudiced", and hence be most extreme--either positively or negatively.

This was fully confirmed in a most clearcut fashion, according to the illustration in Figure 12 above.

It might be remarked that, before the data were in, other members of our Israel Institute objected to this prediction. They thought that only a U-shape curve would result, namely only the middle part of the graph from α to ϵ, so that involvement would resemble intensity. And indeed, involvement does resemble intensity in the region of the zero point--the middle bend γ did essentially coincide with the zero point as determined by intensity. But the extremes are quite different; the writer predicted this difference in advance by generalizing the notion of "prejudice" of extreme groups suggested by the third principal component.

The success of this prediction is further evidence as to the adequacy of our psychological interpretation of the absolute types provided by closure, since it was based on the latter interpretation.

The general name we suggest for fourth components of this type is *involution*. It sounds like "involvement", but actually has no previous use in attitude research[22] to our knowledge. It does suggest a rolling curve; but more important it suggests a turning inward, and this is the kind of thing we want. We seek something that expresses that the respondent is turning the attitude over and over within himself. Non-involution will then mean *no* turning over.

"Involvement" may sound somewhat appropriate for our radio example, but may be misleading for other data. The kind of "prejudice" that is related to lack of involvement in radio might be called that due to *absence* of reasoning, from *lack of personal contact* with radio. But there is another kind of "prejudice" which fits our notion of involution for other data which might be called *cessation* of reasoning, *even though there is close contact*. Let us return for a moment to the previous example of attitude toward remaining in the army. Had we known then what we know now, what should we have suggested as the fourth component of this attitude? Surely not involvement in a sense implying contact, because that would mean that men who most want to stay in the army are least *involved*. According to the third component, the most positive men are those who have definitely made up their minds, and are surely in close contact with the matter. The fourth component should then show them "uninvolved", not because they have no contact with the problem or have never though about it, but *because their minds are at rest with it;* they have stopped turning the matter over. So we prefer to call them non-involuted. Similarly, the most negative men either never weighed the matter reasonably to begin with, or weighed it considerably--were involved--but also stopped debating, having decided to one side; both kinds can be equally negative, and we use the term *non-involuted* for both.

This reasoning shows we should ask questions like: "Are you *debating* with yourself whether or not you ought to stay in the army?" "Do you *spend much time in wondering* whether or not you ought to stay in the army?" Our conjecture would be that such questions would prove scalable, and yield a curve with three bends in it when related to attitude toward remaining in the army. The Israel Institute of Applied Social Research is now experimenting with just such questions, which seem applicable to many attitude problems, especially public opinion. In place of "stay in the army" read whatever the topic is.

It is important to notice that involution is *specific* to the underlying content, just like intensity. This is unlike the example given of closure, which belongs simultaneously to several universes. We studied the involution of approval of "Voice of Israel" without reference to any other universe, just as we studied its intensity without need to refer to other universes. Suppose we wished now to study the closure of this attitude of approval[23]. What should we propose for this closure? We could think of further universes, such as approval of the BBC, the Voice of America, Sofia, and other broadcasting services heard in Israel. Our closure questions could be like: "Considering all these broadcasting services, have you decided which one does the best job?" Such a closure would serve simultaneously for each attitude separately, toward BBC, VOA, etc.

For other kinds of data, closure can be specific to the content and not refer to a universe of universes. A recent example of this occurred in an Israel Institute study of supervisors' ratings of their subordinates. One content area was composed, for example, of questions like: "Does employee X show satisfactory initiative on his job?" The research indicated that a successful closure area for this content should ask questions like: "Do you know employee X well enough to judge his initiative?"

THE INTERLEAVING OF BENDING POINTS

The mathematical equations tell us further important features about the geometrical relationship between the third and fourth principal components of the same attitude. We state these briefly here as follows, taking as an example the above Figure 12 for involution of approval of the Voice of Israel.

The bending point b of the closure must be between α and γ, and bending point of d must be between γ and ϵ. In a large and important class of mathematical cases there will be coincidence between points α and a, γ and c, and ϵ and e. That is, the *crossing* points of the third component (from positive to negative, or from negative to positive) coincide with the *bending* points of the fourth.[24] Similarly, in such cases, crossing points of the fourth coincide with bending points of the fifth, etc. Also the middle bending points of components of even order all coincide with the zero point. We have assumed precisely this in our diagrams. The hypothesis of coincidence of bending and crossing points seems most appropriate to the psychology of our attitudes.

ARE THE PSYCHOLOGICAL FUNCTIONS THE SAME AS THE MATHEMATICAL COMPONENTS?

We have thus demonstrated that empirical psychological variables can be found which, when plotted as functions of the scale ranks of a given attitude, yield curves of the same general shapes as the respective mathematical principal components. Does this prove that these psychological functions are the same as the mathematical components? Could not some other psychological functions be found empirically that will have the same shapes but bend at different places, yielding a different zero point, etc.? There is but one mathematical set of principal components--were the requisite universe parameters known for the equations. But can't there be more than one psychological solution for the same data, with differing absolute types?

It is easy to *disprove* that two or more functions are principal components of the same attitude. For example, assume two functions are hypothesized to be the second and third components respectively but the "closure's" two bending points are found both to be on one side of the "intensity's" arrowhead; then these two functions *cannot* both be principal components.

The law of interleaving of bending points holds mathematically for all the higher components. Each successive component must have its bending points interleave with those of the preceding component. Thus far, only four components have been identified psychologically. [25] But if we could go on and identify all the rest, and show empirically that the interleaving of bending points takes place as specified, then the identity between these functions and the mathematical components is virtually established.

For suppose somebody else came along and suggested a new kind of "intensity" variable, and sure enough it is found empirically to be a U-shaped function of the attitude, but its arrowhead was at an entirely different percentile from the preceding one. This nevertheless cannot be a *principal component*, for it will be incompatible with the bending points of the higher order components in the earlier set. The previous set of functions have among themselves infinitely many mutually compatible bending points, which in the limit define a continuum of absolute types. Any shift in bending point for a given function must then be incompatible with many other components.

To propose an alternative psychology to a given one, it is not sufficient merely to exhibit one function and show it bends in a certain way. One cannot prove that one "intensity" function is "really" the second component and that another is not, without reference to a complete set of higher order components. There is no other way of choosing objectively between empirical psychological functions which have the same general shape.

Thus far we have demonstrated a compatible system of four empirical psychological functions. To this extent we have proved they might also be the mathematical principal components. As we increase their number, this will better the proof and more and more exclude the possibility of alternative psychological functions belonging in the same picture.

COMPONENTS VERSUS FUNCTIONS

It is important to distinguish between a function of the attitude and a *component* of the attitude. Why are the mathematical variables called components and not just functions? The reason is, that the attitude is a *function of these components,* just as much as the components are functions of the attitude scale. Mathematically, we sought a least-squares metric, and found a best set of values of x, say x_I or the first principal component. Then we saw there was a next best solution x_{II}, and and x_{III}, an x_{IV}, etc. But the mathematics says something further and very profound that we have not noted here yet.

Just as each *respondent* has a value on each of these components, just so does each *response* to each item in the universe. For example, the response "Yes" to "War is good" has a set of values w_I, w_{II}, w_{III}, . . ., one for each of the principal components. If we knew the x-values for a given respondent, and the w-values for the response "Yes" to this item, then we could tell exactly whether or not the respondent chose this response. The mathematics says to use the w-values as weights for the x-values, and to form the following arithmetical sum[26]

$$w_I x_I + w_{II} x_{II} + w_{III} x_{III} + w_{IV} x_{IV} + \cdot \cdot \cdot$$

This sum will be *unity* if the respondent did say "Yes", and *zero* if he says "No". The response is a perfect function of the components. In the same way, *every item in the universe is a perfect function* of the components. That is why these mathematical functions are called components. They are functions of the items to be sure, but in turn the items are functions of them.

In psychological terms, this means that if we knew a person's score on the underlying least-squares metric; and his intensity score in its own least-squares metric; and his closure and involution and all higher order component scores, each in its own least-squares metric; then we could predict from weighted sums of these scores exactly what each respondent will do on each item. The response to an item is an exact linear function of a person's metric score, intensity, closure, involution, etc.

That is why it is so important to make sure that we are working not just with functions of an attitude. If we really arrive at psychological components and not just functions, we have an entirely *new frame of reference for the attitude*. Our initial frame of reference was a one-dimensional one: a scalable attitude is one in which each item is a simple function of a single continuum. The functional relation there was non-linear, being expressed by cutting points.

A profound consequence of this one-dimensional property is that it implies at the same time infinitely many dimensions -- namely, the principal components. The same attitude has these infinitely many dimensions, the functional dependence on them now being expressed by linear equations in w's and x's. A scalable attitude is one-dimensional in the sense of rank order, but is a function of infinitely many psychological components.

We had started by seeking certain functions of the attitude. We find them, and find that in turn the attitude is a function of them.

This reverse relationship suggests the difficulty there may be in going empirically beyond the fourth component. For the mathematics shows that the terms in the weighted sums are usually very small after the fourth. The first four terms usually constitute almost the entire sum. Psychologically, this should also mean that the first four components alone should often be very adequate for representing the attitude universe. [27]

Before closing this part of the discussion, we must remark that, in practice, our psychological concepts can only be approximate. Any empirical psychological variable we use will only approximate the unique intrinsic one we seek. There may be several such empirical approximations possible. That we are working in practice with only crude psychological concepts is evident from the scatter present in empirical diagrams of the functions. (This scatter is not due merely to retest unreliability of each variable separately, for scale ranks--both for content and the component--are always highly reliable.) But if different observed variables are really approximating the same psychological component, then--as we have seen--they should all yield the same bending points, no matter how else they differ among themselves. In this case, it makes no difference which one we use in practice, for it is the bending points which are of importance to the analysis of scalable attitudes.

After bending points are determined which are intrinsic to the scale, they may then often prove useful in studying relationships with outside variables. Examples have already been reported in which an outside variable was found to have a bow-shaped regression on a scalable attitude--with the usual amount of regression error found in ordinary correlation scattergrams, which is larger than for intensity scattergrams--and the arrowhead coincided with the scale's zero point as determined by intensity. Thus, a zero point can predict where the bending point of a U-curvilinear regression will take place for an outside variable. [28]

THE INTERPLAY OF PSYCHOLOGY
AND MATHEMATICS

We can now look back on the trail we have followed and
see the intricate connection between our psychology and our
mathematics.

The psychological problem of a consistent meaning for "more
favorable" and "less favorable" for a universe of content led to a
mathematical definition of a perfect scale, with an unequivocal
meaning for rank order. Further psychological problems of *metric*
led to a mathematical maximization problem which brought forth a
host of oscillating principal components with a law of interleaving
of bending points.

Actually, the only clear psychological metric problem we had
was that of question bias, or a zero point. We really didn't know
what we wanted of the rest of the metric, but just felt it would be
nice if there were something "beyond mere rank order", even
though rank order is perfectly sufficient for statistical prediction
of outside variables (changing internal metrics does not change
statistical predictions of outside variables). Seeing that the
mathematical second principal component was U-shaped suggested
that it might be represented by the intensity of an attitude. If so,
this suggested further that the desired zero point could be defined
as where the intensity curve touched bottom. But the mathematics
warned against using the maximizing equations in practice; they
were correct only if the universe parameters were known. Psychologically, we had no way of devising "random" samples of items
to estimate these parameters unbiasedly. Instead, the mathematics
said, if one could observe only rank order on the first component,
and only rank order on the second component, then although the exact metrical equation for the U would be unknown, its bending point
could be estimated unbiasedly from any sample of items, random
or not.

This threw the onus back on psychology--how to get ranks on
intensity. A psychological theory and practical techniques were
devised for doing this. Experiments verified what the mathematics
had said; "mere" ranks on content and intensity for the first time
gave an invariant and objective solution ot the problem of bias.
And the zero point had psychological meaning because it was arrived at by a psychological theory. Mathematics alone couldn't
determine the zero point empirically; psychology alone couldn't
prove the zero point invariant with respect to the sampling of items.

This successful combination of mathematics and psychology suggested it might be worth exploring the third mathematical component by psychological means. The mathematics said with respect to this component, too--as for all the oscillating principal components--That if only rank order could be determined for it empirically, then its bending points on content should be unbiasedly estimated by any sample of items. Such further bending points would subdivide our psychologically positive and negative segments of the underlying coninuum into more differentiated absolute psychological types.

Thus, mathematics challenged our psychological insight. And we failed it. The psychological literature gave us no clue as to anything corresponding to the third principal component. If the mathematical lead was correct, the present psychological literature had something important lacking. Unpremeditatedly, a research project revealed some graphs with some wiggles in them. Ordinarily, we would have thought this some mischief of sampling error--because "everybody knows" that attitudes have nice normal correlations with each other, with linear regressions, etc.; and we would have smoothed the curve. But we recalled that, some years back, mathematics told us to look for a curve like this. So we looked at it again, and it proved to be no sampling fluke after all. The mathematics had been right all the time; something had been missing from the psychological literature. This something we now learned to understand psychologically--since we had an empirical example of it to ponder over--and it was given the name *closure*.

The mathematics lured us on to try for the fourth principal component. The psychology of closure now gave us a boost. The "unreasoning" or "prejudice" principle there could be enlarged to go in the positive direction as well as in the negative. A new psychological variable--involution--was defined accordingly; an experiment deliberately made to test it; and it did behave as if it were the fourth component. This also vindicated the preceding psychology of the third component which led to it.

Further mathematical components lie beyond. The mathematics says they will be harder to get to--especially those of prime order (which then cannot be components of components)--for they contribute relatively little to the total attitude. They are important for only a small minority of the population of respondents. This does not, however, preclude their being identified.

Psychological notions like intensity have been known before. Notions like prejudice, involvement, and the like have been known before. How do we know we have "the" correct notion which corresponds to the mathematical components? The mathematics says, that before social scientists begin to quarrel among themselves as to what is the "best" definition of intensity, say, for a given kind of attitude, they had better see what the higher order components look like first. Only a *set* of psychological functions can be tested to see if it might be a *set* of components, the test being the proper interleaving of bending points. The larger the set of consistent functions, the less argument as to whether they can be the actual components. Arguing on purely "psychological" grounds is not helpful.

DEPTH INTERVIEWS AND PRINCIPAL COMPONENTS

Many social scientists have objected to attitude scales and the like. Attitudes are complex things, they say, and cannot be measured as one does lengths in inches and feet. One must use depth techniques, or non-directed interviews, and probe all the dimensions there are in order really to understand the attitude's structure.

These social scientists are right in large part. Attitudes are complex, with many dimensions. Our mathematics has proved this strikingly for the simple case of perfect scales: there is an infinite number of principal components. In trying to identify these components psychologically, we are led interestingly enough to ask questions somewhat like in a depth interview: involution, closure, intensity. Perhaps the higher order components are further things groped for in depth interviews. We wind up not with inches or feet --though that may be what the underlying least-squares metric is analogous to--but with a *further frame of reference:* an absolute psychological typology. We also know there may be no point going on endlessly in quest of more dimensions, even though we know more exist than depth interviewers may have thought of.

Althogether we have three different kinds of frames of reference: (a) ranks from item cutting points, (b) algebraic principal components, and (c) absolute psychological types. We now have a suggestion for depth interviewers. Our mathematics started out with a simple rank order, and then revealed infinitely many dimensions. The depth analysts start at the other end, by first probing many dimensions which they think are components of the attitude. But perhaps they can complete the circle, and prove that in turn their components are functions of the attitude. In that case, it may turn out that they have an underlying rank order, and have been implying a scale after all.

For the mathematics states paradoxically, that the set of principal components is *not* a scale: it is the original *content* items whose interrelations form the scale pattern and scale types. The principal components interrelations are very complex, as can be seen by plotting the joint scattergram of involution and closure, say. A typical graph that results for a perfect scale in shown in Figure 13,

Figure 13

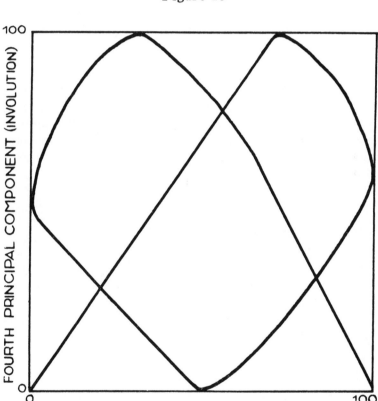

looking much like a doodler's scrawl. Each variable is a three-or four-valued function of the other.

Multivalued relationships like that of Figure 13 help explain why depth interviews appear to be "deep". If one works directly

with higher order components, each has several levels of crossings with the others. To try by direct means to piece out where
and how these crossings take place in empirical data is well-nigh
impossible if error is present. Imagine error scattered about the
curve in Figure 13, and see how the different levels of the curve
easily become blurred together, so that the entire picture can give
the erroneous impression that the two components are almost
statistically independent of each other.

Working with components is certainly a worthwhile approach,
as we have seen. But to work with them efficiently and in a com-
prehensible manner, one should first inquire whether they are not
all functions of a single rank order. If so, their interrelationships
are most easily studied via their individual relationships to that
rank order; namely, by single-valued functions as in Figure 4-7
above.

It is not my intention to imply that depth interviews are
concerned solely with principal components of scales. My point is
that--in the special case where a scale is present--if the components the interview is seeking happen to coincide with the scale's
principal components, then unless one is aware of the scale's existence one will find the interrelationship of the components most
complex and apparently hopelessly entangled, and so be falsely
impressed by the need for intuitive and subjective procedures to
"understand" what is involved. Intuitive interpretation, when error
is present, can hardly be expected to reveal a picture like in
Figure 13 even when the picture is inherent in the interview data.

If intuition and subjectivity fail when unguided by mathematics in the simple case of a scale, how much more easily can they
fail in the more complicated non-scale cases. A mathematical
guide to intuition apparently can be available also for non-scale
cases, as we shall see in our third lecture. There we shall indicate how principal components can arise also for non-scale data,
but with different laws of formation than for scalable data.

FOR THE FUTURE

Besides arriving at an absolute psychological typology by
means of the principal components of a scale, we have learned
many other things from this experience not directly concerned
with ascertaining this typology.

We know now many mistakes we have made in the past in
wording questions for obtaining the basic rank order.

One mistake is to confuse the components with the basic content; such a mixture of questions will usually yield scale error. For example, if you want to know whether the respondent is favorable or unfavorable to something x, don't ask: "Do you prefer x over any other alternative?" At best, this will pick out only those extremely favorable to x, but won't discriminate between those mildly favorable all the way down to those very favorable. This can be seen from the theory of closure, and has been verified experimentally. Closure has been mixed in with the content here, and the mixture yields error in a scale analysis.

Another mistake is to ask questions without having any closure in mind. Our opening example was of this kind: "Is war good?" "Good for what?" a respondent may rejoin. And he is right. There are all kinds of attitudes towards war, depending on the closure or frame of reference in mind. One such might be: for settling international disputes, with closure questions like "Among all ways to settle international disputes, have you decided which one is best?" The basic content then could be: "Is war a good way in which to settle international disputes?" "Does war help or hinder the settlement of grievances among nations?"

We are now experimenting with a technique of trying to study the four principal components simultaneously, instead of each separately. To study each separately requires a series of questions on each. If we can study the first three or four components simultaneously by one or two questions each, we can immensely shorten the questionnaire or interview and yet have the complete requisite information.

In another direction, we have been alerted to wiggly regressions, an keep finding various kinds which would have been dismissed previously as implausible. These are ordinary correlation problems, without reference to components. The regression of personal adjustment on one type of socio-economic status shows a succession of bends in Israel data--tentatively suggesting objective dividing points for *social classes*. Another type of status has but the usual smooth regression for the same personal adjustment. Had we not carefully differentiated initially between the content of these two kinds of status--although they are highly intercorrelated --and had mixed them, this phenomenon would have been obsured.

There is growing evidence that many kinds of oscillatory regressions exist between attitudes. These have never been observed for the reason that universes of content have not been clearly defined and tested for scalability, but conglomerations of varied-- albeit interrelated--data have been used as though they were single variables. Such hodge-podge procedures inevitably lead to smooth monotone regressions, with normal distributions, and with no clear psychological meaning.

But it is particularly to the dynamics of attitudes that new vistas are opened. Allow us to speculate somewhat boldly.

Love and hate are thought to be closely related, yet are opposite extremes. This paradox is easily resolved if love-hate is thought of as a content continuum, and we had an intensity function--the intensity of the relationship involved. Now if a person's intensity is high, then he has either extreme hate or extreme love. Hence, *if his intensity remains constant but his content changes*, this content can change *only to the opposite extreme*.

Similarly, if mania-depression is a content continuum in some sense, and if its second principal component for some reason must remain constant, any change in content must be extreme for extreme people. And so for religion-atheism, etc. It may not be the second component that is constant--it may be the fourth, allowing also a switch to complete neutrality for previously extreme people. Or it may be some other principal component that remains constant.

Finding psychological variables that could be the components in these situations can then give a simple continuous picture that explains radically discrete jumps.

Our final example of where principal component theory can lead is taken from the problem of role conflict. Stouffer and Toby [29] exhibit a series of regressions between two moral attitudes: "universalist" and "particularist". Some regressions are monotone, and some have two little bends suggestive of the third component. But the psychology of the situation definitely does not indicate that closure is involved. Are the bends just flukes, because sometimes they appear and sometimes they don't? Not necessarily. It is easy to show that, if both kinds of attitudes have the same *fourth* principal component in common--if the involutions of the respondents were the same for both systems of morals--but there is a difference in zero points between the two contents, then precisely such two bends can sometimes appear, and other times not.

This role conflict example illustrates how previous attitude research has concentrated on correlating only the content between different universes. But by considering the possible correlations between the higher components--which are psychological functions and hence comparable from universe to universe in a way that content is not--it may be possible to develop theories of whole related systems of attitudes. The higher components can possibly serve as inter-attitude organizers, as well as provide an analysis of each attitude separately.

It is developments of this sort that can be arrived at by studying the psychological and mathematical implications of simple rank order, in terms of the principal components which are tautologically related to the rank order.

6. A New Approach to Factor Analysis: The Radex *

By LOUIS GUTTMAN

The Israel Institute of Applied Social Research

In the preceding lecture,[1] I suggested that the analysis of interrelated data can involve three distinct levels of systems of components. First, one must define the universe or universes of content under consideration; this is the problem of the *semantic* components of the observed variables. Next, one can hypothesize why the observations are statistically interrelated the way they are; this may require a theory of *elementary* components. Third, given a systematic theory for the observed interrelationships, one can inquire into the *principal* components of the system and derive a secondary frame of reference which may be useful.

Each of the three lectures[2] is to discuss one of these three varieties of systems of components. I had pointed out that, for what may be sufficient pedagogical reason, the lectures are being given in the reverse of their logical order. The first lecture dealt primarily with the third-mentioned variety, namely principal components. The present lecture will elaborate on the notion of ele-mentary components. Our final lecture is to deal with semantic component systems.

Actually, the first lecture also discussed elementary compo-nents; but we did not then stress this fact in order not to distract attention from the main object of that lecture. It is now appro-priate to review what was said then from the point of view of the present topic, before we go on to provide new and more involved examples of systems of elementary components.

* In writing this lecture for publication after its original oral presentation at Columbia University, I was greatly aided by a transcription made of another oral version presented later at Harvard Uni-versity. I am deeply indebted to Professor Samuel A. Stouffer and Harvard's Laboratory of Social Relations for providing the recording and typescript of the latter version. Upon my return to Israel, a grant from the Office of Naval Research of the U.S. Department of the Navy made possible a systematic reworking of data already available in the literature, according to the new approach. The first results have been added to this written version of this lecture. The term "radex" is also an innovation in the present writing.

For the case of a perfect scale of qualitative data, there is but one elementary component—the underlying rank order. From a person's scale rank, one can deduce his behavior on each and every item in the universe of content being studied. Thus, a single variable—the scale ranks (or their transformation into any other metric)—accounts for the totality of behavior, and in particular for the interrelationships between the items. We were able to construct the statistical tables of the joint occurrence between any two or more items from knowledge of only the single elementary component involved.

It so happens that our example was of qualitative data, and such data are not expressible as linear nor even algebraic functions of their single elementary component. The notions of cutting points and of discernible intervals express the nonlinear relationships that exist between qualitative items and an underlying rank order. After these nonlinear relationships were known, we were then able to go on to derive equations for the principal components of the system. It turned out that, although only one elementary component was present, it implied a secondary system of infinitely many principal components. Furthermore, the observed qualitative items were expressible as precisely linear functions of these principal components.

From the point of view of the present topic, the moral to be learned from the example of perfect scales is that we could not have gone on successfully to deduce the principal components before we had the more elementary theory of rank order. Any set of items has principal components, but in general without any useful law of formation. For the particular case of a single elementary component of rank order, we found the remarkable laws of oscillation of its principal components which lent themselves to a most fruitful psychological interpretation.

Now we shall go on to more complicated examples of elementary component systems. Greater complication may give us more to sink our teeth into than for the simple case of one component, and so help us better to appreciate the role of an elementary component theory in a structural analysis. Instead of qualitative data, we shall this time use examples of observed interrelated quantitative variables. And instead of attitude data, we shall use illustrative material from mental testing.

Quantitative data are usually not to be treated by cutting points and discernible intervals, but by ordinary algebraic methods. The examples of the present lecture are restricted to the case of linear regressions among the observed variables, and where the interrelations are determined by least-squares and measured by product-moment or Pearsonian correlation coefficients[3]. For this case, elementary component theory is exemplified by what has been known historically in psychology as factor analysis.

I now suggest dividing factor analysis into at least two kinds. The previous approach of Spearman, Thurstone, and others is that of *common*-factors. In contrast to this, in today's lecture I shall introduce the notion of *order*-factors. Toward the end of this discussion, we shall see that there is a connection between the two kinds of factor theories. In a sense, the older theory is a degenerate case of the newer one. In another sense, the newer theory unifies what are otherwise apparently opposing schools of thought within the older kind of theory.

AN OVERVIEW OF RADEX THEORY

A set of variables whose intercorrelations conform to the general order pattern prescribed by the new theory will be called a *radex*. This is a word designed to indicate a "radial expansion of complexity."

Two distinct notions are involved in a radex. One is that of a difference in *kind* between tests, and the other is that of a difference in *degree*. Each of these notions will give rise to a separate concept of order among tests, so that a radex is ultimately at least a doubly-ordered system. In this lecture, we shall treat only the simplest case of the radex which can be completely portrayed by a simple, two-dimensional diagram. The empirical evidence thus far—as I shall exhibit shortly—show that mental test data can be surprisingly well accounted for by such a diagram.

Within all tests of the same kind, say of numerical ability, differences will be in degree. We shall see that addition, subtraction, multiplication, and division differ among themselves largely in the degree of their complexity. Such a set of variables will be called a *simplex*. It possesses a simple order of complexity. The tests can be arranged in a simple rank order from least complex to most complex.

Correspondingly, all tests of the same degree of complexity will differ among themselves only in the kind of ability they define. We shall postulate a law of order here too, but one which is not from "least" to "most" in any sense. It is an order which has no beginning and no end, namely, a circular order. A set of variables obeying such a law will be called a *circumplex*, to designate a "circular order of complexity." Our empirical data will testify that different abilities such as verbal, numerical, reasoning, etc. do tend to have such an order among themselves.

In the more general case, tests can differ among themselves simultaneously both in degree and in kind of complexity, and the general structure here is the radex. Thus, within a radex, one can usually isolate simplexes by keeping the content of the abilities constant and by varying the degree of complexity; and one can also usually isolate circumplexes by keeping degree of complexity constant and then varying the content.

In practice, in this present first effort, we must begin without knowledge of the ultimate map of the radex. So we begin by studying separately defined universes of content and see if each is an approximate simplex. Then by selecting one test from each universe, we see if a circumplex emerges. This lecture is devoted to giving examples of this procedure. On a later occasion, when some current empirical work on the radex is completed, I expect to present a fairly detailed radex map of certain human abilities.

A powerful feature of a simplex structure is its immediate use for prediction purposes. The same holds for a circumplex structure, as well as for the more general radex. This feature seems largely lacking in previous theories of factor analysis. Radex theory opens a clear path to better predictions with less tests.

It may be helpful to review briefly what has gone before in factor analysis, in order better to understand how the new theory differs from its predecessors. This I shall do now. Then I shall present some of the main features of the new theory and some of the available empirical justification.

SPEARMAN'S SINGLE-COMMON-FACTOR THEORY

Let us review the previous theory of common-factors as it developed historically. Spearman and his fellow psychologists in England of fifty years ago were dealing with mental tests. They observed a phenomenon which has continued to be observed—that achievement tests never have negative intercorrelations (at least for the type of tests usually administered to schoolchildren in Western cultures). Tests in history, geography, arithmetic, vocabulary, or what have you, seem always to have positive or zero correlations among themselves.

This finding led to all kinds of conjectures as to what kind of components might underlie these intercorrelations. Spearman observed that for certain batteries of tests the intercorrelations seemed to form a hierarchy. In particular, it seemed that tests

might be arranged in an order such that the correlations between
two tests decreased the farther down the hierarchy they were.
He was able to develop a theory of elementary components that
would give rise to such a hierarchy.

There are several ways of developing this theory. One way
he used was the method of partial-correlation. He said: consider
a battery of tests. Let us take any two tests, t_j and t_k, and compute their observed correlation r_{jk}. Then the hypothesis is that
there exists a single component c—or one general factor—such
that if it were eliminated, then the intertest partial-correlation
would be zero:

$$r_{jk.c} \;=\; 0 \quad (j \neq k) \tag{1}$$

If equation (1) holds with the same c for all possible pairs of
tests in the battery, then this battery is said to have c as its
single common-factor, or to have a single-common-factor
structure.

With the hypothesis of a single-common-factor, Spearman
used the formula for partial-correlation to lead to a certain algebraic system of a simple nature which gives rise to a hierarchy.

The partial-correlation between any two variables x and y,
eliminating any third variable z, is computed by the general
formula:

$$r_{xy.z} \;=\; \frac{r_{xy} - r_{xz}\, r_{yz}}{\sqrt{(1 - r_{xz}^2)\,(1 - r_{yz}^2)}} \;.\tag{2}$$

For the case of tests t_j and common-factor c, the hypothesis is
that if $x = t_j$, $y = t_k$, and $z = c$ in (2), then this partial correlation
vanishes as in (1). In this case, the numerator on the right of (2)
must vanish, whence

$$r_{jk} \;=\; r_{jc}\, r_{kc} \quad (j \neq k) \;.\tag{3}$$

The correlation r_{jc} of a test t_j with the component c is called the common-factor *loading* of the test. Using this language, Spearman's basic equation (3) says that *the correlation between any two tests t_j and t_k is the product of their common-factor loadings*.

Let us take a numerical example of what is implied by this. Suppose that we have five tests, and that we know their correlations with c. Then we can reproduce the correlations between these tests by using formula (3). Call the tests t_1, t_2, t_3, t_4, and t_5 respectively, and suppose that their common-factor loadings are .9, .7, .5, .3, and .1, in that order. Then the correlation between t_1 and t_2 will be $(.9) \times (.7) = .63$. Similarly, all the remaining intercorrelations can be computed. These can be arranged in a square table as follows:

Table 1

Test Intercorrelations for a Hypothetical
Single-Common-Factor Structure

Test		t_1	t_2	t_3	t_4	t_5
Common-Factor Loading		.9	.7	.5	.3	.1
t_1	.9	(.81)	.63	.45	.27	.09
t_2	.7	.63	(.49)	.35	.21	.07
t_3	.5	.45	.35	(.25)	.15	.05
t_4	.3	.27	.21	.15	(.09)	.03
t_5	.1	.09	.07	.05	.03	(.01)

A correlation in row j and column k is the product of the loading in row j and the loading in column k. The table is symmetric, since $r_{jk} = r_{kj}$. The diagonal of the table should express the correlations of each test with itself, or unity. Instead, we have followed formula (3) even for the case $j = k$; that is, we have computed the r_{jc}^2 and placed the answers in parentheses in the main diagonal of Table 1.

This is one kind of hierarchy, in which the correlations go down as you go down the tests. If one starts at the upper left corner and moves anywhere to the right or downward, the correlations taper off.

Now, in trying to apply this hypothesis of hierarchy to observed data, it was found that it didn't work. There was occasionally a tendency to go down, but not as specified by formula (3). The hierarchy was not particularly even; the data often could not be regarded as anything near a hierarchy. In the course of time, the word "hierarchy" has disappeared from the literature of factor analysis. For example, in perhaps the most widely accepted approach of today—that of Thurstone—the term is never mentioned.

In my new theory, particularly in that of the simplex, I propose to revive the concept of hierarchy.

THEORIES OF MULTIPLE-COMMON-FACTORS

What happened historically was this. Since the particular kind of hierarchy specified by formula (3) was discredited, it was not asked: is there some other kind of hierarchy that holds? Instead, the psychologists went off into a different direction entirely, which led to all kinds of complications and controversies.

Various psychologists have used different variations in what was done next, but they all have worked within the same kind of framework. Their general reasoning was as follows. If one common-factor is insufficient to account for the intercorrelations, then there must be at least two common-factors present.

Let the first common-factor be denoted by c_1 and the second by c_2. Let r_{jc_1} be the correlation of test j with c_1, and let r_{jc_2} be the correlation of the same test with c_2. The hypothesis that exactly two common-factors are present can be stated by a partial correlation formula that generalizes formula (2) above. We shall not write the extended formula here. It suffices to state that the hypothesis of two common-factors implies that the partial correlation between any two tests j and k vanishes when c_1 and c_2 are eliminated:

$$r_{jk.c_1 c_2} = 0 \quad (j \neq k) \ . \tag{4}$$

If (4) holds, then a generalization of (3) holds also. In the special case where the two common-factors are uncorrelated $(r_{c_1 c_2} = 0)$ equation (4) can be shown to imply that

$$r_{jk} = r_{jc_1} r_{kc_1} + r_{jc_2} r_{kc_2} \quad (j \neq k). \tag{5}$$

We now have two terms on the right of (5), each derived from loadings on one of the common-factors, compared to but one term in (3).

But even two common-factors usually did not suffice to reproduce the original correlations r_{jk} according to equation (5). So three common-factors would be tried. If that failed, then four were tried, etc.

The general case can be called that of m common-factors: $c_1, c_2, \ldots, c_m$, the general hypothesis being:

$$r_{jk.c_1 c_2 \ldots c_m} = 0 \quad (j \neq k) , \tag{6}$$

leading to the general formula:

$$r_{jk} = r_{jc_1} r_{kc_1} + r_{jc_2} r_{kc_2} + \ldots + r_{jc_m} r_{kc_m} \quad (j \neq k) \tag{7}$$

for the case where all common-factors correlate zero with each other. If the common-factors have mutual intercorrelations different from zero, a more general form of (7) holds, but the special case of uncorrelated or orthogonal common-factors is sufficient here for our purposes.

It can be proved that by keeping on "extracting" common-factors from a finite number of n tests, one is always bound to wind up with some set m of "common-factors" that satisfy (7), where $m \leq n$. Indeed, there always exists a numerically satisfactory set where $m = n$, and another set where $m = n - 1$. Sometimes, for some data, there exist additional sets where $m < n - 1$.

Many psychologists, notably Thurstone, said that it is not very meaningful if m is equal to or close to n. They postulated that the number of common-factors should be small compared to the number of tests, so as to provide a parsimonious explanation of the observed intercorrelations. If the common-factors gave no parsimonious picture of the structure of the original observations, there would be no point in using them in place of the original tests.

When m is greater than one, then there is no need for the observed correlations to follow any hierarchical pattern. Equation (7) for m $>$ 1 generates no gradient for test correlations the way single-common-factor equation (3) does. That is why the notion of hierarchy went out the window with the advent of multiple-common-factor theories.

THE UNKNOWN COMMUNALITIES

There has been a great deal of controversy about attempts to find a small system of m common-factors to explain the inter-correlations of a large system of n tests.

One of the difficulties is purely arithmetical. The usual computing routines operate like a sort of "grinding machine" for grinding out common-factors. If one common-factor doesn't suffice to reproduce the r_{jk} , grind out another. If these two together don't suffice, grind out a third, etc., until the approximation to the r_{jk} according to formula (7) is regarded as adequate. But the computing routines used for these successive grinds are strictly legitimate only if certain parameters called *communalities* are known in advance.

Formula (7) holds if j $\neq$ k. However, if the right member is written with k = j, the resulting quantity is called the communality of test j, and is denoted by h_j^2:

$$h_j^2 = r_{jc_1}^2 + r_{jc_2}^2 + \ldots + r_{jc_m}^2 \tag{8}$$

According to (8), the communality of a test is the sum of the squares of all its m common-factor loadings (provided the common-factors are all mutually uncorrelated). The left member of (7) becomes unity for j = k, for then it is the correlation of test j with itself, which is perfect. The left and right members of (7) are not in general equal for j = k; the communality is at most equal to the self-correlation, and in general is less than the self-correlation if m $<$ n. Thus, inequality (9) always holds if (7) holds:

$$h_j^2 \leq r_{jj} = 1. \tag{9}$$

In Table 1 above, for Spearman's case of m = 1, it is the communalities that we have entered in the main diagonal of the table in place of the self-correlations.

In numerical computations, the work cannot properly be begun until the n communalities h_j^2 are known (except for Spearman's case where m = 1). On the other hand, these communalities cannot be ascertained exactly unless m—the number of common-factors—is specified. But m cannot be known in general until the grinding-process is completed. On another occasion, I shall show in detail the unsatisfactory state of affairs that results from these considerations, and shall prove that there can be no general solution to this problem[4] (just as there is no general way of trisecting an angle in the classical geometric problem).

For the present, let us take for granted the fact that there is as yet no mathematically acceptable basis for the various computing routines now being used in practice for determining a parsimonious number of common-factors for a given set of data. Controversies legitimately continue as to what the minimum possible number is for certain empirical data. Controversies also exist as to whether the minimum number—were it ascertainable— is the best way of "explaining" the data.

THE CONTROVERSIES ABOUT ROTATION OF AXES

An entirely different sore-spot of common-factor theories is the problem called that of *rotation of axes*. Assuming the communalities are all known, and that exactly m common-factors completely reproduce the r_{jk} as in equation (7), this still does not guarantee that there is but one solution. To the contrary, if m > 1, then there are infinitely many solutions to the problem. If there are m common-factors $c_1, c_2, \ldots, c_m$, with loadings satisfying (7), then there is an alternative set of m common-factors—say $d_1, d_2, \ldots, d_m$—also satisfying (7), which equation can be written then instead as

$$r_{jk} = r_{jd_1} r_{kd_1} + r_{jd_2} r_{kd_2} + \ldots + r_{jd_m} r_{kd_m} \qquad (j \neq k). \tag{10}$$

The communality of test j is exactly the same numerically as before. Only the separate loadings r_{jc} have been exchanged for loadings r_{jd}, but the sum of squares of the new m loadings stay put, giving the same h_j^2 numerically as in (8).

If both (7) and (10) hold simultaneously, and with the same set of communalities h_j^2, then it can be shown that the d's are linear functions of the c's, and vice-versa. Indeed, *any* nonsingular linear transformation of the c's yields a new set of m common-factors which retains the original communalities. Geometrically, such transformations represent rotations of axes, whence the name of the problem. With $m > 1$, indefinitely many different rotations of axes can be made, given an initial set of m common-factors.

Here apparently is where the sharpest controversies lie. There are perhaps six or seven different schools of thought on where or how the reference axes of the common-factors should ultimately be placed. This it should be noted, is more a psychological problem than a mathematical one. Given only hypothesis (7), mathematics has nothing to say on the problem of rotation. (On the other hand, the mathematics does say that before worrying about the rotation problem, one should make sure there are m common-factors possible in the first place; that is, if the problem of communalities is not solved, further problems may be concerned only with nonexistent variables.)

Thus, we see the path taken by psychologists when Spearman's single-common-factor theory failed. They went on to multiple-common-factors, and splintered off into six or so different schools, despite the lack of a rigorous mathematical foundation when m exceeds unity.

My own first attempt at an alternative theory to Spearman's was a mathematical success[5], but an empirical failure. It had beautiful mathematical properties not possessed by any common-factor theory, but I could find no data for which the mathematics was appropriate in practice. More recently, I have learned how to modify my theory, and correspondingly have found it actually useful for certain empirical data. This theory I call that of the *simplex*. A related theory I call that of the *circumplex*. The more comprehensive theory of the *radex* (which combines simplexes and circumplexes simultaneously) has properties which severally have been emphasized or sought for by one or more of the existing common-factor schools. In a sense, the new approach unifies all the older approaches simultaneously. Each older approach will find its main point more or less justified by the radex, and not at all in contradiction to the main points of other schools. On the other hand, this new approach does away with some of the preconceptions of the older approaches; only by so doing could the older theories be unified.

Let us first examine the simplex theory, and then the circumplex. It will then be seen how they blend into the radex. Finally, we can compare the previous common-factor schools with the new one of order-factors.

AN ALTERNATIVE SINGLE-FACTOR THEORY:
THE PERFECT SIMPLEX

If Spearman's single-common-factor hypothesis is negated, we shall now seek an alternative kind of single factor, and not go on to an m-common-factor theory. A suggestion as to how to do this comes from scale analysis (reviewed in the previous chapter). In scale analysis we were concerned with order among *people*. But how about a concept of order among *variables*? Is it possible to attach a meaning to a rank order among quantitative[6] variables? If so, we can return to the notion of a hierarchy which has been abandoned by those seeking multiple-common-factors.

I propose that such a meaning is possible. For mental tests at least, it seems feasible—both theoretically and in practice—to use a notion of complexity as an attempted basis for comparing different variables.

Suppose we are given n tests $t_1, t_2, \ldots, t_n$ which differ only on a single complexity factor. (What we mean by this we shall explain first verbally here, and mathematically later.) Test t_1 is the least complex. Test t_2 is next; it requires everything t_1 does, and more. Similarly, t_3 is more complex than t_2, requiring everything t_2 does and more. In this case, t_3 is clearly also more complex than t_1. In general, test t_{j+1} is more complex than t_j, and hence requires what all preceding tests require, plus something more. Let g denote the total complexity factor, of which all the tests are composed in various degrees. Thus g is like an additional test beyond the most complex given test t_n. Then our basic hypothesis can be stated as:

$$r_{jg.k} = 0 \quad (j < k). \tag{11}$$

If t_k is more complex than t_j – or $j < k$ – then partialing t_k out of t_j and out of g will leave nothing left in common between t_j and g.

Using hypothesis (11) in general formula (2), setting $t_j = x$, $g = y$, and $t_k = z$, shows that a consequence of the hypothesis is that

$$r_{jg} = r_{jk} r_{kg} \qquad (j < k) . \qquad (12)$$

But we are interested in "explaining" r_{jk}, so we prefer to write (12) in the form:

$$r_{jk} = \frac{r_{jg}}{r_{kg}} \qquad (j < k) . \qquad (13)$$

Equation (13) shows again the importance of the notion of order among the variables, since this order determines which coefficient goes in the numerator of the right member, and which in the denominator.

Equation (13) can be compared with Spearman's formula (3). In each case, only correlations with a single factor are involved. In Spearman's case, these correlations are multiplied by each other; in our case, division is used. Spearman's case requires no particular initial ordering of the observed variables; our formula (13) is meaningless without such an ordering.

Each case leads to a hierarchy of observed intertest correlation coefficients. We have seen, in Table 1, that Spearman's hypothesis leads to a gradient that descends as one departs from the upper left corner of the table to the lower right corner. Let us now see what an analogous table looks like for the new order-theory.

An important case is where the tests are "equally-spaced" in their complexity; here $r_{j,j+1} = r_{k,k+1}$, or the correlation between any two adjacent tests is constant. As a numerical example of such a case, suppose we have five tests – t_1, t_2, t_3, t_4, and t_5 – which satisfy (11) and (13), and for which the complexity loadings are .07776, .1296, .216, .36, and .6 respectively. (These are simply the first five powers of .6 in reverse order.) Then according to formula (13), the intercorrelation table for the original five tests is shown in Table 2.

The hierarchical gradient in Table 2 is quite different from that in Table 1. This time, the largest correlations are all next

Table 2

Test Intercorrelations For a Hypothetical,
Equally-Spaced, Perfect Simplex

Test		t_1	t_2	t_3	t_4	t_5
	Complexity Loading	.07776	.1296	.216	.36	.6
t_1	.07776	1.0	.6	.36	.216	.1296
t_2	.1296	.6	1.0	.6	.36	.216
t_3	.216	.36	.6	1.0	.6	.36
t_4	.36	.216	.36	.6	1.0	.6
t_5	.6	.1296	.216	.36	.6	1.0
Total		2.3056	2.7760	2.9200	2.7760	2.3056

to the main diagonal, and taper off as one goes to the upper right and lower left of the table.

If the tests are not equally-spaced in their complexity, then the gradient will not be as neat as in Table 2, but will still maintain the general northeast-southwest character. The largest value in any row (column) will be next to the main diagonal of that row (column), and the correlation coefficients will decrease as they depart from the main diagonal either to the left or the right (upwards or downwards). An example of a nonequally-spaced simplex is shown in Table 3.

A set of tests whose observed intercorrelations satisfy a condition like (13) will be said to form a *perfect simplex*. They have a simple order of complexity. We shall later introduce non-perfect simplexes. The case in Table 3 is "perfect" because equation (13) holds for $j = k$ as well as for $j \neq k$; for it reads $r_{jj} = 1$ when $j = k$. In Tables 2 and 3 we have entered unity, or the total self-correlation, in the main diagonal, since this is directly consonant with equation (13).

An important feature of a perfect simplex when the tests are equally-spaced, is shown by the totals of the columns (or rows) which we have entered at the bottom of Table 2. The lowest totals are at the extremes of the tables — for the least and most complex tests — and reach a maximum at the middle of the table. These

Table 3

Test Intercorrelations For a Hypothetical,
Nonequally-Spaced, Perfect Simplex

Test		t_1	t_2	t_3	t_4	t_5
Complexity Loading		.10	.12	.30	.85	.90
t_1	.10	1.00	.83	.33	.12	.11
t_2	.12	.83	1.00	.40	.14	.13
t_3	.30	.33	.40	1.00	.35	.33
t_4	.85	.12	.14	.35	1.00	.94
t_5	.90	.11	.13	.33	.94	1.00
Total		2.39	2.50	2.41	2.55	2.51

totals are helpful in practice in determining the rank order of tests
when the correlation table is not initially given in the simplex
order. If the tests are not equally spaced, there will be a close but
not necessarily exact curvilinear correspondence between rank of
column totals and order of test (cf. Table 3).

A FACTOR THEORY IS NOT
MATHEMATICALLY ESSENTIAL

We have developed the idea of a perfect simplex by introducing the notion of a complexity factor. We have done it this way for
two reasons. One is to be able to use a language somewhat comparable to that of the earlier theories. The other is to pave the
way for seeking a physiological basis for the observed intercorrelations.

Actually, the important mathematical properties of the simplex do not at all depend on any factor hypothesis, and the mathematical theory can be developed without reference to any hypothetical variable g at all.

First, we should note that equation (13) does not lead to any
unique determination of the complexity loading r_{jg}. If we are given
a set of loadings r_{jg} (j = 1, 2, . . . , n), and multiply each by an

arbitrary constant A to define $r'_{jg} = Ar_{jg}$, then the new values r'_{jg} satisfy (13) just as well as do the original r_{jg}.

In particular, we could assign the most complex test, t_n, the loading $r_{jn} = 1$, or imply it is the total complexity factor itself. This would mean for the example of Table 2 that the new loadings would be .1296, .216, .36, .6, and 1 respectively for the five tests in the order given there. This would in no way change the observed correlation coefficients in the body of the table.

Another feature that equation (13) does not determine by itself is: what is the *direction* of increasing complexity? For example, Table 2 is completely symmetric with respect to the minor diagonal as well as to the main diagonal. If we were to say now that the order of complexity is the precise reverse of that originally stated, and assign the loadings in the order .6, .36, .216, .1296, .07776 to the tests t_1, t_2, t_3, t_4, and t_5 respectively, this would in no way change the observed intercorrelations. From the observed r_{jk} alone, it is not possible to determine the direction of complexity of the tests; the direction may be from least complex to most complex, or vice versa. This is true for unequally-spaced tests as well as for those with equal spacing.

The only thing about order that the observed r_{jk} can determine is that a test t_j is intermediate between t_{j-1} and t_{j+1}, no matter what the direction of increasing complexity may be. That is, the r_{jk} can rank the tests unambiguously, even though it is not known whether the ranking is from lowest to highest or from highest to lowest.

These two kinds of indeterminacies are reflections of the fact that a hypothetical variable g was not needed in the first place to arrive at the order structure of the observed correlations. Indeed, we can start all over again without any reference to an explicit order-factor g. Let us adopt the following definition:

Definition. A statistical variable z will be said to be intermediate to x and y if the following partial-correlation vanishes:

$$r_{xy.z} = 0. \tag{14}$$

Then, if we are given a set of n variables t_1, t_2, . . ., t_n, this set will be said to form a perfect simplex in this rank order if

$$r_{jh.k} = 0 \qquad (j < k < h). \tag{15}$$

According to (15), each test is intermediate in the sense of (14) to any two tests on opposite sides of it in the rank order. If n is the last subscript in the rank order, then using n for h in (15) makes (15) analogous to (11) — but without any hypothetical g. We have

$$r_{jn} = r_{jk} r_{kn} \qquad (j \le k),\tag{16}$$

which is analogous to (12). Equation (16) holds for $j = k$, and this we have noted in the right side. Alternatively, if 1 is the first sub-script in the rank order, we could use 1 in place of j in (15). Changing subscripts, (15) can be written:

$$r_{1k} = r_{jk} r_{1j} \qquad (j \le k).\tag{17}$$

From (16) we have:

$$r_{jk} = \frac{r_{jn}}{r_{kn}} \qquad (j \le k),\tag{18}$$

and from (17):

$$r_{jk} = \frac{r_{1k}}{r_{1j}} \qquad (j \le k).\tag{19}$$

Formulas (18) and (19) are analogous to (13), but involve no hypo-thetical variables.

What is important for our present mathematical purpose is to note that a perfect simplex, whether defined with or without a hypothetical order-factor g, can have its observed correlation co-efficients expressed in the form

$$r_{jk} = \frac{a_j}{a_k} \qquad (j \le k),\tag{20}$$

where a_j is some parameter belonging to test j. The parameters a_j may be defined only up to a constant of proportionality, but that is sufficient for our purposes. For a given ranking of the tests, examples of possible sets of a_j that we have shown are the sets of correlations r_{jg}, r_{jn}, and r_{1j}^{-1} ($j = 1, 2, . . .,n$) respectively, the latter two sets involving no hypothetical variables. It will be convenient from now on to regard equation (20) as *defining a perfect simplex matrix of intercorrelations*.

We learn an interesting property immediately from equation (20) namely, that any second order minor determinant in the observed correlation matrix vanishes if all four of its elements are on one side of the main diagonal. For such a minor can be written and expanded as:

$$
\begin{vmatrix} r_{jk} & r_{j,k+q} \\ \\ r_{j+p,k} & r_{j+p,k+q} \end{vmatrix}
=
\begin{vmatrix} \dfrac{a_j}{a_k} & \dfrac{a_j}{a_{k+q}} \\ \dfrac{a_{j+p}}{a_k} & \dfrac{a_{j+p}}{a_{k+q}} \end{vmatrix}
= 0
\qquad
\begin{matrix} (\, j \le k \,) \\ \\ (\, j + p \le k + q \,) \end{matrix}
\qquad (21)
$$

On the other hand, a minor which contains elements from both sides of the main diagonal does not vanish in general.

Second order minors are what Spearman called "tetrad-differences". In his case, there is no order of complexity among the variables, so the problem of crossing the main diagonal does not arise. According to Spearman's formula (3) above, all tetrad-differences vanish (assuming communalities are written in the main diagonal).

Much more is to be learned mathematically about a correlation matrix which is expressible in the form (20). Before we go on with the mathematics, let us turn now to the question of whether the simplex theory is supported by empirical data.

AN EXAMPLE OF VERBAL ABILITY TESTS

In going over tables of intercorrelations of mental tests published in the literature, I found none that conformed to the perfect simplex structure. The reason for this is clear. The complexity factor attempts to account for too much -- namely, the total variance of each test. In equation (20), the formula holds for j = k, or for the total self-correlation. This is in contrast to Spearman's case and to the multiple-common-factor cases, where communalities less than unity result in (7) when j = k. The presence of re-test unreliability alone may throw the main diagonal off. And surely

even tests with the same general content differ among themselves
in some aspects besides their relative complexities on their common content. By modifying the order-factor theory to allow also
for an unreliability factor, and/or for what are called "specific"
factors in common-factor theory, we find it more suitable to empirical data. Let us look at some data now, and later discuss the modification of the mathematics.

The first example I have tried was borrowed from the Thurstones' monograph describing a large factor analysis project.[7]
Twenty-one tests were administered to 437 eighth-grade children
in Chicago schools, and all the intercorrelations were computed.
Seven common-factors had been "ground" out of the correlation
table. The twenty-one tests had deliberately been assembled to
reveal seven such factors on the basis of a previous analysis of a
large battery of sixty tests.

According to my own approach, it is first necessary to define
a universe of content without reference to any statistical manipula-
tions. Just as in scale analysis, so also for factor analysis is it
important first to clarify the content of interest, and then to make a
hypothesis as to the statistical structure appropriate to such a universe.

I first tried to classify the content of the tests into distinct
universes, just by studying the type of questions used in the tests.
The hypothesis of ordered complexity was to be made for each universe separately and was to be tested for each universe separately.

The only universe I could define which had an adequate number
of tests from the twenty-one to enable a proper empirical study of
the simplex hypothesis was that which we shall call *verbal ability*.[8]
Nine of the twenty-one tests I classified as sampling this universe.
They are listed here as named and numbered in the Thurstone monograph (p. 28):

(21)	Letter Grouping	(9)	Completion
(19)	Letter Series	(12)	Suffixes
(20)	Pedigrees	(10)	First Letters
(7)	Sentences	(11)	Four-Letter Words
(8)	Vocabulary		

Doubt was had about the content of Test 20 on Pedigrees, but it was
included in our analysis anyway. It did turn out to fit adequately into the picture. The intercorrelations found by the Thurstones for
these nine tests are shown in Table 4.

In Table 4, the tests are arranged in a rank order determined
with the aid of the totals we have entered at the bottom of the table.

Table 4

Intercorrelations of Nine Verbal Ability Tests for
437 Chicago Eighth-Grade School Children[9]

Test	Letter Grouping 21	Letter Series 19	Pedigrees 20	Sentences 7	Vocabulary 8	Completion 9	Suffixes 12	First Letters 10	Four Letter Words 11
21	--	.610	.496	.425	.381	.396	.303	.398	.381
19	.610	--	.613	.492	.468	.446	.305	.391	.367
20	.496	.613	--	.555	.525	.523	.319	.355	.323
7	.425	.492	.555	--	.829	.768	.407	.419	.356
8	.381	.468	.525	.829	--	.775	.482	.472	.415
9	.396	.446	.523	.768	.775	--	.433	.428	.354
12	.303	.305	.319	.407	.482	.433	--	.557	.514
10	.398	.391	.355	.419	.472	.428	.557	--	.654
11	.381	.367	.323	.356	.415	.354	.514	.654	--
Total	3.390	3.692	3.709	4.251	4.347	4.123	3.320	3.674	3.364

The rank of the totals is unchanged by non-inclusion of the self-correlations of unity in the main diagonal. We prefer to leave the main diagonal blank here since Table 4 obviously does not reveal a perfect simplex.

The largest total belongs to Test 8 (Vocabulary); this test therefore was placed in the middle row and column of the table. The two tests with next largest totals were seen to show gradients going in opposing directions, and so were placed on either side of Test 8. Test 20 (Pedigrees) had the fourth highest total, and was seen to follow the gradient going leftwards, so was placed before Test 7. Similarly, the remaining tests were placed, one by one, in order of their column total and according to the gradient of correlation coefficients.

This method of ranking the tests is perfectly justified for an equally-spaced and perfect simplex. For nonequally-spaced and/or nonperfect simplexes, it gives only a first approximation to the correct rank order. Inspecting the results of our first ranking showed that Test 12 (Suffixes) appears to belong better between Tests 9 and 10, than at the extreme right where it was originally placed according to its column total. This way, nonvanishing tetrads come from minors that cross the main diagonal. Table 4 shows the tentative ranking our final inspection suggested, the only departure from the rank of column totals being for Test 12.

NONPARAMETRIC ANALYSIS OF THE HIERARCHY

Just staring at Table 4 seems sufficient to verify that some kind of hierarchy is present among these verbal ability tests. There is an unmistakable general trend for the largest correlations to be next to the main diagonal, and to taper off to the upper right and lower left corners.

On the other hand, it is also quite evident that a perfect simplex is not present. The correlations don't taper in the manner required by a perfect simplex. It may be then that we have a nonperfect simplex, or as we prefer to call it, a *quasi-simplex.*

The situation is similar to that of scale analysis. Often data do not form a perfect scale, but show definite gradients that indicate that nevertheless a meaningful rank order may be possible, although it alone will not reproduce the observations. Such data are said to form a *quasi-scale,* and there are many varieties of quasi-scales possible, in contrast to the unique definition of a perfect scale.

(Lazarsfeld's latent distance model is one example of a quasi-scale;[10] the nodular scale is a more general type;[11] and an even more general type is defined by image analysis.[12])

Shortly, we shall present some precise mathematical definitions for some kinds of quasi-simplexes. But at the moment, we wish to point out that one of the features of rank theories is that the general nature of the order is often empirically evident by inspection alone, without any calculation of parameters or precise mathematical specifications.

Just as mathematical statisticians are finding good reason for turning more and more to order statistics in sampling theory, and to nonparametric tests of hypotheses, just so may it be worthwhile in factor analysis to see what aspects can be delineated without parametric considerations.

I submit that a hierarchy, if it really exists, may often reveal itself to inspection alone. Not always, to be sure; we shall see reasons why a hierarchy can sometimes be obscured to direct inspection. But surely the converse holds; if inspection reveals a hierarchy, then the hierarchy exists. Knowing it exists should spur efforts to reveal its nature in more detail, and may perhaps ultimately lead to an exact parametric theory for it.

The verbal ability tests do reveal a hierarchy to the eye. We do not at this stage know its exact parametric nature; but this parametric ignorance should not blind us to the fact that there is a hierarchy among the correlation coefficients.

Let us look at the content of the tests themselves, and see if intuitively the tests do seem to be in order of increasing complexity. Judging by their respective contents, we seem to have arranged the tests in order from least complex to most complex, the simplest being Letter Grouping and the most complicated being Four-Letter Words.

The Letter Grouping Test, as described by the Thurstones, contains questions like the following:

> Look at the four groups of letters below. Three of the groups are alike in some way. Mark the one that is different from the other three.

> AABC   ACAD   ACFH   AACG

The correct answer is the third group, since all others are alike in having two A's. The rest of the test contained similar questions. Experience with the alphabet is clearly involved here.

The second test in our hierarchy is Letter Series. Typical problems are:

Read the series of letters below, and indicate what the next
letter in each should be:

```
c   d   c   d   c   d   ----
a   a   b   b   c   c   d   d   ----
a   b   x   c   d   x   e   f   x   g   h   x   ----
```

This test is apparently more complex than the preceding one since
it requires not just recognizing when two letters are alike, but also
facility with sequences of letters of the English alphabet.

Let us now jump to the other end of our hierarchy. Next to
the end is First Letters. The instruction for this test was simply:

Write as many words as you can which begin with S.

The most complex of the nine tests, according to our hierarchy, is
Four-Letter Words. The instructions for this were:

Write as many words as you can which have four letters
and begin with C.

Surely, restricting oneself only to four-letter words is a more
complicated operation than not having such a restriction. Our
hierarchy concurs, by saying that Four-Letter Words is a more
complex operation than First Letters.

Also, thinking up words is a more complex operation than just
recognizing similar letters or series of letters. Our hierarchy has
placed tests that deal with words at a higher level than tests that
deal only with letters.

Thus, intuitive consideration of the content of the tests tends
to confirm the hierarchy arrived at by examination of their intercorrelations.

This is not to be taken to imply that such an intuitive confirmation is either necessary or sufficient. For some of the more
intermediate tests, it is difficult to make an intuitive estimate of
their rank order. In some other data, a ranking by correlations
may conceivably contradict intuition. (Let us never forget that if
we were to depend on intuition or "common sense" alone, we would
still believe that the world is flat and not round.) My point is that
we here have the comfortable circumstance that intuition is clear
enough on some of the tests to make us happy about the order the
correlations have established for us previously. This is a contribution to our peace of mind rather than to rigor of proof, but such
a contribution is not to be disdained in working with a new theory.

ANOTHER EXAMPLE OF VERBAL ABILITY TESTS

The example taken from the Thurstones is the first set of data I had examined with a quasi-simplex in mind. Further confirmation of a hierarchy for such tests can now be given with another example based on a more adequate number of cases. Table 5 shows a set of intercorrelations which had been studied previously by three different writers from three different points of view. I have copied the data from Peatman (who gave the latest of the treatments). He studied the intercorrelations of ten tests, all told, using Tryon's technique of cluster analysis. From these ten tests I selected the six in our Table 5 as having a common content largely of verbal ability. (The remaining four tests were: History, Fine Arts, Mathematics, and General Science.) Peatman found the above six tests to belong to two different "operational unities". But a glance at Table 5 shows but a single order present, or a quasi-simplex.

The nonparametric aspect of order theory does bear some resemblance to cluster analysis, but we now see that previous cluster techniques need to be modified if they are really to be useful for specific structural theories like that of the simplex. Without a preliminary order hypothesis, it does not seem possible to interpret correlation profiles properly.

Studying the order of the tests in Table 5 again gives us the satisfaction of seeing that it agrees with "common sense". The direction of increasing complexity is clearly from Spelling to Foreign Literature; and each test, according to our intuitive judgment, does seem to involve a more complex verbal activity than the preceding one.

Because of the relatively large number of cases this example is based on, we shall give it a more parametric treatment shortly, when we come to discuss the problem of external prediction from simplexes. The greater clarity of the hierarchy to the eye is undoubtedly due in part to the larger size of sample here than in the previous example. Sampling errors alone can of course blur a hierarchy if N is not sufficiently large. A further reason for the clearer hierarchy here may be the better technical quality of the tests themselves, since reliabilities of over .90 were reported for each test in Table 5.

Table 5

Intercorrelations of Six Verbal Ability Tests
for 1046 Bucknell College Sophomores[13]

| Test | Spelling | Punctuation | Grammar | Vocabulary | Literature | Foreign Literature |
	A	C	B	D	E	H
A	--	.621	.564	.476	.394	.389
C	.621	--	.742	.503	.461	.411
B	.564	.742	--	.577	.472	.429
D	.476	.503	.577	--	.688	.548
E	.394	.461	.472	.688	--	.639
H	.389	.411	.429	.548	.639	--
Total	2.444	2.738	2.784	2.792	2.654	2.416

AN EXAMPLE OF NUMERICAL ABILITY TESTS

Another type of content that seems to form a quasi-simplex is that of numerical ability. There were only four tests in the Thurstones' monograph that I could classify as primarily numerical, even when I examined the content of all sixty original tests. The intercorrelations of these four tests conform generally to the hypothesis of a quasi-simplex, but four is too small a number for an adequate analysis.

In L. L. Thurstone's earlier monograph, which became available to me only later,[14] intercorrelations are given for a set of fifty-six tests administered to 240 schoolchildren. The size of sample here is not too large. Also, the intercorrelations were computed by means of tetrachoric coefficients, which adds further to sampling error. However, among the six tests I selected as being primarily of numerical ability, we can nevertheless see an unmistakable hierarchy. The intercorrelations are shown in Table 6.

It is gratifying to see that the order of these six tests as determined by their intercorrelations turns out to accord with the traditional view of arithmetic. Table 6 proves that subtraction is more complex than addition, multiplication is more complex than subtraction, and division is more complex than multiplication. This should not be surprising, for each kind of operation does involve the preceding one explicitly. The Numerical Judgment test involves all the four arithmetical operations, and is shown by the simplex table to be the most complex of all.[16]

"DEGREE OF COMPLEXITY" VERSUS "DIFFICULTY"

There is some danger of confusing the notion of degree of complexity with that of difficulty. If we say subtraction is more complex than addition, we do not mean by this that subtraction is necessarily more difficult than addition. Complexity and difficulty have no necessary connection with each other in our theory.

"Difficulty" has a conventional meaning in test theory that is related to a group average. For example, if less people answer correctly one (dichotomously scored) item than another, the first item is said to be more difficult than the second. Or if one spelling test composed of fifty items turns out to have a lower population mean than another spelling test also composed of fifty items, the first test is said to be more difficult than the second for this population. Comparative difficulty in this sense implies only a comparison of group averages.

Table 6

Intercorrelations (Tetrachoric) of Six Numerical Ability Tests for
240 Chicago Schoolchildren[15]

Test	Addition 31	Subtraction 32	Multiplication 33	Division 34	Arithmetical Reasoning 39	Numerical Judgment 38
31	--	.62	.62	.54	.29	.28
32	.62	--	.67	.53	.38	.37
33	.62	.67	--	.62	.48	.52
34	.54	.53	.62	--	.62	.57
39	.29	.38	.48	.62	--	.64
38	.28	.37	.52	.57	.64	--
Total	2.35	2.57	2.91	2.88	2.41	2.38

Order of "complexity", on the other hand, we have defined in terms of correlation coefficients as in equation (15) above. A correlation coefficient is invariant under any linear transformations of scores. Hence, changing group averages need not change correlation coefficients.

Returning to subtraction and addition, it is entirely possible to make an addition test far more difficult than a subtraction test. For example, for a given population, select a set of ten addition items all of which were missed by at least 70% of the population. The mean total score on such a test will then be less than 3. Select ten subtraction items all of which were answered correctly by at least 70% of the population. The mean total score on subtraction will then be at least 7. Hence the population mean on subtraction is greater than for addition, or this particular subtraction test is less difficult than this particular addition test. However, the intercorrelation between these two tests can be precisely the same as for tests in which subtraction is made more difficult than addition. Furthermore, the intercorrelations with other tests in a simplex can be essentially the same, no matter if orders of difficulty are reversed.

Pearsonian correlations need not, of course, remain precisely the same if test difficulties are altered. However, if each test belongs to a scalable universe,[17] then it is easy to see that the rank correlation coefficient between any two tests does not essentially depend on the difficulties of the tests. Making one test more difficult or less difficult (by selecting appropriate items from the scalable universes) does not at all change the rank order of the *people* on the test; only their apparent scores change, but not the rank order of these scores within the test. Hence, ranks and their intercorrelations do not depend on test difficulty. It follows that Pearsonian coefficients – such as are used in factor analysis generally and in the present lecture – usually cannot vary much, since they are usually closely (albeit curvilinearly) related to rank correlations. Indeed, if difficulties (i.e., population means) are varied, but population variances are kept constant, Pearsonian coefficients can vary relatively little.

Our simplex theory hypothesizes that order of complexity has little to do with the relative difficulties of the particular tests used. Were the difficulties to be changed, the hypothesis is that this will not change the complexity rankings of the tests nor their general gradients. Modifications of correlation coefficients due to modification of test difficulties should take place systematically in accordance with the gradients. This will always tend to be true if our tests are from scalable universes. This emphasizes the importance of first examining the structure of each test individually by scale analysis before attempting a factor analysis of correlations between tests. It may well be that some of the departure from the simplex structure in our examples above (and from the circumplex in the examples to come below) is due to lack of scalability of some of the tests used.

THE ARBITRARINESS OF OBSERVED METRICS

It should always be remembered that the directly observed metric of a test is essentially arbitrarily determined by the investigator. He can make the test as easy or hard as he pleases by his selection of items or by altering time limits. Furthermore, it may sometimes be difficult, if not impossible, to compare the observed scores on two different tests. Take for example two of the verbal ability tests used in Table 4. The test on First-Letters consists of but a single question, and a test score is simply the number of words a testee writes from memory that begin with a certain letter. Another test, Letter-Series, consists of twenty-five dichotomously scored items. How compare two mean scores from such tests? The notion of relative "difficulty" seems to be undefined for such an example, for the observed metrics are not in quite the same kind of units. One test has only one question and the other has the arbitrary number of twenty-five questions. The scores have different meanings.

Even though difficulties may be noncomparable, because of a lack of comparable metrics, complexities remain comparable since they are defined by dimensionless correlation coefficients. Letter-Series can be said to represent a less complex verbal activity than does First-Letters, despite the fact that the two activities are observed with noncomparable metrics.

Simplex theory has a further contribution to make to this problem of metric, which we shall examine when we return shortly to mathematics to develop further parametric aspects of simplex analysis.

ORDER OF LEARNING
AND ORDER OF COMPLEXITY

Why should one task be more complex than another? Is order of complexity inherent in the nature of the tasks, or is it an
artifact of the learning process? The answer seems to include
both possibilities. Order of complexity can often be largely a cultural phenomenon as well as a result of an inherent relationship
between the abilities involved.

In the case of our arithmetic tests, each successive task did
require the preceding ones. Multiplication cannot be done without
using addition. Division requires multiplication and subtraction.
Conceivably, one could learn to subtract without learning to add;
but this is never done. We are taught subtraction in terms of addition; or better we are taught subtraction after we are taught addition.[18]

In contrast, the verbal ability tests have no such clearcut order of learning or of direct involvement of one task in the next.
Why should thinking of words ending in 'tion' (Suffixes Test) be
less complex than thinking of words beginning with 'p' (First-
Letters)? The answer may lie in the culture of the Chicago school
system and the role that words ending in 'tion' play in that culture

Let us look at a final example of a quasi-simplex which may
have some bearing on this problem of order of learning and relative complexity.

Some investigators have tried to see whether Spearman's
single-common-factor theory holds for learning experiments
among certain animals. Spearman's hypothesis has been rejected
on the basis of data reproduced in Table 7. Spearman's hypothesis
is properly to be rejected for Table 7 because a tetrad does not
vanish which involves elements on opposite sides of the main diagonal. However, Table 7 sustains our new alternative hypothesis
that a quasi-simplex is present in the data. We have inserted our
usual row of totals at the bottom of the table. The simplex order
turns out to be the order in which the experiments were recorded.

Of course, only four[19] variables are involved in Table 7, and
this is much too small a number to allow for any safe generalization. I cite this example largely to indicate a line of experimentation that might profitably be followed.

The U-Maze Reversed appears more complex than the U-
Maze. Similarly the Elevated Maze Reversed appears more complex than the Elevated Maze. Could this be because the rats had to
unlearn the original maze in order to succeed in the Reversed

Table 7

Intercorrelations Among Four Learning Experiments
on the Albino Rat[20]

	Warden U-Maze	U-Maze Reversed	Miles Elevated Maze	Elevated Maze Reversed
Experiment	1	2	3	4
1	--	.55	.47	.33
2	.55	--	.52	.41
3	.47	.52	--	.51
4	.33	.41	.51	--
Total	1.35	1.48	1.50	1.25

Maze? What if they were to try a Reversed Maze first, and then
the maze unreversed; would the order of complexity be altered?
It would be interesting to have systematic experiments made with
reversal of order of learning.

On the other hand, both forms of Elevated Maze seem more
complex than both forms of U-Maze. Perhaps order of learning of
the mazes is not a controlling factor here, but the relative complexities are in the nature of the tasks. This too is a hypothesis
worth testing systematically.

If learning takes place by organization of the nervous system,
then it may be that things learned first establish some kind of organization which then has to be altered or superimposed on by
things learned later – provided the later things are of the same
general nature and require the same elements of organization.

Simplex theory thus has a contribution to make to learning
theory by suggesting this problem of order of learning for study and
by giving some specific preliminary tools for its analysis. Previous
experiments on learning seem to have emphasized largely the aspects of speed and difficulty. Simplex theory suggests study of certain aspects of the *organization* of learning.

PREDICTION FROM A PERFECT SIMPLEX

We now return to some mathematics. Only the perfect simplex has been defined mathematically to this point of our lecture.
There is only one kind of perfect simplex in our approach, but
there may be several varieties of quasi-simplexes. Lest we get
lost in the trees of quasi-simplexes later on when we attempt a
parametric treatment of them, it may be well first to learn one of
the most striking features of the perfect simplex, for this carries
over in part to quasi-simplexes.

Granted we know a correlation matrix is of the form specified by equation (20). What can we do with this information?

Tests are usually administered in order to help predict some
external criterion or criteria. Or a test may often serve as a criterion itself — as something to be predicted. Knowing that the
structure of a set of variables is a simplex provides a powerful
method for handling each of these kinds of prediction problems.

The most compact way of discussing the linear multiple-
regressions among variables is by means of the inverse of their
correlation matrix. From this inverse are easily computed all the
multiple-correlation coefficients and all the multiple-regression
weights.

The inverse of a perfect simplex correlation matrix has a
very simple form, with profound implications for prediction problems. Consider the previous numerical example in Table 2. The
inverse of the correlation matrix there is shown in Table 8. The
striking feature is that all elements are precisely zero except for
those in the three central diagonals. The main diagonal elements
are all positive; the elements in the two diagonals surrounding the
main diagonal are all negative; and all other elements are zero.

The hypothetical tests in Table 2 were equally-spaced. This
is reflected in Table 8 by the fact that — except for the first and
last entries — elements in the same diagonal are all equal. Except
for tests 1 and 5, the main diagonal elements are all equal to 2.1250
here, and the elements in the neighboring diagonals are all equal to
- .9735. There is a "border effect" on the first and last tests,
which makes main diagonal elements different from the corresponding ones of the remaining tests.

The general law of formation of Table 8 holds for any perfect
simplex, whether equally-spaced or not. The main diagonal elements may not all be equal, but they will be positive. Next to the
main diagonal, the elements may not all be mutually equal, but they
will be negative and smaller numerically than the main diagonal.

Table 8

The Inverse of the Equally-Spaced, Perfect,
Simplex Correlation Matrix of Table 2

Test	t_1	t_2	t_3	t_4	t_5
t_1	1.5625	-.9375	0	0	0
t_2	-.9375	2.1250	-.9375	0	0
t_3	0	-.9375	2.1250	-.9375	0
t_4	0	0	-.9375	2.1250	-.9375
t_5	0	0	0	-.9375	1.5625

And there will always be a border effect on the first and last tests, tending to reduce numerically their nonzero elements compared to those of other tests. The border effect is due to an end test not being enclosed by a less complex or a more complex test, as the case may be, so that it has only one immediate neighbor. All other tests have two immediate neighbors.

As an example of an unequally-spaced simplex, let us consider again the hypothetical case of Table 3. The inverse of this correlation matrix is shown in Table 9 following.

Table 9

The Inverse of the Unequally-Spaced, Perfect,
Simplex Correlation Matrix of Table 3

Test	t_1	t_2	t_3	t_4	t_5
t_1	3.273	-2.727	0	0	0
t_2	-2.727	3.463	-.476	0	0
t_3	0	-.476	1.333	-.403	0
t_4	0	0	-.403	9.399	-8.743
t_5	0	0	0	-8.743	9.257

Notice again the positive main diagonal elements, the negative elements next to the main diagonal, and the zero elements everywhere else.

It is well-known that, if r^{jk} denotes the element in row j and column k of the inverse matrix of the r_{jk}, and if w_{jk} is the weight of t_k in the multiple-regression for predicting t_j, then[21]

$$w_{jk} = \frac{-r^{jk}}{r^{jj}} \ (j \ne k) ,\qquad (22)$$

assuming all tests are in standard form (i.e. with unit standard deviations). According to (22), if we reverse the sign of each non-diagonal element in row j of Table 8 (or Table 9) and divide by r^{jj} — the diagonal element of that row — then the resulting values will be the multiple-regression weights for predicting t_j from the n-1 remaining t_k. Carrying out this process for each row of Table 8 yields all the regression coefficients for all five multiple-regressions of each test on the remaining four tests, as in Table 10.

Table 10

Multiple-Regression Weights for Predicting Each Test
from the Remaining Four Tests
in the Equally-Spaced, Perfect Simplex of Table 2

Criterion	Predictor					Multiple-Correlation Coefficient
	t_1	t_2	t_3	t_4	t_5	
t_1	--	.6	0	0	0	.6
t_2	.4412	--	.4412	0	0	.73
t_3	0	.4412	--	.4412	0	.73
t_4	0	0	.4412	--	.4412	.73
t_5	0	0	0	.6	--	.6

For the present discussion, the most important feature of Table 10 is the location of the zero regression weights. The same pattern of zeros necessarily holds – according to formula (22) – for the regression coefficients as for the inverse matrix. We have left the main diagonal of Table 10 blank, since a test is not used in predicting itself; formula (22) is only for $j \neq k$.

In order to predict the first test from the remaining tests, we use the weights in row 1 of Table 10. We see that only the second test gets a nonzero weight, namely, .6. The other tests do not at all help in the prediction. Similarly, to predict the last test from the remaining tests, only the next to the last test gets a nonzero weight; the earlier tests help not at all.

To predict an intermediate test, nonzero regression weights exist only for two predictors, the ones immediately before and after it in order of complexity. For example, to predict test 2 from the remaining tests – according to row 2 of Table 10 – tests 1 and 3 get weights of .4412; and the remaining tests get zero weights, or don't help at all.

The same general law of formation of regression weights holds for unequally-spaced tests. Table 11 shows the regression weights for the hypothetical tests of Table 3, computed from the inverse matrix in Table 9 according to formula (22).

Table 11

The Multiple-Regression Weights for Predicting Each Test
From the Remaining Five Tests
in the Unequally-Spaced, Perfect Simplex of Table 3

| Criterion | Predictor | | | | | Multiple Correlation Coefficient |
	t_1	t_2	t_3	t_4	t_5	
t_1	--	.83	0	0	0	.833
t_2	.79	--	.14	0	0	.843
t_3	0	.36	--	.30	0	.500
t_4	0	0	.04	--	.93	.945
t_5	0	0	0	.94	--	.944

The multiple-correlation coefficient for each test as criterion is shown in the last columns of Tables 10 and 11. Each is easily computed from the corresponding main diagonal element of the inverse matrix by the formula[22]:

$$r_j = \sqrt{1 - \frac{1}{r^{jj}}}, \qquad (23)$$

where r_j denotes the multiple-correlation coefficient of test j on the remaining n-1 tests.

Border effects again are noticeable. The two extreme tests have lower multiple-correlation coefficients than do the intermediate tests. Indeed, for the extreme tests we have

$$r_1 = r_{12} \ , \quad r_n = r_{n-1,n} \qquad (24)$$

or each multiple-correlation coefficient is precisely the same as the zero-order correlation with the neighboring test. This again reflects the fact that nonneighboring tests do not help in prediction. Each test at either end of the rank order has but one neighbor, and all others have two neighbors. In an equally-spaced series, end tests are always less predictable than intermediate ones; in an unequally-spaced series, the end tests will usually tend to be the least predictable.

Suppose we wished to improve the predictability of a given test t_j by bringing in additional tests from the same universe of content (i.e., from the same perfect simplex). What kind of test will be most helpful? The answer is very clear. Any additional test that is less complex than t_{j-1} or more complex than t_{j+1} will not help at all. Only by bringing in a test which is intermediate to t_{j-1} and t_j, or intermediate to t_j and t_{j+1}, can the multiple-correlation for t_j be raised. In such a case, the new regression weight of the old t_{j-1} or of the old t_{j+1} will become zero.

The predictability of an end test ordinarily can best be enhanced by bringing in an even more extreme test, so that it will then have two neighbors instead of one.

PREDICTION FROM A QUASI-SIMPLEX

Since perfect simplexes are not to be expected in practice, let us return to our empirical examples of quasi-simplexes and see how prediction works for them.

The multiple-regression weights from the 9x9 intercorrelation matrix of the Thurstones' verbal ability tests are shown in Table 12. This table was computed by first computing the inverse matrix, and then using formula (22). The column of multiple-correlation coefficients was computed from the inverse matrix by formula (23). The first-order enlargement method [23] was used for computing the inverse matrix; this has advantages here over other methods in providing a sequence of successively larger inverses which is itself of interest for showing what happens as more predictors are added to a set of variables.

Table 12 differs of course from the perfect Tables 10 and 11. There are at least two reasons for this. One is that now a quasi-simplex is involved rather than a perfect simplex. Another is that actual empirical correlations are involved – rather than hypothetical, ideal coefficients – based on a sample of only 437 cases. This is not too large a number of cases for computing multiple-regression weights based on so many as eight predictors. Regardless, we see the same general pattern among the regression coefficients as for a perfect simplex. The highest regression weights usually go to the two neighbors of an intermediate test. These two weights are always positive; all the other weights tend to be closer to zero and are not restricted to being positive.

The weights that do not neighbor on the main diagonal are not necessarily zero even theoretically for a quasi-simplex. The deviations from zero in Table 12 are not due only to sampling error, but could be approximately of the present order of magnitude even if there were no sampling error due to selection of a limited number of schoolchildren. The deviations from zero are attributable primarily to the fact that Table 4 represents a quasi-simplex, which is a perfect simplex plus deviations.

THE MATHEMATICAL DEFINITION
OF AN ϵ-SIMPLEX

We shall now offer one kind of mathematical definition of a quasi-simplex. Other kinds will be made shortly. Let us consider an infinite universe of tests which forms an infinitely finely graded

Table 12

The Multiple-Regression Weights for Predicting Each Verbal Ability
Test from the Remaining Eight Tests of Table 4

Criterion	Letter Grouping (21)	Letter Series (19)	Pedigrees (20)	Sentences (7)	Vocabulary (8)	Completion (9)	Suffixes (12)	First Letters (10)	Four-Letter Words (11)	Multiple-Correlation Coefficient
21	--	.42	.13	.12	-.13	.06	.01	.09	.10	.657
19	.36	--	.34	.08	.07	-.01	-.02	.06	.05	.721
20	.12	.36	--	.17	.06	.13	.02	-.00	.01	.694
7	.05	.04	.08	--	.55	.27	-.02	.00	-.02	.861
8	-.06	.03	.03	.53	--	.29	.09	.04	.05	.868
9	.04	-.01	.08	.36	.39	--	.06	.04	-.03	.814
12	.01	-.03	.02	-.05	.22	.10	--	.29	.22	.634
10	.08	.05	-.00	.00	.09	.06	.23	--	.43	.725
11	.09	.05	.01	-.04	.11	-.04	.19	.48	--	.692

quasi-simplex. That is, between any two given tests in the rank order, there is always an indefinitely large number of intermediate tests. If t_a and t_b are any two tests, then there are infinitely many tests t_k with quasi-simplex rank between those of t_a and t_b. Then we shall define an ϵ-*type of quasi-simplex* – or an ϵ-*simplex*, as follows.

Definition of an ϵ-simplex. Consider an infinite universe of variables observed for an infinite population of people. Assume the variables can be arranged in a continuous rank order among themselves such that the following properties hold. Let t_a and t_{a_1}, be any two variables from the universe, and let t_{a_2} be any other variable whose rank is between the ranks of t_a and t_{a_1}. In general, let t_{a_n} be some variable with rank between t_a and $t_{a_{n-1}}$ ($n = 2, 3, \ldots$). Let $w_{aj}^{(n)}$ be the multiple-regression weight of t_{a_j} for predicting t_a in the regression of t_a on the n variables t_{a_k} ($k = 1, 2, \ldots, n$). Then the universe will be said to constitute an ϵ-simplex if and only if

$$\lim_{n \to \infty} w_{aj}^{(n)} = 0 \quad (j = 1, 2, \ldots, n-1) , \qquad (25)$$

for all t_a and all possible selections of sequences of t_{a_k} ($k = 1, 2, \ldots, n$).

According to this definition, an ϵ-simplex differs from a perfect simplex in that zero weights for nonneighboring tests hold only in the limit as $n \to \infty$ for the ϵ-type, whereas zero weights hold for any value of n in the perfect type. The two kinds of simplex are similar in the effect induced by changing the immediate neighbors of a test through inserting new and closer neighbors; in each case the old neighbors have their weights reduced (to zero in the case of a perfect simplex, and usually substantially close to zero in an ϵ-simplex).

To have weights vanish in the limit does not mean that therefore the corresponding tests do not help in prediction. Let $t_{ai}^{(n)}$ denote the predicted value of t_a for person i from n tests t_{a_j} ($j = 1, 2, \ldots, n$) which are successively closer neighbors to t_a. Then

$$t_{ai}^{(n)} = w_{a1}^{(n)} t_{a_1 i} + w_{a2}^{(n)} t_{a_2 i} + \ldots + w_{an}^{(n)} t_{a_n i} \qquad (26)$$

According to (25), if the universe is an ϵ-simplex, then each term on the right of (26) has a zero limit as $n \to \infty$, except possibly for the last term. There are $n-1$ terms with zero limits, but the *number* of such terms increase with n. Hence the sum

$$w_{a1}^{(n)} t_{a_1 i} + w_{a2}^{(n)} t_{a_2 i} + \ldots + w_{a,n-1}^{(n)} t_{a_{n-1} i} \qquad (27)$$

need not vanish in the limit as $n \to \infty$, even though each term vanishes separately. The limit of the sum need not be the sum of the limits. The vanishing of the weights in the limit implies that no one of the nonneighboring predictors plays any important role in the prediction.

ON THE APPROACH TO ZERO OF REGRESSION WEIGHTS OF NONNEIGHBORING TESTS

Our second example of verbal ability tests, in Table 5, is based on over 1,000 cases, and apparently involves tests which are technically superior to those of the previous examples (in view of the high reliability coefficients reported). It seems then worth making a more detailed analysis of these data, since sampling unreliability and internal inconsistency will interfere less than in the previous case.

In Table 13 are shown the multiple-regression weights for predicting each test from the remaining five tests, as computed by formula (22). Formula (23) was used for the multiple-correlation coefficients shown in the last column of Table 13.

The regression weights neighboring on the main diagonal of Table 13 are the dominant ones in the table and are all positive. Again there is a border effect on the first and last rows, both with respect to weights and multiple-correlation coefficients.

We have just defined an ϵ-simplex as a system of interrelated variables wherein all nonneighboring multiple-regression weights tend to zero as more tests are inserted among those first given. Since the present example won't let us go beyond $n = 6$ and is based on a thousand cases, sampling stability here should be sufficient for us to examine empirically what happens as n increases.

Table 13

The Multiple-Regression Weights for Predicting Each Verbal Ability
Test from the Remaining Five Tests of Table 5

Criterion	Predictor						Multiple-Correlation Coefficient
	Spelling	Punctuation	Grammar	Vocabulary	Literature	Foreign Literature	
	1	2	3	4	5	6	
1	--	.41	.14	.16	-.03	.09	.660
2	.28	--	.54	-.02	.10	.02	.786
3	.10	.55	--	.24	-.01	.04	.783
4	.12	-.02	.26	--	.46	.10	.756
5	-.02	.11	-.01	.45	--	.36	.760
6	.09	.03	.06	.13	.47	--	.668

Let us begin with the two tests which are ultimately farthest apart, so that we can see what happens as we keep inserting tests between them. Spelling and Foreign Literature are at the two extremes of the ranking of our six tests. They correlate .389 with each other, according to Table 5. Hence the multiple-correlation of each on the other alone is the same .389, as is also the weight of each for predicting the other. We record this information for n = 2 in Table 14(a).

Next, consider the multiple-regressions when n = 3, the third test being Punctuation with rank intermediate to Spelling and Foreign Literature. The weights and coefficients are as in Table 14(b). Next we insert Grammar to make n = 4, Grammar being between Spelling and Foreign Literature in the simplex ranking; the results are shown in Table 14(c). For n = 5, Vocabulary is added to the previous four tests, and is even closer to Foreign Literature; the resulting weights and coefficients are recorded in Table 14(d). Finally, if we add Literature to make n = 6, with Literature being even closer to Foreign Literature than the other tests, we arrive at the previously presented Table 13.

Focussing on the multiple-regression weight of Spelling for predicting Foreign Literature, we see it takes on the following values as n goes from 2 to 6 by adding tests which are closer and closer to Foreign Literature (and farther and farther from Spelling): .39, .22, .18, .10 and .09. The weights of Punctuation in the same series of regressions (for n = 3, 4, 5, 6) are respectively: .28, .13, .09 and .03.

The biggest drop in weight usually takes place for the test which was the closest neighbor previously but is superseded by an even closer neighbor. For example, to predict Foreign Literature with n = 5 in Table 14(d), Vocabulary got a weight of .42; this weight dropped to .13 in Table 13 when Literature was added.

On the other hand, for predicting Spelling when n = 3, Punctuation received a weight of .55, which changed only to .42 for n = 4, the new predictor Grammar not being a better neighbor to Spelling. As tests even more distant from Spelling were introduced into the regressions for n = 5 and 6, Punctuation's weight remained at .41, and the weights of the other predictors also did not change much.

The growth of the multiple-correlation coefficients followed the same pattern. The multiple-correlation coefficient for Foreign Literature grew as follows as n went from 2 to 6: .389, .445, .471, .577 and finally .668. As tests were added that were closer to Foreign Literature, the correlation increased. Actually, the final coefficient of .668 is not strikingly better than the simple correlation of .639 with neighbor Literature alone in Table 5. The nonneighbors

Table 14

The Changes in Multiple-Regression Weights and Multiple-Correlation
Coefficients as Tests are Added with Simplex Rank Intermediate
to Spelling and Foreign Literature in Table 5

(a) n = 2

Criterion	Predictor Weight		Multiple-Correlation Coefficient
	Spelling	Foreign Literature	
Spelling	- -	.39	.389
Foreign Literature	.39	- -	.389

(b) n = 3

Criterion	Predictor Weight			Multiple-Correlation Coefficient
	Spelling	Punctuation	Foreign Literature	
Spelling	- -	.55	.16	.638
Punctuation	.54	- -	.20	.648
Foreign Literature	.22	.28	- -	.445

(c) n = 4

Criterion	Predictor Weight				Multiple-Correlation Coefficient
	Spelling	Punctuation	Grammar	Foreign Literature	
Spelling	--	.42	.19	.13	.651
Punctuation	.28	--	.56	.06	.783
Grammar	.14	.60	--	.13	.762
Foreign Literature	.18	.13	.24	--	.471

(d) n = 5

Criterion	Predictor Weight					Multiple-Correlation Coefficient
	Spelling	Punctuation	Grammar	Vocabulary	Foreign Literature	
Spelling	--	.41	.14	.14	.08	.659
Punctuation	.28	--	.55	.02	.05	.784
Grammar	.10	.55	--	.23	.04	.783
Vocabulary	.14	.03	.33	--	.34	.677
Foreign Literature	.10	.09	.06	.42	--	.577

really don't help much. An even closer neighbor than Literature –
could one be found – would help even more, and could possibly reduce Literature's weight virtually to zero; or a neighbor on the opposite side – more complex than Foreign Literature – could also
be of substantial aid in this regression.

In contrast, the growth of the multiple-correlation coefficient
for Spelling is not aided much by bringing in more and more complex tests. We find Spelling's predictability starting at .389 from
Foreign Literature alone, jumping to .638 for n = 3 as its best
neighbor available (Punctuation) is added, and remaining at about
the same level thereafter as n continues from 4 to 6 by bringing
in tests farther and farther from Spelling, the coefficients being
.651, .659, and .660 respectively. Really to improve Spelling's
predictability, we should seek a test with rank intermediate to that
of Spelling and Punctuation, and a test which neighbors on Spelling
on the opposite side of lesser complexity.

EXTERNAL PREDICTION FROM A SIMPLEX

The ordinary problem of prediction is not of the type we have
just been discussing. Predicting one test from others from the same
universe might be called *internal* prediction. But the ordinary problem of prediction is that of *external* prediction, namely predicting
something outside the universe from one or more variables within
the universe.

Ultimately, we would like to be able to predict, for example,
success as a clerical worker from verbal ability. Under certain
hypotheses, the simplex pattern offers a powerful basis for aiding
in such external predictions.

The Psychological Testing Unit of the Israel Defence Army recently came to me with a problem of external prediction. They had
administered a battery of nine tests to a group of soldiers before
they entered a course, and also had a final grade for each upon completion of the course. The problem was how best to use these data
in the future to weed out new candidates most likely to fail the course.

First I examined the content of the nine predictors, and conjec-
tured they would form an approximate circumplex – the kind of structure we come to next in this lecture. However, when I was shown the
intercorrelations, I found the tests did not depart radically from being a quasi-simplex, which is quite possible for certain circumplexes.
Therefore, I decided to regard the predictors as part of a quasi-
simplex (although strictly they were not), and asked: with which one

of the nine predictors did the criterion (the course grade) correlate most highly? With the sixth test in my simplex ranking, was what the Army testers told me. In that case, I said, I conjecture that the two next highest criterion correlations come from the tests to which I had assigned ranks five and seven, and the correlations taper off markedly for the other tests.

The Army testers looked at their data, and sure enough my conjecture was correct.

For predicting the criterion, then, I advised using only the multiple-regression on tests five, six, and seven, and to omit the other tests completely; this would give a more reliable prediction from the point of view of sampling error than would using the regression on all nine predictors.

Because of the relatively small size of the sample of these particular Israel Army data, and the fact that a typical simplex was not involved, I shall not present here the actual regressions computed for the external prediction problem. Instead, to illustrate external prediction, let us return to the verbal ability data of Table 5, which are based on a thousand cases. Besides these verbal ability tests, four others of different content were administered to the same sample: History, Fine Arts, General Science, and Mathematics. The correlations between these four tests and the six verbal ability tests are shown in Table 15.

Interestingly enough, these tests external to the verbal ability universe reveal a gradient in their relationship to this universe. History correlates most highly with Foreign Literature (.646), and its correlations decline systematically along the rank order, being lowest with Spelling. The same is true for Fine Arts. General Science, on the other hand, correlates best with Vocabulary; and its row of correlations shows a tapering off in both directions from Vocabulary. Mathematics does not correlate significantly with any of the verbal ability tests (although curiously its negligible correlations also reveal a peak at Vocabulary and a tapering off in both directions).

From the gradients in Table 15, we should guess that the law of formation of regression coefficients for predicting the external tests should be similar to that for internal prediction. And so it is. The multiple-regression weights for predicting each external test from the quasi-simplex of verbal ability are shown in Table 16.

The inverse matrix of the intercorrelations of the predictors is involved in external prediction, as well as in internal. If r_{jk} is

Table 15

The Correlations of Four External Tests With Six Verbal Ability Tests[24]

External Test	Verbal Ability Test					
	Spelling	Punctuation	Grammar	Vocabulary	Literature	Foreign Literature
History	.328	.339	.383	.546	.574	.646
Fine Arts	.344	.407	.426	.494	.541	.691
General Science	.044	.102	.159	.334	.202	.258
Mathematics	-.022	.014	.013	.030	.002	-.035

Table 16

The Multiple-Regression Weights for Predicting Each External Test in Table 15

External Test (Criterion)	Verbal Ability Test (Predictor)						Multiple-Correlation Coefficient
	Spelling	Punctuation	Grammar	Vocabulary	Literature	Foreign Literature	
History	.01	-.04	.04	.19	.16	.44	.694
Fine Arts	-.02	.06	.07	.07	.09	.55	.714
General Science	-.16	-.04	.03	.40	-.12	.18	.386
Mathematics	-.05	.04	.00	.08	-.00	-.08	.081

the correlation between predictors t_j and t_k, if r_{uj} is the correlation between criterion u with t_j, and if $w_{uj}^{(n)}$ is the weight for t_j for predicting u in the regression of u on n predictors (so that n + 1 variables are now involved all told), then

$$w_{uj}^{(n)} = r_{u1}r^{j1} + r_{u2}r^{j2} + \ldots + r_{un}r^{jn} \quad (j = 1,2, \ldots ,n),(28)$$

where r^{jk} is again the element in row j and column k of the inverse matrix of the r_{jk}. If the r_{jk} formed a perfect simplex, then all but some three consecutive terms in (28) would vanish for each j. In an ϵ-simplex, all but three consecutive terms would tend to vanish. If in addition, the r_{uj} have a gradient related to the ranking of the tests in the quasi-simplex, we get a law of formation for predicting such an outside variable u.

Table 16 was computed by using formula (28) on Table 15 and on the inverse matrix of Table 5. The multiple-correlation coefficients in the last column were computed by the formula

$$r_{u.123 \ldots n}^2 = r_{u1}w_{u1}^{(n)} + r_{u2}w_{u2}^{(n)} + \ldots + r_{un}w_{un}^{(n)}. \quad (29)$$

As expected from the gradients in Table 15, both History and Fine Arts get large weights on Foreign Literature (.44 and .55, respectively), and much smaller weights on all other predictors. Their multiple r's, in consequence, are not improved much over their respective simple correlations with Foreign Literature (.694 compared with .646, .714 compared with .691).

General Science correlated best with an intermediate test, Vocabulary, which also gets the most important regression weight. The remaining tests do not help much in the regression, and the multiple-correlation is .386 compared to .334 with Vocabulary alone.

Mathematics has no significant multiple-correlation here. It is helpful to consider its row in Table 16 to get an empirical idea of how large sampling error can be in regression weights when based even on 1000 cases. The Mathematics row in Table 16 should apparently ideally be all zeros, but weights as large as .08 appear in the sample.

IMPLICATIONS FOR PRACTICAL PREDICTION PROGRAMS

The implications of the simplex structure for practical prediction programs should now be obvious.

Suppose we wished to predict success on a certain job that required verbal ability among other things. What verbal ability test
or tests should we use? By relating the criterion to a sequence of
verbal ability tests of varied complexity, we can find which two or
three tests come closest to having the desired complexity. If these
do not provide a satisfactorily high prediction, we will nevertheless
have a clue as to how to go about making up new tests that will yield
a better prediction. The new tests should fall at a simplex rank order nearer to the complexity the criterion seems to require.

Similarly, if numerical ability is needed as a predictor, the two
or three tests from their simplex with the most appropriate complexity should be used. And so for prediction from any simplex.

One criterion may require one level of complexity, and another
criterion may require another level. We have seen how Fine Arts
is best predicted from the level of verbal ability that Foreign Literature represents, while General Science is best predicted from the
lower level of Vocabulary.

We should emphasize again that it is levels of complexity involved here, and not levels of difficulty. Changing tests internally
by eliminating or adding items will not affect the prediction process
we are describing, especially if each test is an approximate scale.

Traditional item analysis techniques for external prediction
can be seen to be beside the point when the predictors form a simplex. Item analysis would try to assemble those items from all the
tests that individually "discriminate" best. But this need not at all
yield the best prediction composite. If each test is an approximate
scale, and all the scales form an approximate simplex, then we know
how to use this structural information to yield maximum predictability with minimum effort. Two or three tests of the most appropriate level of complexity can yield almost as good predictability as
would infinitely many possible tests from the universe of content;
and within each of these two or three scalable tests, only a relatively
small number of items need be used, chosen to give the shape of distribution of test scores most appropriate for the given prediction
problem.

Using but a very small number of tests as predictors has the
further advantage in practice of minimizing the sampling error resulting from using a previously computed regression in a new sample. This problem of using in a new sample a regression based on

an earlier sample (where the criterion was already known so that
the regression could be computed) has not yet attracted all the attention it deserves. It does not yet seem widely known that a sample correlation coefficient may sometimes be significantly different
from zero, but the resulting regression equation worse than useless
for a new random sample from the same population.

In an experiment I conducted some years ago[25], I computed a
multiple regression of a criterion on 63 predictors for a sample of
136 cases. The multiple-correlation coefficient turned out to be
.73. Using this regression on a strictly comparable sample (the
two samples were actually obtained by dividing a larger sample into two random halves), the new correlation between criterion and
predictions (using the old sample weights) was .04, or virtually
zero. Using simple arbitrary weights – the same weights in both
samples – yielded a stable correlation of about .25.

The random sampling error in multiple-regression weights can
be too considerable for use in a new sample. And use in a new sample is the realistic problem. This dangerous sampling error can be
minimized to some extent by using as few predictors as possible
that will still yield high predictability. The simplex structure is
fortunately of the type that permits just such a minimization of sampling error.

FURTHER TYPES OF QUASI-SIMPLEXES [26]

The time has come for us to return to certain theoretical matters, so that we can ultimately tie up our new approach with the
previous one of common-factors.

We have thus far discussed a quasi-simplex rather vaguely as
a perfect simplex plus deviations. The only concrete definition we
have offered to this point has been that of an ε-simplex, pivoting
only on what happens in the limit as the number of tests increases.
It is of interest, however, to consider also types of quasi-simplexes
where certain definite properties hold for any finite number of tests
from the universe. To this end, we shall now define four more types
of quasi-simplexes in mathematical terms. They differ among themselves with respect to their laws of deviation from a perfect simplex.

Given any tests t_j which come from a universe which is a quasi-
simplex, we assume each observed score can be expressed as the
sum of two components: a score on an underlying perfect simplex,
and a deviation score. Let s_{ji} be the underlying perfect simplex
score for person i on test t_j, and let e_{ji} be the deviation score for

that person on that test. Then

$$t_{ji} = s_{ji} + e_{ji} \; . \tag{30}$$

That the variables s_j form a perfect simplex, we shall state by the formula – following (20) –

$$r_{s_j s_k} = \frac{a_j}{a_k} \quad (j \leq k) \tag{31}$$

where a_j is some parameter belonging to test t_j .
By an α-simplex (alpha-simplex) we shall mean the type of quasi-simplex for which the law of deviation is as follows:

$$r_{e_j t_k} = 0 \quad (j \neq k) \; . \tag{32}$$

The law (32) states that the deviation part of the test t_j is uncorrelated with the observed scores on any other test.
By a β-simplex (beta-simplex) we shall mean a quasi-simplex with the following law of deviation:

$$r_{e_j s_k} = 0 \quad (j,k = 1,2, \ldots) \; . \tag{33}$$

Here a deviation is uncorrelated with the underlying perfect simplex rather than with the original observations on other tests in the simplex.
For a γ-simplex (gamma-simplex), the law of deviation is:

$$r_{e_j e_k} = 0 \quad (j \neq k) \; , \tag{34}$$

or the deviations are uncorrelated with each other.
By a δ-simplex (delta-simplex) we shall mean a quasi-simplex in which all three laws (32), (33), and (34) hold simultaneously[27].

Another useful concept for quasi-simplexes is one I propose for any kind of structural analysis, namely that of *determinateness*. A quasi-simplex will be said to be determinate if and only if the underlying perfect simplex can be estimated exactly in the limit as the number of observed variables increases. That is, if $r_{s_j.12 \ldots n}$ is the multiple-correlation coefficient of s_j on some n observed t_k, then the simplex structure will be said to be determinate if and only if there exists a sequence of tests in the simplex such that

$$\lim_{n \to \infty} r_{s_j.12 \ldots n} = 1 \quad (j = 1, 2, \ldots) . \tag{35}$$

The sequence of predictors can be different for each s_j. The implication of determinateness is that, by increasing the number of tests, we can get more and more closely at the actual scores on the underlying perfect simplex.

If we now consider the meaning of a determinate α-simplex, we see it has a most familiar characteristic. Suppose we were to predict t_j from $n-1$ other tests. Then t_j would be broken into two parts; its predicted values and its errors of prediction. According to the normal equations of least-squares, the errors are uncorrelated with each predictor separately, or (32) holds. But then the predicted part is always determinate, being by definition a perfect linear function of the predictors, or (35) holds. Thus, in a determinate α-simplex, the perfect simplex part is what I have termed elsewhere the total image space.[28]

The δ-simplex is a special case of each of the α-, β-, and γ-types separately, since it involves the laws of all three. The relationships of types α through δ to the ϵ-simplex we shall have to discuss on another occasion. For our present purposes, it is relevant to take a closer look only at the δ-simplex, since its law of deviation coincides with that of the earlier common-factor theories of Spearman, Thurstone, et al. This we do after some further preliminaries that now follow.

EXPANSION OF A SIMPLEX INTO COMMON-FACTORS

We have now arrived at a stage where we can, in part, relate mathematically our new theory of order-factors with the previous approach of common-factors. If we are given n tests from a quasi-simplex, let us express the s_{ji} in (30) as the sum of n orthogonal or uncorrelated common-factors in the following manner. Let c_{pi} be score of person i on the pth common-factor, and let

$$s_{ji} = c_{1i} + c_{2i} + \ldots + c_{ji} \quad (j = 1, 2, \ldots, n). \tag{36}$$

According to (36), the perfect part of t_j is the sum of the first j common-factors. Each succeeding test in the rank order involves one more common-factor than the preceding one. It may be help-ful to write this in more expanded notation, which we now do for the full expansion of the observed tests according to (30) and (36):

$$
\begin{aligned}
t_{1i} &= c_{1i} && + e_{1i} \\
t_{2i} &= c_{1i} + c_{2i} && + e_{2i} \\
t_{3i} &= c_{1i} + c_{2i} + c_{3i} && + e_{3i} \\
&\cdots \cdots \cdots \cdots \cdots \cdots \cdots \\
t_{n-1,i} &= c_{1i} + c_{2i} + c_{3i} + \ldots + c_{n-1,i} + e_{n-1,i} \\
t_{ni} &= c_{1i} + c_{2i} + c_{3i} + \ldots + c_{ni} && + e_{ni}
\end{aligned} \tag{37}
$$

In (37) we shall not assume that the t_j are in standard form but only that the means are zero. The c_p and the e_j are each also assumed to have zero means. The variances we need will be de-noted by

$$\sigma^2_{t_j}, \ \sigma^2_{s_j}, \ \sigma^2_{c_p}, \ \sigma^2_{e_j} \quad (j, p = 1, 2, \ldots, n).$$

We assume uncorrelated common-factors:

$$r_{c_p c_q} = 0 \quad (p \neq q). \tag{38}$$

From (36) and (38) it follows that[29]

$$\sigma^2_{s_j} = \sigma^2_{c_1} + \sigma^2_{c_2} + \ldots + \sigma^2_{c_j}. \tag{39}$$

According to (39), the variance of the simplex part of a test increases with the rank j of the test.

To prove that (37) can possibly define a quasi-simplex, we prove that (36) defines a perfect simplex. For this, we first deduce from (36) and (38) that the covariance between any two s_j and s_k is simply the variance of the earlier of the two variables in the rank order:

$$\text{cov}(s_j, s_k) = \sigma^2_{s_j} \quad (j \leq k). \tag{40}$$

Therefore, the simple correlation between s_j and s_k is

$$r_{s_j s_k} = \frac{\sigma^2_{s_j}}{\sigma_{s_j} \sigma_{s_k}} = \frac{\sigma_{s_j}}{\sigma_{s_k}} \quad (j \leq k). \tag{41}$$

But the last member is precisely of the form of (31), setting $\sigma_{s_j} = a_j$. Therefore the s_j as defined by (36) and (38) do form a perfect simplex, and the resulting (37) can be a quasi-simplex of which the s_j are the perfect part.

The proof just given does not establish that (37) is necessarily a quasi-simplex. That depends on the law of deviations of the e_j. Any n variables can be written in the form (37) and satisfy (41) if no restrictions are laid on the deviations e_j. A definition of a quasi-simplex is incomplete if it does not specify some restrictive law of deviation; otherwise the notion becomes trivial.

THE δ-SIMPLEX AND COMMON-FACTOR THEORY

The law of deviation for the δ-simplex is of special theoretical interest to us here, since it is the same as the law of deviations for the previous common-factor theories of Spearman, Thurstone, and others. In these earlier theories a unique-factor – including specific-factors – correlates zero with: (a) all tests except the one including it, (b) all common-factors – be they orthogonal or oblique, and (c) all other unique-factors. These three conditions are the same as (32), (33), and (34) above.

Therefore, a δ-simplex expressed in the form (37) can be regarded as a common-factor structure with n - 1 common-factors.

The common-factors are the first $n-1$ c_j since each of these occur in at least two tests, and hence actually are "common" to more than one test. The unique-factor for the last test is the sum $c_n + e_n$, for c_n belongs specifically to t_n. In a sense, then, the δ-simplex is a special case of Spearman-Thurstone common-factor theory.

In another and most important sense, the δ- simplex differs radically from the Spearman-Thurstone approach. This can be seen by asking: What happens as the number of tests increases? In the Spearman-Thurstone approach, if m is the total number of common-factors for the entire universe of content, then if $n > m$ tests are selected from the universe, the communalities of each of the n tests is theoretically fixed. Nothing happens to the common-factor structure of the n tests as more are added to them from the universe.

Not so for the expansion (37), with its implied simple order of complexity for the entire universe from which the n tests were drawn. If we assume a continuous ranking exists for the infinitely many tests in the universe, then between any two tests of different rank we can insert a third test of intermediate rank. For example, let us select another test t^* from the universe whose rank is between those of the tests t_2 and t_3 in (37). That is, if $t^* = s^* + e^*$, where s^* is the perfect simplex part of t^*, then s^* is intermediate to s_2 and s_3.

How can we express s^* in terms of the common-factors c_p of (36) and (37)? s^* must contain what s_2 does, and more, but less than s_3. Therefore, it must be that c_3 is divisible into two parts, say c_3^* and c_3^{**}, so that $c_3 = c_3^* + c_3^{**}$, and

$$s_i^* = c_{1i} + c_{2i} + c_{3i}^* . \tag{42}$$

Similarly, if we insert a new test between any two previous tests, it must divide one of the common-factors in two. Each new test implies one more common-factor.

Conversely, if we omit a test, then two of the previous common-factors are no longer distinguishable, and can be regarded as but one common-factor. For example, if we omit t_3 in (37), then c_3 and c_4 are no longer distinguishable from each other, and their sum can be treated as but one common-factor.

It is the property of separability of common-factors that distinguishes order-theory from previous common-factor theory. It is this property that gives us in general as many discernible c_p in

(36) as there are tests, so that a perfect simplex matrix is in general nonsingular (and has an inverse). For an infinite universe, a nonsingular simplex has an infinite number of common-factors. The notion of a parsimonious number m of ordinary common-factor theory is completely irrelevant here. *A simplex has a parsimonious structural representation even though it may be of infinite rank in the common-factor sense.*

The common-factor "pattern" of (36) and (37) superficially resembles that obtained by what Thurstone calls the "diagonal" method for factoring a correlation matrix, or what is better known to mathematicians as Schmidt's process of orthogonalization. It should be noted, however, that (37) implies a restrictive law on the factor loadings. We have not assumed that any of the variables in (37) are in standard form, but only that all means are zero. If we inquire into the pattern of correlations of the t_j with the c_p, or of the common factor loadings, it is as follows:

$$
\begin{array}{llll}
\dfrac{\sigma_{c_1}}{\sigma_{t_1}} & & & \\[2ex]
\dfrac{\sigma_{c_1}}{\sigma_{t_2}} & \dfrac{\sigma_{c_2}}{\sigma_{t_2}} & & \\[2ex]
\dfrac{\sigma_{c_1}}{\sigma_{t_3}} & \dfrac{\sigma_{c_2}}{\sigma_{t_3}} & \dfrac{\sigma_{c_3}}{\sigma_{t_3}} & \\[2ex]
\cdots\cdots\cdots\cdots\cdots\cdots\cdots\cdots & & & \\[2ex]
\dfrac{\sigma_{c_1}}{\sigma_{t_n}} & \dfrac{\sigma_{c_2}}{\sigma_{t_n}} & \dfrac{\sigma_{c_3}}{\sigma_{t_n}} \quad \cdots & \dfrac{\sigma_{c_n}}{\sigma_{t_n}}
\end{array}
\tag{42}
$$

or

$$
r_{t_j c_p} = \begin{cases} \sigma_{c_p}/\sigma_{t_j} & p \le j \\ 0 & p > j. \end{cases}
\tag{43}
$$

Column p in (42) is proportional to σ_{c_p}, and row j in (42) is inversely proportional to σ_{t_j}.

The pattern (42) therefore is highly restrictive, and cannot be obtained for an arbitrary correlation matrix by the diagonal method. Indeed, all tetrad-differences in (42) vanish that do not involve a main diagonal element.

AN ALTERNATIVE EXPANSION OF A SIMPLEX

Perhaps a more striking way of showing the difference between order-theory and common-factor theory is by exhibiting an alternative expansion of the simplex. Why should we restrict ourselves to an additive system of the c_p in (36) and (37)? Consider the following alternative system.

Let u be a variable with a zero mean and that is statistically independent of the c_p. The c_p will be assumed now all to have nonzero means. That is, if $\bar{c}_p$ is the mean of c_p then $\bar{c}_p \neq 0$ $(p = 1, 2, \ldots, n)$. Assume further that all the c_p are completely statistically independent of each other (not merely uncorrelated). Let γ_p^2 denote the mean of squares of c_p.

Now, let

$$s_{ji} = u_i c_{1i} c_{2i} \cdots c_{ji} \quad (j = 1, 2, \ldots, n). \tag{44}$$

Here, s_j involves the product of the c_j, instead of the sum as in (36).

Since all variables on the right of (44) are completely mutually statistically independent, the mean of their product is the product of their means, and must vanish since the mean of u is zero. Hence, the mean of each s_j is zero. Therefore, the covariance between s_j and s_k is simply the mean of the products $s_{ji} s_{ki}$. From (44) and the notation just defined, we have

$$\text{cov}(s_j, s_k) = \sigma_u^2 \gamma_1^2 \gamma_2^2 \cdots \gamma_j^2 \bar{c}_{j+1} \bar{c}_{j+2} \cdots \bar{c}_k \quad (j \leq k), \tag{45}$$

and in particular

$$\sigma_{s_j}^2 = \sigma_u^2 \gamma_1^2 \gamma_2^2 \cdots \gamma_j^2 \quad (j = 1, 2, \ldots, n). \tag{46}$$

Therefore,

$$r_{s_j s_k} = \frac{\text{cov}(s_j, s_k)}{\sigma_{s_j}\, \sigma_{s_k}} = \frac{\overline{c}_{j+1}\overline{c}_{j+2}\cdots \overline{c}_k}{\gamma_{j+1}\gamma_{j+2}\cdots \gamma_k} \quad (j < k). \tag{47}$$

If we define

$$a_j = \frac{\gamma_1 \gamma_2 \cdots \gamma_j}{\overline{c}_1 \overline{c}_2 \cdots \overline{c}_j} \quad (j = 1, 2, \ldots, n), \tag{48}$$

then (47) becomes

$$r_{s_j s_k} = \frac{a_j}{a_k} \quad (j \le k). \tag{49}$$

But this is identical with (20). Hence, the s_j defined by (44) form a perfect simplex.

Thus we see a profound truth regarding our elementary component expansion into common-factors. The fact that a correlation matrix is of the form (20) is of no help in trying to ascertain a unique form for an underlying common-factor system. An additive system like (36) and a multiplicative system like (44) yield exactly the same answer.

Unless it be proved otherwise, there may be even other types of functional forms than additive or multiplicative that may yield the same (20).

This indeterminacy of functional form is a more profound type of indeterminacy than that of rotation of axes of common-factor theory. There, the choice is between different additive systems. Here, the question is open as to whether the system is additive in the first place.

The hopes that common-factor theory might ultimately help in external prediction problems (like vocational guidance) have been based on the hypothesis that a particularly useful rotation of axes might be found that would identify additive common-factors that might be fundamental to prediction. Actually, there is no real general theory of prediction at present for common-factor structures.

In contrast, the predictive properties of a simplex do not at all depend upon how the order-factor is resolved into common-factors. The same matrix form (20) or (49), holds for the perfect part, regardless of what the underlying resolution may be. The inverse matrix depends only on the correlation coefficients, and the nature of this dependence is the same whether the additive scheme (36) or the multiplicative scheme (44), or some other scheme holds. It is the inverse matrix that governs the prediction problem, so we can have a complete theory of prediction for a simplex without any deep knowledge of its elementary components. All we need is the law of formation of the observed correlation coefficients, and this we have by virtue of the order-theory involved.

It is one of the striking properties of an ordered system that it lends itself to useful prediction purposes despite the lack of basic knowledge as to *why* the order exists. Insofar as common-factor theory is orderless, it cannot lend itself well to prediction purposes until its basic problems of factor identification are solved. Not so for the simplex, circumplex, and the radex. Knowledge of their general order features alone is quite adequate for many theoretical and practical purposes.

SPEARMAN'S CASE AS A DEGENERATE δ-SIMPLEX

Let us again look at the δ-simplex, using for convenience additive expansion as in (37). We now wish to show how Spearman's single-common-factor theory can be regarded as a special case of the δ-simplex.

According to the laws of deviations (33) and (34), we derive from (37) that

$$\text{cov}(t_j, t_k) = \text{cov}(s_j, s_k) \quad (j \neq k). \tag{50}$$

Hence, the simple correlation between two observed tests is, from (50) and (40):

$$r_{jk} = \frac{\sigma_{s_j}^2}{\sigma_{t_j} \sigma_{t_k}} \quad (j < k). \tag{51}$$

Equation (51) does not hold in general for $j = k$; in this case, the left member is the self-correlation of unity, while the right member is only the communality of t_j.

Let A be an arbitrary constant, and let

$$a_j = A \frac{\sigma_{s_j}^2}{\sigma_{t_j}}, \quad b_j = \frac{1}{A\sigma_{t_j}} \quad (j = 1, 2, \ldots, n). \tag{52}$$

Then a_j and b_j are two parameters belonging to t_j, and (51) can be written

$$r_{jk} = a_j b_k, \quad (j < k). \tag{53}$$

In (52), a_j and b_j were defined only up to a constant of proportionality, but (53) does not at all depend on this constant.

Equation (53) can be regarded as a generalization of equation (20). If $b_j = a_j^{-1}$, then (53) reduces to (20). In this case, according to (52), $\sigma_{s_j}^2 = \sigma_{t_j}^2$, or $\sigma_{e_j}^2 \equiv 0$ in (30), and we have a perfect simplex.

Another interesting special case of (53) turns out to be our old friend, Spearman's single-common-factor structure. For if $b_j = a_j$, then (53) becomes of the same form as (3), with $a_j = r_{jc}$. Also, (53) then becomes symmetric in j and k, so the order restriction $j < k$ no longer holds.

If $a_j = b_j$, then from (52) we have

$$\sigma_{s_j}^2 = \frac{1}{A^2} \quad (j = 1, 2, \ldots, n), \tag{54}$$

of the total common-factor variance for each test is constant. From (39), this means that $\sigma_{c_p}^2 = 0$ for $p = 2, 3, \ldots, n$, or only one common-factor can be present. Equations (37) reduce to Spearman's equations[30]

$$t_{ji} = c_{1i} + e_{ji} \quad (j = 1, 2, \ldots, n). \tag{55}$$

The simplex, then, provides a framework which includes Spearman's original theory as a special case. According to (52), if we choose A so that $0 < A \leq 1$, then we see that

$$a_j \leq b_j \leq \frac{1}{a_j} \quad (0 < A \leq 1). \tag{56}$$

If the equality sign holds on the left for all j, we have Spearman's correlation matrix according to (53). If the equality holds on the right for all j, we have a perfect simplex correlation matrix from (49). Intermediate values of b_j give us different δ-simplexes from these two extremes. Thus conditions (3) and (13), which initially looked like belonging to two entirely different theories, actually are but the opposite extremes of the same theory of the δ-simplex.

ORDER OF COMPLEXITY VERSUS
ORDER OF SATURATION

We can now regard Spearman's case as that of a degenerate δ-simplex wherein all tests have the same complexity. We have $s_{ji} \equiv c_{1i}$, or there is no change in the s_j from test to test: $s_{ji} \equiv s_{ki}$ for all j and k. Why then does Spearman's case reveal a hierarchy as in Table 1?

The answer is that Spearman's hierarchy is not based on order of complexity – it has none – but on the relative sizes of the communalities, or the saturations with the single-common-factor. Formula (3) is symmetric in j and k, and so implies no order among the tests. But we nevertheless arranged the tests in Table 1 in order according to the sizes of their common-factor loadings.

The implications of this kind of order can be seen from the multiple-regression weights that result from Table 1 for predicting the tests from each other. These are shown in Table 17.

Table 17

The Multiple-Regression Weights for Predicting Each Test
from the Remaining Four Tests in the Hypothetical
Single-Common-Factor Structure of Table 1

| Criterion | Predictor | | | | | Multiple-Correlation Coefficient |
	t_1	t_2	t_3	t_4	t_5	
t_1	--	.51	.25	.12	.04	.688
t_2	.58	--	.08	.04	.01	.636
t_3	.37	.11	--	.03	.01	.459
t_4	.22	.06	.03	--	.00	.276
t_5	.07	.02	.01	.00	--	.092

In each row of Table 17, the largest weight is always the one farthest to the left. t_1 bears the brunt of the prediction in every regression involving it, and the multiple-correlation coefficients of the remaining tests are not much more than their simple correlations with t_1 alone in Table 1. The reason for this is that their multiple-correlations cannot exceed their respective correlations with the single common-factor[31] and t_1 already correlates .9 with this common-factor.

To improve predictability here, then, one should seek tests even closer to the common-factor than t_1. Adding other tests from the same structure will not help much if they are chosen to have loadings similar to that of the criterion test. It is not closeness of ranks of predictors to the rank of the criterion that counts here, but closeness to the common-factor.

If one goes on to multiple-common factors and inquires what happens to the inverse matrix and multiple-regression weights, one again sees why the general m-common-factor theory is orderless. There is no longer a uniquely defined single-common-factor to get closer to, but all kinds of rotations of axes are possible. It has been shown that under certain general conditions, if m remains finite while n increases, then *all* multiple-regression weights tend to zero.[32] It doesn't make much difference what tests are used to predict the criterion under such circumstances. Again the communality is an upper bound to the square of the multiple-correlation for any test. There is no general rule for the general case of m-common-factors telling how to choose a small number of tests that will enable predictability that is close to the maximum allowed by the criterion's communality.

THE PRINCIPAL COMPONENTS OF A PERFECT SIMPLEX[33]

A theory of elementary components led us to deduce the perfect simplex law that $r_{jk} = a_j/a_k (j \leq k)$. The elementary theory involved only a single order-component g, which could also be expressed as a set of additive or of multiplicative elementary components.

Given the simplex structure, we can now inquire into its principal components. Any structure has principal components, but usually with no particular law of formation nor psychological meaning. Principal components have rightly been criticized by many psychologists as being meaningless if used automatically for any set of data.

Mathematically, principal components can always be computed for any set of intercorrelated variables. One basis for their derivation is as follows. Consider n tests t_j, with t_{ji} as the score of person i on test t_j. The mean over i will be assumed zero for each test. Let w_j $(j = 1, 2, \ldots, n)$ be a set of weights to be determined, and let

$$x_i = w_1 t_{1i} + w_2 t_{2i} + w_n t_{ni} . \tag{57}$$

Thus, x_i is the score of person i on a new variable x which is a linear function of the original tests. Let y_j be the correlation of x with t_j:

$$y_j = r_{xt_j}, \tag{58}$$

and let 2λ be the sum of squares of the y_j:

$$2\lambda = \sum_{j=1}^{n} y_j^2 . \tag{59}$$

If we seek that set of weights w_j which yields the variable x which maximizes λ, we are led to the equations for the principal components of the t_j. It turns out that one can solve for the maximized correlations y_j directly without solving explicitly for the weights w_j. These y_j satisfy the following equations:

$$\sum_{j=1}^{n} y_j r_{jk} = \lambda y_k \quad (k = 1, 2, \ldots, n). \tag{60}$$

Those familiar with matrix algebra will realize that the values y_j satisfying (60) form a latent vector of Gramian matrix $||r_{jk}||$, associated with latent root λ. There are n solutions λ to (60), and associated with each is a latent vector. The largest latent root provides the maximum for (59), and the smallest provides the minimum. The weights w_j in (57) for a given solution to (60) are computed by:

$$w_j = \frac{\sigma_x}{\sigma_{t_j}} y_j , \tag{61}$$

so the stationary weights w_j are closely related to the stationary correlations y_j.

Since there is more than one solution to (60), let us add another subscript to distinguish between solutions. Thus, let λ_p denote the pth latent root, y_{pj} the jth element of the pth latent vector, w_{pj} the weight derived according to (61) from the pth solution, and x_{pi} the score of person i on the pth solution x_p according to (57). Then it can be shown that always:

$$t_{ji} = y_{1j}x_{1i} + y_{2j}x_{2i} + \ldots + y_{nj}x_{ni} \quad \begin{pmatrix} i = 1, 2, \ldots \\ j = 1, 2, \ldots, n \end{pmatrix} \tag{62}$$

The x_p began as functions of the t_j in (57), but the t_j turn out in turn to be functions of the x_p according to (62). Hence, the x_p are components as well as functions of the tests. They are called principal components because of their stationary properties, yielding solutions from the maximum to the minimum of (59).

All this algebra holds, as stated, for any set of variables t_j, and need have no particular scientific meaning apart from its purely mathematical properties. However, let us see what happens in the special case where the t_j form a perfect simplex. We do not have space here for the mathematics, which will be published later, but only sketch some of the results.

Using equation (20) for the perfect simplex, (60) can be written as

$$\sum_{j=1}^{k} y_j \left(\frac{a_j}{a_k} \right) + \sum_{j=k+1}^{n} y_j \frac{a_k}{a_j} = \lambda y_k (k = 1, 2, \ldots, n). \tag{63}$$

Let z_j be defined as

$$z_j = a_j y_j \quad (j = 1, 2, \ldots, n). \tag{64}$$

Then (63) can be written also as:

$$\sum_{j=1}^{k} z_j + a_k^2 \sum_{j=k+1}^{n} a_j^{-2} z_j = \lambda z_k \quad (k = 1, 2, \ldots, n). \tag{65}$$

Differencing both members of (65) with respect to k, rearranging the terms, and differencing again, yields the following second-order difference equation in z_k:

$$\Delta \left[\left(a_{k+1}^2 - a_k^2 \right)^{-1} \Delta z_k \right] + \lambda^{-1} a_{k+1}^{-1} z_{k+1} = 0 \quad (k = 1, 2, \ldots, n-2). \quad (66)$$

Difference equation (66) is precisely of the same form as that arising for the principal components weights of a perfect scale of dichotomies.[34] The parameters involved have quite different meanings for the scale of qualitative data as for the present simplex of
quantitative variables. Also, the boundary conditions for the respective difference equations are different. The boundary conditions for (66) turn out to be, from (65):

$$\Delta a_1^{-2} z_1 = \lambda^{-1} \left(a_2^{-2} - a_1^{-2} \right) z_1 \quad (67)$$

$$\Delta z_{n-1} = \lambda^{-1} \left(1 - a_n^{-2} a_{n-1}^2 \right) z_n. \quad (68)$$

Despite the change in boundary conditions, the essential kind
of mathematical properties remain as were found for the scale of
dichotomies. If (66), (67), and (68) are reexpressed in terms of
the y_j instead of the z_j, then the coefficients of the y_j define a
Gramian matrix which is precisely the inverse matrix of (20).
That is, (66), (67) and (68) are equivalent to

$$\sum_{j=1}^n y_j r^{jk} = \lambda^{-1} y_k \, (k = 1, 2, \ldots, n), \quad (69)$$

where r^{jk} denotes again the element in row j and column k of
$\|r_{jk}\|^{-1}$. Thus, (69) is equivalent to a second-order difference
equation and its two boundary conditions. That is why all elements
r^{jk} are zero that are outside the three central diagonals, as in
Tables 10 and 11 above.

It was this and other comparable properties of the scale of
dichotomies that made me seek a structural theory for quantitative
variables with such features, and that is how I was led to the simplex originally.

Another property that holds is the *law of oscillations* for the
principal components. For the simplex, this law holds for the z_j
as defined by (64). Again, we need to distinguish among the n different solutions to (60) or (69), and will accordingly let z_{pj} be the
jth element in the pth solution, as obtained by (64) from y_{pj}. We

assume the λ_p arranged in order of magnitude so $\lambda_1 > \lambda_2 > \ldots$
$> \lambda_n$ (it is known they must be distinct if the a_j are distinct).
Then the z_{1j} have no sign changes; they are all positive, say. The
z_{2j} have one sign change, and have a monotone relation to j, say
z_{2j} increases monotonely with j, beginning with z_{21} negative and
ending with z_{2n} positive. The z_{3j} have two sign changes, and a U-
shaped relationship to j. In general, the $z_{p+1,j}$ have one more sign
change and one more bend in their relationship to j than do the
z_{pj}.

This law of oscillation is very similar to that which I described in the previous lecture, for the principal components of
scalable attitudes. An important difference must be emphasized.
There, I was discussing the *score* components, or what are equivalent to the x_{pi} of (57) in our present case. Here, I am treating
essentially the *weight* components w_{pj}, via the z_{pj}. For a perfect
scale of dichotomies, both score and weight principal components
enjoy laws of oscillation. But for the perfect simplex, in general
only the weight components have a law. From (20) alone, there
are no restrictions on the score components. Indeed, if the observed tests have a normal multivariate distribution, then the
score components x_{pi} are not merely uncorrelated with each other
linearly (as they must be for any structure, whether a simplex or
not) but are completely statistically independent of each other and
can have no further law of formation.[35] For quantitative variables,
we can expect to have laws only for weights and not for scores.
For qualitative data, laws both ways may be possible.

Let me repeat again that the present treatment of the simplex is for the case of multivariate linear regressions. Such a
structure does not hold for a scale of dichotomies. Therefore,
even though the simple point product-moment correlations of a
perfect scale of dichotomies always satisfy equation (20) above[36]
of the perfect simplex, the respective theories of elementary components are quite different for the two cases, as are also the respective theories of principal components, despite some close similarities in the latter.

What is the meaning here of the principal components of a
perfect simplex, as distinguished from that of elementary components? How does the resolution of the t_{ji} according to (62) differ
from that according to (36) or (44)? The answer must be post-
poned, apparently, until the principal components can be identified
directly. In the case of scalable attitudes of the previous lecture,
we saw how the principal components gave a new frame of reference for the data, but this became useful only after we could

identify and observe the components directly. The same may hold for the simplex of a universe of mental tests. It may be that in some sense the elementary components provide a "particle" theory for the data, whereas the principal components provide a "wave" theory; and both are necessary for a full comprehension of the observed phenomena.

In any event, it should be clear that the principal components of a simplex are not simply a particular "rotation of axes" from another system of components, as they would be regarded in previous theories of factor analysis. Indeed, such a notion of rotation holds only from an additive system like (36); it does not hold from a multiplicative system like (44).

I prefer to regard the principal components as a different level of analysis, rather than as a competitor on the same level as elementary components. There is no need to choose between the two in simplex theory, as there is in previous common-factor theory. The principal components have special properties in their own right for the perfect simplex, which are of basic importance to the structure. Indeed, through them we learned the nature of the inverse of the observed correlation matrix, and the consequent compact powers of prediction of the simplex.

The elementary components will be found ultimately, I believe, to refer to neurons when the data are of mental abilities. It was thinking in terms of elementary components that led to the theories of the circumplex and the radex.

Before going on to the circumplex, may I add a word about data other than from mental tests. One field where I believe the new order-theories will be found useful is that of time-series. If an autocorrelation matrix has the simplex structure, then its principal components will give an automatic Fourier analysis of the series – *but without need for preliminary specification of the type of orthogonal functions involved.* Instead of fitting arbitrary oscillating orthogonal functions to the data as is conventional, the research worker can let the data themselves determine the orthogonal series implicit in themselves. The same will hold for the circumplex.

THE CIRCUMPLEX

We have seen how verbal ability tests can form a simplex among themselves. We have also seen how numerical ability tests can form a simplex among themselves. As further areas of content are studied along these lines, we can possibly find that geometrical visualization, types of mechanical abilities, various musical abilities, etc., each form simplexes by themselves.

Then we shall be in the position to ask: What is the struc- ture of the interrelationships among different simplexes? One possible structural theory is what I call that of a circumplex. Let us examine this concept.

For simplicity, let us first consider that only one test is taken from each simplex, and let us consider a set of n simplexes. Thus we again have a set of n tests before us. But this time each is from a different universe of content. These different universes of content, however, all belong to the same superuniverse. For our ability tests, the superuniverse is that of mental abilities, and each universe that yielded a simplex is of a different type of mental ability. The superuniverse must be defined before one begins, just as the subuniverses must be defined before any statis- tical analysis is initiated. Otherwise a structural analysis will not be very meaningful, as one won't know what total structure is being referred to, and won't know how to sample the superuniverse.

Within a simplex, we can speak of one test being more com- plex than another. But how about comparing tests *between* simplexes?

Is a numerical ability less or more complex than some ver- bal ability? Than some musical ability? I suggest that such com- parisons in general will not be meaningful, until a theory for com- paring content is developed. As a structural hypothesis for inter- relations of different kinds of tests, I suggest again a theory of order, but this time not of degree of complexity. The new hypoth- esis is that the different kinds of abilities should have an order among themselves, but not of such a nature that there is a ranking from highest to lowest.

Is it possible to have an ordering without a head and foot to it? Yes, quite simply, by having it *circular*. Then the order has neither beginning nor end. All variables have an equal rank, but still there is a law of neighboring that holds. A system of vari- ables which has a circular law of order is a circumplex.

The law of rank order of the simplex and the circular order law of the circumplex seem the simplest possible. In developing new theories, it seems well to explore thoroughly the simplest possibilities before going on to more complicated ones, for to complications there is no end.

THE UNIFORM, PERFECT, ADDITIVE CIRCUMPLEX

To fix ideas, let us start with a very specialized example of a circumplex. We shall state its structure initially in terms of an additive elementary component system, and use a conventional diagrammatic scheme to portray it.

Suppose we have five tests t_1, t_2, t_3, t_4, and t_5 which have a circular order determined by five elementary components c_1, c_2, c_3, c_4, and c_5. We shall call a circumplex *uniform* if each test is a function of an equal number of the n elementary components. If our $n = 5$ tests form a uniform circumplex with $m = 3$, and if the components are additive, the structure in terms of components can be written as follows:

$$
\begin{aligned}
t_{1i} &= c_{1i} + c_{2i} + c_{3i} \\
t_{2i} &= \phantom{c_{1i} + {}} c_{2i} + c_{3i} + c_{4i} \\
t_{3i} &= \phantom{c_{1i} + c_{2i} + {}} c_{3i} + c_{4i} + c_{5i} \\
t_{4i} &= c_{1i} \phantom{+ c_{2i} + c_{3i} + {}} + c_{4i} + c_{5i} \\
t_{5i} &= c_{1i} + c_{2i} \phantom{+ c_{3i} + c_{4i} + {}} + c_{5i}
\end{aligned}
\tag{70}
$$

Clearly, it is arbitrary where we begin to number the tests and the components. We could just as well write (70) as, say,

$$
\begin{aligned}
t_{3i} &= c_{3i} + c_{4i} + c_{5i} \\
t_{4i} &= \phantom{c_{3i} + {}} c_{4i} + c_{5i} + c_{1i} \\
t_{5i} &= \phantom{c_{3i} + c_{4i} + {}} c_{5i} + c_{1i} + c_{2i} \\
t_{1i} &= c_{3i} \phantom{+ c_{4i} + c_{5i} + {}} + c_{1i} + c_{2i} \\
t_{2i} &= c_{3i} + c_{4i} \phantom{+ c_{5i} + {}} + c_{2i} \, .
\end{aligned}
\tag{71}
$$

The sets of equations (70) and (71) are identical, but (70) gives the appearance that t_1 and c_1 are the first test and component respectively, while (71) makes t_3 and c_3 appear first. The assigning of subscripts is arbitrary, as long as the circular order is maintained, with subscript 1 following subscript n. In general, for a uniform circumplex we can write

$$
t_{ji} = \begin{cases}
c_{ji} + c_{j+1,i} + \ldots + c_{j+m-1,i} & (j \leq n - m + 1) \\[2mm]
(c_{1i} + c_{2i} + \ldots + c_{j-n+m-1,i} + (c_{ji} + \ldots + c_{ni}) & (j > n - m + 1)
\end{cases}
\tag{72}
$$

One way to visualize this circular order is as in Figure 1. Figure 1a shows the five elementary components schematically as segments of a circle. Figure 1b shows t_1 and t_4 as embracing

Figure 1

A Hypothetical Uniform Circumplex

a. The Sectors   b. Two Tests

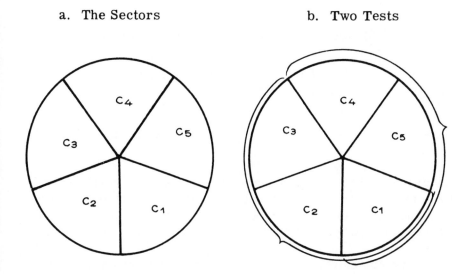

their three respective components; these two tests have c_1 in common. Similarly, the remaining tests can be indicated in Figure 1b, each comprising its three consecutive elementary components.

THE EQUALLY-SPACED, UNIFORM, PERFECT,
ADDITIVE CIRCUMPLEX

In order to see what the observed intertest correlations r_{jk} should be like if the structure is that of a uniform, additive circumplex, we can calculate them from (72). We again assume all elementary components to be uncorrelated, or

$$r_{c_p c_q} = 0 \quad (p \neq q). \tag{73}$$

The most important features will be revealed if we restrict ourselves to the special case where all elementary components have
equal variance, say σ^2:

$$\sigma^2_{c_1} = \sigma^2_{c_2} = \ldots = \sigma^2_{c_n} = \sigma^2, \qquad (74)$$

and where

$$m \geq n/2 . \qquad (75)$$

If (74) and (75) hold, then it can be seen from (72) that

$$r_{jk} = \begin{cases} 1 - \dfrac{k-j}{m} & 0 \leq k-j < n-m \\[4mm] 1 - \dfrac{n-k+j}{m} & n-m \leq k-j < n. \end{cases} \qquad (76)$$

The proviso (75) is to limit the number of zero correlations between tests. If m were less than $n/2$, then $r_{jk} = 0$ if $k-j > m$
(modulus n). Since a large bloc of zero correlations is not to be
expected in practice, the more interesting case for us is when (75)
holds.

As a numerical example of (76), consider the case where
$n = 6$ and $m = 4$. Then (76) can be expressed as in the following
Table 18.

The fact that the circumplex in Table 18 is perfect is shown
by the values of unity in the main diagonal. The total self-correlation of each test is completely accounted for, and (76) holds for
$j = k$ as well as for $j < k$. That the circumplex is equally-spaced
is indicated by the equality of values along each diagonal parallel
to the main diagonal. The correlation of test t_j with test t_{j+a},
where a is any positive or negative integer, is the same as for
t_k with t_{k+a}, with the convention that $k+a = k+a-n$ if $k+a > n$.

If we add the totals in each column of the table, we find them
all equal for this equally-spaced case. Each row of the table has
the same entries as the preceding row, but moved, one space to
the right, the end one moving to the beginning. Technically, such
a matrix is called a *circulant*. The particular circulant defined by
(76) is symmetric.

Table 18

The Intercorrelations for an Equally-Spaced, Uniform,
Perfect, Additive Circumplex
When n = 6 and m = 4

Test	t_1	t_2	t_3	t_4	t_5	t_6
t_1	1.00	.75	.50	.25	.50	.75
t_2	.75	1.00	.75	.50	.25	.50
t_3	.50	.75	1.00	.75	.50	.25
t_4	.25	.50	.75	1.00	.75	.50
t_5	.50	.25	.50	.75	1.00	.75
t_6	.75	.50	.25	.50	.75	1.00
Total	3.75	3.75	3.75	3.75	3.75	3.75

If the circumplex is not equally-spaced, then the column totals of the correlations need not be equal. The correlation matrix is then no longer a circulant. There will be a tendency for the largest correlations to be next to the main diagonal and in the upper-right and lower-left corners, as in Table 18, but this will only be a tendency and not a strict rule. Unequal spacing occurs in an additive, uniform circumplex whenever any two $\sigma_{c_p}^2$ are unequal.

A quasi-circumplex can be defined, analogously to a quasi-simplex, as a perfect circumplex plus deviations. Different laws of deviations give rise to different types of quasi-circumplexes, just as they do for quasi-simplexes.

EMPIRICAL EVIDENCE AS TO A CIRCUMPLEX
OF VARIOUS MENTAL ABILITIES

Consider the pattern of the correlation coefficients between the six tests in the following Table 19. There is an unmistakable trend for the largest correlations to be next to the main diagonal, to taper off as they depart from the diagonal, and then to increase again at the northeast and southwest corners.

Table 19

Intercorrelations Among Tests of Six Different Kinds of
Abilities for 710 Chicago Schoolchildren[37]

Test	Association	Incomplete Words	Multiplication	Dot Patterns	ABC	Directions
	6	32	37	17	1	12
6	1.	.446	.321	.213	.234	.442
32	.446	1.	.388	.313	.208	.330
37	.321	.388	1.	.396	.325	.328
17	.213	.313	.396	1.	.352	.247
1	.234	.208	.325	.352	1.	.347
12	.442	.330	.328	.247	.347	1.

The first test (Association) has two immediate neighbors, namely the second (Incomplete Words) and the last (Directions). There really is no "first" or "last" test here, for any rotation of the order of the tests would leave the same pattern of neighboring. Table 19 reveals the same general kind of gradient as does Table 18.

Of course, Table 19 differs from hypothetical Table 18 in that it represents neither a perfect circumplex nor an equally-spaced one. An idea as to the nature of the quasi-circumplex involved here empirically is given by the pattern of the multiple-regression weights for predicting each test from the remaining five. These weights and the corresponding multiple-correlation coefficients are shown in Table 20. The pattern is again that to be expected from a quasi-circumplex. Neighbors get the relatively large positive weights, and nonneighbors get weights that are closer to zero. Unlike in the quasi-simplex, the "first" and "last" tests here have two neighbors. It so happens that the multiple-correlation coefficients are all very similar. This indicates that the tests are not very unequally spaced, and also cannot vary too much in the amount of deviation each has from an underlying perfect circumplex (the "communalities" cannot differ widely).

Let us look more closely at the content of these tests, for now we are approaching an actual theory of the structure of intelligence.

THE NATURE OF THE CIRCLE OF MENTAL ABILITIES

The test called Association in Table 19 had the following instructions: "Write as many words as you can that are names of things to eat or drink." This task calls for both verbal ability and also guided initiative. It is not surprising to find that its neighbors are Incomplete Words and Directions.

Incomplete Words is a more purely verbal task. A sample item is:

> "Write a letter in each blank below to complete each word:
> l__mp, de__k, wi__dow."

The test of Directions consisted of reading certain instructions and then carrying them out. For example:

> "If the word *cat* has three letters, write 4 here ____."

Table 20

The Multiple-Regression Weights for Predicting Each Test
in Table 19 from the Remaining Five Tests

| Criterion | Predictor | | | | | | Multiple-Correlation Coefficient |
| | Association | Incomplete Words | Multiplication | Dot Patterns | ABC | Directions | |
	6	32	37	17	1	12	
6	--	.30	.10	-.01	.04	.30	.553
32	.31	--	.20	.15	-.02	.09	.540
37	.10	.21	--	.23	.14	.11	.534
17	-.01	.16	.25	--	.23	.04	.486
1	.04	-.02	.15	.23	--	.23	.465
12	.31	.10	.11	.03	.21	--	.533

The instructions usually cannot be carried out without being cautious against responding in an automatic fashion. Apparently the freedom of thought required here overlaps that required for free association of words.

Thought of a somewhat different kind is required by the ABC test. This is essentially an exercise in abstact algebra. For example, if AB = C and CA = B, what is ABA equal to? The two neighbors of this ability are Directions and Dot Patterns. Directions, as we have seen, requires a certain kind of nonrigidity of thought, which apparently overlaps that required to learn a new pattern of reasoning. Dot Patterns overlaps the ABC test on the other side, with respect to the notion of patterning; it involves a geometric or visual law whereas ABC involves an algebraic or literal law.

Multiplication turns out to have as its best neighbors (among the given tests) Dot Patterns and Incomplete Words. As we shall see in further examples of empirical data, numerical ability seems to be between geometrical and verbal.

The circle of human mental abilities as revealed thus far by Tables 19 and 20, runs then, from nonrigidity of thought, through verbal, numerical, and geometrical ability in turn, winding up back again at nonrigidity of thought. Many other kinds of abilities can conceivably be interposed among these, making closer and closer neighbors within the circumplex.

FURTHER EVIDENCE AS TO THE CIRCLE OF MENTAL ABILITIES

In a radex, only if tests of different kinds of content have comparable degrees of complexity will they tend to show a circumplex pattern. Apparently, then, the six tests of Table 19 are roughly of the same degree of complexity, each within its own simplex. We can select more tests from the same research project, but belonging to a different level of complexity, and see the same kind of circle emerging as before.

All the simplexes involved have not yet been studied in full, and indeed some cannot be for lack of appropriate tests in the published literature. Only in a new battery of tests especially designed for the purpose can we expect to find tests of all the varied degrees of complexity and content needed to plot out a full radex. Regardless, Table 21 shows further evidence as to the same general circle of abilities that Table 19 revealed.

Table 21

Intercorrelations Among Six More Tests of Different Kinds
of Abilities for 710 Chicago Schoolchildren[38]

Test	Ryhming Words	Digit Span	Arithmetic	Geometrical Forms	Identical Pictures	Picture Naming
	50	11	5	28	31	41
50	1.	.260	.222	.126	.144	.358
11	.260	1.	.254	.115	.073	.115
5	.222	.254	1.	.248	.090	.010
28	.126	.115	.248	1.	.307	.081
31	.144	.073	.090	.307	1.	.243
41	.358	.115	.010	.081	.243	1.

Table 22

The Multiple-Regression Weights for Predicting Each Test in
Table 21 from the Remaining Five Tests

Criterion	Predictor						Multiple-Correlation Coefficient
	Rhyming Words	Digit Span	Arithmetic	Geometrical Forms	Identical Pictures	Picture Naming	
	50	11	5	28	31	41	
50	--	.175	.164	.030	.028	.327	.455
11	.196	--	.201	.035	.007	.038	.333
5	.178	.194	--	.208	.009	-.095	.375
28	.032	.034	.207	--	.283	-.005	.382
31	.030	.006	.009	.283	--	.209	.379
41	.341	.036	-.092	-.005	.201	--	.417

In Table 21, correlations are highest along the main diagonal, decline, and then rise again in the northeast and southwest corners. The circle of abilities runs from verbal, through arithmetical and geometrical, and back to verbal again.

This time, we could find no reasoning test in the published data of the requisite degree of complexity to fit into Table 21, parallel to the ABC and/or the Directions tests in Table 19. A numerical memory test--Digit Span--was found to interpolate between the verbal and the arithmetical ability tests. Instead of one kind of geometrical test--Dot Patterns--in Table 19, Table 21 has three kinds: Geometrical Forms, Identical Pictures, and Picture Naming.

Rhyming Words, in Table 21, belongs essentially to the same simplex as does Association in Table 19, but is more complex (we do not pause here to show the simplex correlations involved). Similarly, Arithmetic in Table 21 belongs to the same simplex as does Multiplication in Table 19, but is more complex. In general, then, the circumplex of Table 21 shows essentially the same circle as does Table 19, but at a higher level of complexity. To combine the pictures of Tables 19 and 21 requires the concept of radex, wherein tests differ both in degree of complexity and in content.

Before closing this section, allow me to remark that work in progress on data available for adults from the Bellevue-Wechsler tests tends to show the same circle as do the Thurstone data: thinking ability, verbal, numerical, geometrical and back again. [39]

The multiple-regression weights for the data of Table 21 are recorded in Table 22, further to verify the law of circular neighboring.

THE RADEX CONCEPT

We have portrayed a circumplex schematically in Figure 1 as a circle divided into sectors, each sector representing a discernible elementary component. Each kind of content was represented as a connected set of some of these sectors.

If we wish to portray a simplex on the same kind of diagram, it can be done as follows. We restrict ourselves to one kind of content, or to a segment of the circle, as in Figure 2a. If the five sectors are labelled a, b, c, d, and e, then our particular hypothetical simplex is assumed to be comprised of the four sectors a, b, c, and d.

Within this simplex, we can now discern different degrees of complexity. Figure 2b assumes four tests are available for the

Figure 2

A Schematic Diagram of a Simplex

a. The Total Simplex   b. Levels of Complexity
                                 Within the Simplex

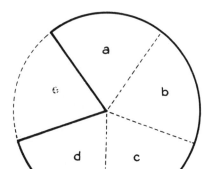 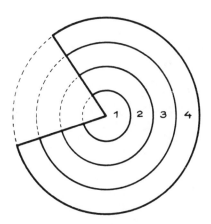

simplex, distinguishing between four particular levels of complexity. The least complex test is composed of the subarea labelled 1. The second test contains what the first does--and more; it covers both subareas 1 and 2. The third test covers subareas 1, 2, and 3, and so on to the most complex test which covers the entire simplex area.

It is now clear how to draw a radex diagram, wherein tests can differ both in kind and in degree. Let us assume we have, as in Figure 2, five different kinds of content and four different levels of complexity. This enables us to discern 5x4, or 20 elementary components, as in Figure 3. The letter denotes the sector and the numerical subscript the level of complexity of each elementary component.

In the general radex a test is no longer restricted to belonging either to a simplex or to a circumplex. Figure 3b shows a hypothetical test comprised of ten of the elementary components of Figure 3a. This test is least complex in sector a, more complex in sector b, most complex in c, and drops one stage of complexity in d. Such a test will not fit into the simplex of Figure 2b, since it is not uniform in its complexities on all the sectors involved. Nor will it fit into an ordinary uniform circumplex.

Figure 3

A Schematic Diagram of a Radex

a. Twenty Discernible   b. A Hypothetical Test
   Elementary Components

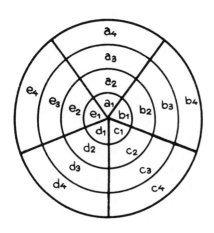

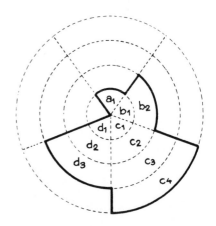

If we consider further that a radex is in general composed of indefinitely many sectors--not just five as in Figure 3--we see an important reason why the empirical examples of this lecture should not be expected to conform too closely to the simplex and circumplex hypotheses. Even though we tried to select tests which differ only in degree of complexity and not in kind of content, it is inevitable that no straight boundaries exist for such empirical selections as Figure 2 implies. Some variation in content must be expected in practice, so that we get only approximate simplexes, or, say, Figure 2 with jagged boundaries for sectors a and d.

Similarly, our circumplexes in practice could not be selected to have all tests on one level of complexity on all sectors. The profile of each test is undoubtedly more jagged, say like that in Figure 3b than in ideal Figure 1.

Current work in progress at the Israel Institute of Applied Social Research is to plot on a map like Figure 3a each of a large battery of tests. Each test will thus have its own profile, like in Figure 3b. The map, of course, will not be limited to a base of 20 elementary components. Once such a map is available, it will allow easy selection of a battery of tests for any given prediction problem. If the radex profile of the criterion is known, the small-est number of available tests which will approximate the profile can easily be ascertained, so that maximum predictability can be obtained with least effort.

Theoretically there can be an infinite number of elementary components. The five sectors shown in Figure 3 can be subdivided indefinitely, as can the four zones. Ultimately, each point in the circle can be regarded as an elementary component; the notation of components c_j we have been using in this lecture is really that of clusters of point components. These clusters are combinable and separable; they are the discernible features of the radex made possible by the particular empirical data at hand.

FUNCTIONAL INTERPRETATION OF THE RADEX

Ultimately, I believe, the radex of mental abilities will be found to have a physiological basis. The point elementary components may be found to be associated with neurons. The principle of neighboring may be found to correspond to neural pathways, or better, to a distribution of electro-chemical activity.

The principle of neighboring can arise out of a functional growth of abilities. The progress from less complex to more complex should clearly involve expansion and/or reinforcement of certain patterns of neural activity. The actual physiological pattern can of course be entirely different from the schematic diagrams we are using here; for example, it can be that of a multiple-branching process. We have not attempted to portray physiological patterns, but only statistical ones.

By positing contiguity of elementary components as in Figure 3, radex theory implies a certain functional interdependence between mental abilities, whether they differ in kind or in degree, and in a manner which seems to lend itself better to a physiological inter-pretation than do previous common-factor theories.

It might be asked: why limit the picture to that of a plane? Why not volumes, say, instead of areas for the discernible element-ary components? With respect to mental tests, the plane hypothesis seems fairly plausible if we regard the neural activity involved to take place primarily in the cerebral cortex. Only empirical data can tell us how best to modify the present hypothesis.

Mathematically, it is quite simple to go on to define discern-ible elementary components in terms of volumes and higher dimen-sional spatial segments. These will be higher dimensional radexes

than the two-dimensional one I have portrayed here. Going on to
more dimensions will not, however, involve any new concepts over
our two basic ones: difference in kind and difference in degree.
More dimensions will merely allow more room for variation with
respect to these two concepts; no essentially new concept will be
added.

Also, once we focus on the notion of order amongst variables,
alternative theories of order are possible--even in a plane--apart
from those of the simplex, circumplex, and radex. One can imagine
strings of elementary components, with loops in them, etc.

I have tried to present the simplest possible theory with a
simple law of functional interdependence, based on the principles of
contiguity and of combinability-separability of discernible elementary components.

I have further tried to emphasize that this particular theory
is at present especially designed for mental test data. I do not
propose it as a general theory for any system of intercorrelated
variables. For example, I do not believe it appropriate for a type
of attitude data discussed in my previous lecture in this series.
As I pointed out there, it is the psychology of their *principal* components that may underlie the interrelations of certain sets of attitudes. These lead to curvilinear and multivalued relationships; the
approach of this lecture is correspondingly inappropriate.

An example of another field where the concepts of simplex
and circumplex may be appropriate is that of time-series. I have
already indicated the possibility of the utility there of the theory of
the principal components of the simplex. The same holds for the
principal components of a circumplex, which unfortunately we have
had no time to discuss in this lecture.

The Israel Institute has now found some Rorschach data to
form an approximate simplex, and some data from the Minnesota
Multiphasic Psychoneurotic Inventory to form an approximate circumplex. In personality data, negative correlations can occur. It
is easy to extend radex theory to allow for negative correlations,
and I shall show how to do this on another occasion; indeed, this
can lead to an even better physiological and functional interpretation of the elementary components, as well as allowing a closer
statistical fit between theory and data even for the case of only
positive correlations.

Radex theory has been presented here as for quantitative
variables. With appropriate changes in the algebra required, the
entire theory can be restated as for qualitative data. The perfect
simplex is then analogous to a perfect scale; a perfect scale of
dichotomies can also be portrayed as by Figure 2b, the points

within the area now being *people* or respondents, and combinations
of zones being categories of the dichotomous items. A circumplex
and radex can correspondingly be defined for qualitative data, using
diagrams just like in Figures 1 and 3, but with reinterpretation of
the details involved.

RELATIONSHIP TO THURSTONE'S CONCEPT OF
SIMPLE STRUCTURE

The circumplex concept for quantitative variables is closely
related to one of the most important concepts of traditional factor
analysis, namely that of *simple structure* as introduced by Thurstone.[40] Our special concern here is where the common-factors
correlate zero with each other, or the case of *orthogonal* simple
structure.

Thurstone's definition runs as follows. If a set of n tests
has r uncorrelated, additive common-factors, but each test individually correlates zero with at least one common-factor, then the
tests will be said to have an orthogonal simple structure. Thurstone's practical techniques are aimed at obtaining as small a number r of common-factors as possible, but for which in turn each
test would be the sum of as few of the m common-factors as possible. For example, with n = 9 and r = 3, Thurstone has prepared a
hypothetical table, Table 23, to indicate where zero correlations
occur between tests and common-factors if orthogonal simple
structure holds. An entry in the table in row j and column p indicates the correlation between test t_j and factor c_p. A zero entry
means a zero correlation, and a check mark ($\checkmark$) means a nonzero
correlation. The first three tests are taken to be those that correlate with only one common-factor. Each of the remaining six
tests has one of the six possible combinations of nonzeros from
two common-factors out of the three.

Now, we can make a table like this also for the additive,
uniform circumplex. Here the number of common-factors r may
be equal to n, the number of tests--and so we shall assume the
case to be--so no "parsimony" is reached in this respect. But m,
the number each test individually contains, can be much less than
n; indeed it can reach as low as $n/2$ without introducing observed
correlations of zero. For example, with n = 6 and m = 4, we can
construct Table 24. The apparent absence of parsimony in Table
24, compared to Table 23, with respect to the number of common-
factors is of course more than made up for by the law of order

Table 23

Hypothetical Zero Correlations between Tests
and Common-Factors For Thurstone's
Orthogonal Simple Structure[41] ($n = 9$, $r = 3$)

	Common-Factor		
Test	c_1	c_2	c_3
t_1	✓	0	0
t_2	0	✓	0
t_3	0	0	✓
t_4	✓	✓	0
t_5	✓	0	✓
t_6	0	✓	✓
t_7	✓	0	✓
t_8	0	✓	✓
t_9	✓	✓	0

Table 24

Hypothetical Zero Correlations Between Tests and Common-
Factor For a Perfect, Additive, Uniform Circumplex ($n = 6$, $m = 4$)

	Common-Factor					
Test	c_1	c_2	c_3	c_4	c_5	c_6
t_1	✓	✓	✓	✓	0	0
t_2	0	✓	✓	✓	✓	0
t_3	0	0	✓	✓	✓	✓
t_4	✓	0	0	✓	✓	✓
t_5	✓	✓	0	0	✓	✓
t_6	✓	✓	✓	0	0	✓

among tests which Table 24 enjoys and Table 23 does not. A further difference is that the nonzero entries in Table 23 are completely arbitrary, but in Table 24 they are not. From (72) it can be seen that if $r_{t_j c_p}$ is not zero, then it is equal to $\sigma_{c_p}/\sigma_{t_j}$:

$$r_{t_j c_p} = \begin{cases} \sigma_{c_p}/\sigma_{t_j} \\ 0 \end{cases} \tag{77}$$

Thus [42] all entries in column p of Table 24 are proportional to the $1/\sigma_{t_j}$, and all entries in row j are proportion to the σ_{c_p}.

If we remove the restriction of uniformity from the circumplex, and--like Thurstone--consider the case where each test can have up to r-1 out of r common-factors, we can obtain a table like Table 25. For convenience, we choose r = 4, for which it turns out that the maximum for n is n = 12.

Table 25

Hypothetical Zero Correlations Between Tests and Common-Factors for a Perfect, Additive, Nonuniform Circumplex (n=12, r=4)

Test	Common-Factor			
	c_1	c_2	c_3	c_4
t_1	✓	0	0	0
t_2	0	✓	0	0
t_3	0	0	✓	0
t_4	0	0	0	✓
t_5	✓	✓	0	0
t_6	0	✓	✓	0
t_7	0	0	✓	✓
t_8	✓	0	0	✓
t_9	✓	✓	✓	0
t_{10}	0	✓	✓	✓
t_{11}	✓	0	✓	✓
t_{12}	✓	✓	0	✓

Not all possible combinations of common-factors can occur in a circumplex; the circular order must be maintained. For a given r, fewer distinct patterns are possible for a circumplex than for Thurstone's more general and unordered simple structure. In Table 25, r =4, and yields n = 12, whereas Thurstone can obtain n = 14 for r = 4. In general, for the nonuniform circumplex, the maximum n is $r(r-1)$, while for Thurstone's case it is $2^r - 2$. Again, restriction (77) holds in Table 25, and not in Thurstone's case.

POSSIBLE ARRANGEMENTS WITHIN A
NONUNIFORM CIRCUMPLEX

The nonuniform circumplex in Table 25 can be regarded as composed of three separate uniform circumplexes. The first four tests have m = 1, the next four have m = 2, and the last four have m = 3. In general, a nonuniform circumplex with r additive common-factors can yield $n = r(r-1)$ different kinds of tests, which can be considered as grouped into r-1 uniform circumplexes, one for each value m = 1, 2,..., r-1.

Alternatively, the structure can be regarded as of r simplexes each with m = 3. For example, the rows of Table 25 can be reshuffled as in Table 26 below. Here, four simplexes appear, each with three common-factors and three tests. (The last two simplexes in the table need the columns rotated to be read in direct fashion.)

In a sense, then, a nonuniform circumplex can be regarded as a circle of overlapping simplexes. That is why, in borderline cases, a circumplex may often look like a simplex.

Most mental test data, of course, will not conform to the specialized patterns of the simplex nor of the uniform circumplex. The nonuniform circumplex allows for a much more variegated system, but one also that requires greater care in working with in practice. This is even more true of the further generalization beyond the nonuniform circumplex, namely that of the radex.

Table 26

A Rearrangement of Table 25 Into Simplexes

| | Common-Factor | | | |
Test	c_1	c_2	c_3	c_4
t_1	✓	0	0	0
t_5	✓	✓	0	0
t_9	✓	✓	✓	0
t_2	0	✓	0	0
t_6	0	✓	✓	0
t_{10}	0	✓	✓	✓
t_3	0	0	✓	0
t_7	0	0	✓	✓
t_{11}	✓	0	✓	✓
t_4	0	0	0	✓
t_8	✓	0	0	✓
t_{12}	✓	✓	0	✓

THE RADEX AND PREVIOUS FACTOR THEORIES [43]

This is as far as we can carry radex theory in the present lecture. I shall close by very briefly trying to indicate how the new theory seems to unify various aspects of previous theories. It at the same time justifies some criticisms made of various parts of previous theories.

When Godfrey Thomson demonstrated that Spearman's type of hierarchy could tend to be accounted for by a theory of random sampling of "bonds" in the mind, Spearman objected on the grounds that mental activity was certainly not random. Our new theory is essentially one of "ordered-bonds" in the mind; Thomson's bonds in a sense remain, and Spearman's objection to randomness is sustained (but Spearman's hierarchy is displaced from its previous central importance).

Of all previous approaches, Thurstone's simple-structure theory is the closest to my own. We have seen how closely it is resembled by the nonuniform circumplex. The emphasis that Thurstone makes on patterns of zero factor loadings is reechoed in the additive forms of both the circumplex and the simplex. Had the notion of a simplex hierarchy been available before, one might have arrived at the radex theory via Thurstone's approach. As it is, the absence of the notion of a simplex lends some justification to the claim of critics that the common-factors of Thurstone and others are statistical artifacts. Consider, for example, Thurstone's analysis of the numerical ability tests of Table 6 above. In the larger battery which contained these tests, he defined one reference axis to be numerical ability, and the correlations of the tests with this common-factor he found to be as in Table 27.

Table 27

Thurstone's Loadings of Six Tests with a Common-Factor of Numerical Ability[44]

	Addition	Subtrac-tion	Multipli-cation	Divi-sion	Numerical Judgment	Numerical Reasoning
Loading	.755	.670	.810	.619	.432	.383

Multiplication turns out to be closest to the common-factor ($r=.810$). As might be expected from what we now know of simplex theory, the remaining correlations in Table 27 taper off to the right and to the left (with a bit of deviation for Addition, which we already have seen has a special link with Multiplication that Subtraction does not). Now, Thurstone's common-factor here is essentially the centroid or arithmetical mean of these tests, by virtue of the computing procedures he used for rotation of axes. Clearly, the centroid of a simplex will tend to be at a test of some middle rank. And that seems to be the case here. If less complex or more complex tests were added, the centroid would shift; we might find Division closest to the common-factor, or else Subraction might be. The interpretation of the common-factor of Table 27 as "Numerical Ability" does seem artificial. This implies that Division is less numerical

than Multiplication, and that a test involving all elementary numerical operations is less purely numerical than is one of the operations.
Radex theory requires no such artificial interpretation, for it merely recognizes the law of order existing among the tests without need
for any reference axes, arbitrary or not.

In the same way, radex theory upholds those who have argued
against the hypothesis that mental abilities can be accounted for
by a relatively small number of common-factors. We can now see
that in a radex with empirically distinguishable simplexes, centroids
of the simplexes will tend to be the reference axes of a Thurstone-
type analysis. Thus, the number of common-factors found previously will tend to correspond to the number of simplexes employed.
Actually, if a simplex is represented by many tests, it will yield
more than one reference axis in the usual type of factor-grinding
operations. The earlier tests will seem to form a separate cluster
from the later tests, because of the gradient in correlation coefficients. The actual theoretical expansion of a simplex is into n-1
additive common-factors; current computing methods would stop
far short of this because of their unsolved problem of when to stop
grinding.

Simplex and circumplex theory resemble cluster analysis
techniques of Tryon, Cattell, and others. The "correlation profile"
technique of Tryon, we have seen, breaks down on data like those in
Table 5. The reason is similar to that given in the previous paragraph; in a lengthy simplex, the earlier and later parts will seem
to form separate clusters because of the smaller correlations in the
northeast and southwest corners of the correlation table. Cattell has
come close to the idea of the simplex correlation table, but lacked
the distinction between differences in kind and in degree which is
essential for making the idea pan out.

Truman Kelley has made a case for not using standard scores
as a metric for tests in factor analysis. While radex theory differs
from his in the details, it does agree that ultimately there may be
a metric for tests which will be more useful than standard scores.
This may be so especially in the simplex, where a more complex
test might be assigned a larger variance than a less complex test,
say according to equation (36) above. This may ultimately be found
to have a physiological meaning.

And finally, radex theory lends support to those who have
argued the merits of principal components in factor analysis. It
also supports those who have argued against principal components.
Without a law of order, principal components are not likely to be
psychologically meaningful. The simplex and the circumplex seem
to be the first examples of structures for factor analysis with a law

of order which makes the role of principal components unmistakably important. But our new emphasis is that principal components are not to be confused with, nor thought to compete with, the concept of elementary components to which this lecture has been devoted. The concepts are complementary.

7. A Conceptual Introduction to Latent Structure Analysis

By PAUL F. LAZARSFELD

Columbia University

The present paper deals with the application of a mathematical model to one problem of measurement in the social sciences. Many research areas make use of a type of measurement which we shall call the procedure of itemized tests. It consists of making a number of qualitative observations on a person, and then attributing to him a "measure" of some kind by which he can be compared with other persons who have also undergone the test. The observations can be of various kinds. For example, does he behave in a particular way in a certain situation? Does he answer "yes" or "no" to a given question? Has he undergone a particular experience?

In principle, it is not necessary to confine these observations to dichotomies--we could deal with questions which might be answered with a "yes," "no," or "don't know" response. But for the sake of simplicity in our discussion, we shall assume in this paper that all items of observation are of a dichotomous nature. We shall arbitrarily call one of the two alternatives the "positive response." The word "response" will be used not only for answers to questionnaire items, but for all other observations, such as having a specific property or performing a certain act.

The question of how such sets of qualitative observations are translated into measurement will be the focal point of our attention. The kinds of treatment to which such itemized tests can be subjected are limited. The purpose of latent structure analysis is to provide mathematical models by which the various uses of itemized tests can be related to each other. The main purpose of the model is *to bring out the assumptions which are implicit in this type of "measurement."* It is not claimed that the people who do the measuring are aware of these assumptions. It is also not claimed that another model would not reproduce equally well the various operations which have been developed or which could be thought of. But

349

it is claimed that latent structure analysis puts practices and
discussions in the measurement field into reasonable axiomatic
form, and that its axioms permit algebraic operations which lead
to hitherto unobserved relationships and suggest more precise
meanings of the notion of measurement in the social sciences.

The mathematics of latent structure analysis has been set
forth in various places.[1] More recent developments are available
in mimeographed memoranda issued jointly by the RAND Corporation and by the Department of Sociology of Columbia University.
The Department of Social Relations at Harvard University has recently started a series of investigations concerning new developments on specific applications. There seems to be no need, therefore, for a mathematical presentation. Many reviewers, however,
have criticized the lack of a systematic presentation of the general
considerations underlying latent structure analysis.

The following pages, then, will deal with what one might call
a conceptual introduction to latent structure analysis. Nine main
ideas and operations are put forward, separated by appropriate
sub-titles, so that for discussion purposes any specific point can
be singled out. The order of these ten points cannot be derived from
any systematic considerations. They all play a role in the general
picture, but the best sequence in which they should be introduced
is not easily determined. None of these points has any special
importance by itself. As a matter of fact, one point attempts nothing else than to clarify in what sense the term probability is used
in latent structure analysis; it makes no new contribution to discussions of probability theory. It is the sum total of the nine points,
and their specific applications to the problem of measurement,
which matters.

1. SOME TRADITIONAL PROBLEMS OF
CONCEPT FORMATION

All social sciences meet with the problem of making inferences from simple observations to more complex "things." The
graphologist wants to infer the true character of a person from his
handwriting. More generally, projective tests are used to derive
certain basic personality traits from reactions to unstructured
material. But the problem is by no means restricted to individual
psychology. Sociometrists wonder how best to measure the cohesion of a small group. Seemingly the only thing to do would be to
combine various observations into an index of cohesion. But if one
reads these sociometric studies carefully, it seems that such

indices measure an underlying characteristic of the group which could be equally well measured by a variety of indices.

Modern logicians talk of these problems under the general heading of "disposition concepts." Typically, these are defined as concepts which do not refer to a directly observed characteristic, but rather to a disposition on the part of some objects to display specific reactions under specified circumstances.[2] The logician would add that these concepts still create many logical difficulties.

Meantime social scientists make abundant use of them. When Max Weber wants to define a social relationship, then he talks of the "probability of the repeated occurrence of certain behavior." "Friendship" is one of the concrete relationships with which he is concerned; he puts his idea in the following way:

> "...it is only the existence of the probability that, ...a certain type of action will take place which constitutes the 'existence' of the social relationship. Thus *that a 'friendship' exists* or has existed *means this and only this:* that we, the observers, judge that there is or has been a probability that on the basis of known subjective attitudes of certain individuals *there will result in the average sense a certain specific type of action.*"[3]

There is, on the one hand, the *"underlying"* concept; on the other hand there are *observed items of behavior* from which inferences are made as to the existence or the kind or the intensity of "friendship."

The same idea reappears when William James discusses what is meant by a "trait:"

> "...Suppose, e.g., that we say *a man is 'prudent.'* Concretely, that *means that he takes out insurance, hedges in betting, looks before he leaps* ...As a constant habit in him, a permanent tone of character, it is convenient to call him prudent in abstraction from any one of his acts, ...There are peculiarities in his psychophysical system that make him act prudently...."[4]

The historian also turns to dispositional concepts. Macaulay compares the Italian cities of the Fifteenth Century with the countries north of the Alps, especially England, France and Germany. He wants to make the point that they had what we today call different value systems. *"While courage was the point of honor in other (northern) countries, ingenuity became the point of honor in Italy."* For evidence, he compares the two "cultures" in various ways: they admired different kinds of heroes, they had different ways of waging war, the vices they condemned and those they condoned were different, and so on.

In his notion of "attitudes," the psychologist has an especially characteristic disposition concept. Psychological literature
abounds in definitions of the following kind:[6]

> "primarily a way of being 'set' toward or against certain things"
>
> "a readiness for attention or action, of a definite sort"
>
> "a more or less permanently enduring state of readiness of mental
> organization which predisposes an individual to react in a char-
> acteristic way to any object or situation with which it is related"

Inversely, when a textbook discusses "methods by which the
present needs and demands can be ascertained" it suggests, as the
first method, "inferences from present behavior."[7]

To such references every reader can add examples from
daily experience. The physician who uses all sorts of symptoms to
diagnose an illness, the FBI which fills its files with innumerable
details to judge finally the loyalty of a person--both of these efforts
establish a link between an array of available data and a more
basic classification which is their main focus of interest. And this
is also what men have tried to do over the centuries when they have
asked their sweethearts: "Do you *really* love me?"

Some writers have made an effort to formulate this whole
matter more precisely. L. J. Henderson, for instance, discusses
Pareto's notion of "sentiments." He calls them hypothetical enti-
ties figuratively referred to by words and phrases like: a desire
to solve a scientific problem, a sense of loyalty to a community,
a sexual complex. He then adds:

> "Sentiments are not here regarded as facts. The actions and ex-
> pressions of men are facts. In some instances these *actions and*
> *expressions are regarded,* for convenience, *as manifestations of*
> *sentiment.* Sentiments are not regarded as either real or unreal.
> In this respect they are regarded as forces are regarded in mod-
> ern dynamics...with the aid of the assumption,...a uniformity in the
> facts is discovered, and in this case the assumption is retained for
> further use; or a uniformity is not discovered, and in this case the
> assumption is abandoned."[8]

In more modern language Henderson would say that sentiments,
like forces or other dispositional concepts, are constructs, the
merits of which have to be decided on the basis of the order which
they bring into the data accessible to observation and testing.

While Henderson tries to clarify the role of the "underlying"
concept, another writer has given primary attention to the

observational elements which form the basis of the necessary inferences. L. Guttman has coined the important notion of a *universe of attributes*. He developed it in connection with the concept
of attitude, but it is obvious that it applies to all dispositional
concepts:

> "In social research, a universe is usually a large class of behav-
> ior,...(which) is being investigated, like marital adjustment,
> opinion of British fighting ability, knowledge of arithmetic, etc.
> *The universe consists of all the attributes that define the concept.*
> Another way of describing the universe is to say it consists of
> all the attributes of interest to the investigation which have a
> common content, so that they are classified under a single head-
> ing which indicates that content." [9]

There is a question, of course, as to which items belong to a
universe that is coordinated with a particular disposition concept.
Guttman feels that in general this must be left to the decision of
the investigator. Whether his choice is justified depends mainly
on whether he ends up with findings which are worthwhile in an
empirical investigation or in a theoretical context:

> "An attribute belongs to the universe by virtue of its content. *The
> investigator indicates the content of interest by the title he chooses
> for the universe, and all attributes with that content belong in the
> universe.* There will, of course, arise borderline cases in prac-
> tice where it will be hard to decide whether or not an item belongs
> in the universe. The evaluation of the content thus far remains a
> matter that may be decided by consensus of judges or by some
> other means." [10]

This then is the type of material and the kind of problem
with which we will deal in the present paper. For our specific
purpose, however, a more precise formulation will be necessary.

All the remarks quoted so far have a variety of elements in
common. On the one hand, we have empirical observations of
some kind. Their selection has been decided upon by the investigator, who was guided by theoretical considerations, or hunches,
or previous experiences. These observations we shall call
manifest data.

From these manifest data inferences are to be made to a
latent structure. By these terms we try to indicate what the main
purpose of "underlying" concepts seems to be. The writers quoted
above are obviously not looking for an absolute definition. They
are confronted with concrete cases of "friendship" or "prudence"
and want to know how to recognize them, how to relate them to

each other, and so on. If we could ask these writers some further questions, they would say something like this: They want to distinguish "types of friendship," or "degrees of prudence," or they want to distinguish between "friendship" and "love," or between "prudence" and "distrust." In order to do this, some inferences from manifest data to a latent structure are necessary. Up to this point we have added nothing but two terms to the kind of descriptions quoted above.

But how are manifest data and latent structure related? It is on this point that most authors are very vague. If a consistent system of ideas, including concrete operations, is to be developed, then a decision must be made as to *how precisely inferences from concrete observations to "underlying" concepts are to be made.*

In this paper we shall explore one such possibility. No claim will be made that it is the only or even the best one. But as far as we know, it is the first effort to carry out concretely the program implied in the kind of thinking which Weber, James and Henderson considered a fruitful approach in the social sciences.

A number of simple notions will be needed in the presentation of the total argument.

2. PROBABILITY MECHANISMS

No social scientist seems to have any difficulty dealing with concepts such as "primary group," "social structure," or "value system." But when it comes to a term like *probability,* he fears that "mathematics" is involved, and he becomes restless. Most likely he would feel more comfortable if some other term like "propensity to act" were used. This is indeed one meaning which the term probability has in the present text. But we need to clarify how we shall use the term and what we shall mean by it.

We shall continuously make statements of the following kind: "An individual has a certain probability of responding positively to specified questions." No effort will be made to trace such statements back to their ultimate logical foundations. But it is necessary to indicate in what way we intend to use the notion of probability. We accept as our foundation the so-called frequency interpretation as developed, for example, in Ernest Nagel's *Principles of the Theory of Probability*.[11] We start out with a *Reference class* R of n elements of which s have a certain property A; our attention is then directed toward the proportion p = s/n. Suppose now we have reason to believe that the value of p will remain about the same, whether we increase the size n of the Reference class or whether we inspect only an arbitrarily selected part of it. Or, to put it more in mathematical terms, all the p values so formed crowd around a certain value which is called the limit. This idealized proportion of elements, then, having the property A in the Reference class R is called the probability of A in R. Thus people 30 years of age (Reference class) have a probability of .95 to survive at least one year (property A). Nagel makes a comment which is very significant for our present purpose:

> "a) No meaning can be attached to any expression which, taken literally, assigns a probability to a single individual as having a specified property. Statements of probability predicate something of an individual (e.g., Tom Brown) only in so far as he is an element in a specified reference class. Probability statements which do not do so *explicitly* must be regarded as incomplete if they are to be significant: they must be understood as making an implicit specification of the reference class within which the designated property occurs with a certain relative frequency." (Page 23)

Now it so happens that it is possible to assign a probability to Tom Brown individually, without violating this general rule. Suppose we ask him several times the question, "Do you expect a third world war?" Suppose that each time the question is asked we "wash his brain", so that he forgets what answer he gave at previous interviews. Common sense (and actual experiments) lead us to expect that Tom Brown will sometimes say "Yes" and sometimes "No". We can then compute the proportion of times he says "Yes", as the number of interviews increases and thus establish the probability of a positive answer, along the lines of reasoning just developed. Such a probability would be a useful measure of whether Tom Brown is pessimistic regarding the political future. Here the Reference class is the set of repeated interviews under "brain-wash" conditions. This is, of course, an idealization which in concrete situations can only be approximated. But the "class of all thirty-year olds", as it would be used in current probability calculus turns out, upon further reflection, to be also an idealization which requires its own approximations in actual research.

In the present context it is not necessary to enter into a
serious logical discussion. It will suffice for the reader to
remember that when we speak about probabilities in this paper,
the reference classes are always hypothetical repeated interviews or observations, *made on the same individual*, under the
assumption that all previous responses are forgotten by our
subject as soon as they are made. This corresponds to the
common sense terminology in which we say that Tom Brown has
a propensity toward flying off the handle, that he is likely to
"see Helena in every woman", etc.

A probability notion which reproduces the traditional idea
of propensity leads to a consequence which has to be traced out
with some care. A man might be friendly when sober, but belli-
gerent when intoxicated; his probability of performing aggressive acts changes as a function of the alcohol he has consumed.
This might at first seem somewhat surprising: a probability is
an idealized ratio taken presumably over a long time period of
repeated observation; nevertheless we say that this probability
can change from one minute to the next. However, we are
accustomed to this character of all ratios in other contexts. We
might say that a man slowed down from "sixty miles an hour" to
"forty miles an hour", as soon as he saw a policeman. Speed is
distance over time, under the assumption that things remain the
same as they are at the moment; the next moment the situation
is different and the new speed is the one which would prevail if
the new situation now remained stable. In the same sense,
propensities and probabilities may change over time and still be
defined in terms of a reference class of repeated inquiries which
would presumably be made under stable conditions.

The reader should have a concrete model in mind from
which the properties of probabilities can be derived; this will be
helpful if later on we have to proceed to slightly more complicated combinations of the basic ideas. We shall therefore briefly
go over the ground once more and introduce the notion of a
probability mechanism.

How would we build a mechanism which has a probability of
.75 of yielding positive responses to a particular question? It
might be constructed in the following way: A tube is divided into
two branches and one of these is divided once more into two more
branches. At the bottom of the mechanism there is a box which
is divided into two compartments. The left-hand one is labelled
"positive," the right-hand one "negative." Figure 1 shows in
diagramatic form what such a contraption might look like.

Suppose, now, that we pour a large number of marbles into the opening of the tube. Common sense, and simple mechanical considerations, lead us to expect that about three fourths of the marbles will fall into the "positive" compartment and one fourth into the "negative" side.

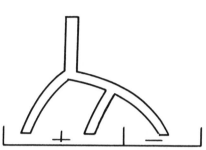

Figure 1

Whenever a marble falls into the positive compartment, we shall say that the machine has yielded a positive response. If we start just one marble through the mechanism, we cannot tell where it will end. But we are quite confident that the more marbles we pour in, the closer the proportion of positive responses will come to .75. If the machine is properly constructed, experiments will bear out our expectations.

Clearly, this is not the only way in which we could construct such a probability mechanism. Let us consider a roulette wheel which is conventional in having 36 compartments. But, unlike the usual wheel, on which the compartments alternate in color, the first 27 compartments of our wheel are red, and the last 9 black.

Now we start the wheel spinning. Again, we expect that the more spins we make, the more exactly will we find that 75 per cent of the spins end with the ball in a red compartment. If we equate red compartments with positive responses, and black with negative responses, we have here another machine with a probability of .75 of yielding positive responses. (We shall use this mechanism in much of the following discussion.)

A probability mechanism is thus any kind of structure which, through repeated trials, yields results approximating more and more closely a previously determined proportion of positive replies. *The probability is therefore a property of the structure.* Our examples show that such probability mechanisms can be constructed and tested empirically. We shall not be concerned here with the question of how, in any specific case, one would know the probability characteristic of the structure. We shall call two probability mechanisms *equivalent* when, on the basis either of our knowledge of their physical structure or the findings of previous experiments, we expect each of them to yield the same proportion of positive responses in the long run. Equivalent mechanisms can vary greatly in internal complexity. Some mechanisms may be chemical or physiological; in many cases,

we may not know the precise blueprint of the structure. But even
in these cases, repeated and controlled tests may make us
confident that, for all practical purposes, the structure does have
a positive-response probability of its own.

The notion of such probability mechanisms is only a slight
abstraction of much common sense experience. What do we mean
when we call one person irascible and another even-tempered?
We imply that the two individuals differ in their neurological and
glandular structure, with the result that one has a high probability
of becoming excited while the other does not. We may not know
exactly what this probability is, but it is not illogical to assume
that a super-physiologist could establish it, just as we established it in the two cases which we have considered.

It is important to realize that the probability of such a
mechanism is established for a certain moment. It is true that
the statement about the specially constructed roulette wheel
reads: In the long run the proportion of positive answers will be
75 per cent. But the statement is made by inspection of the
structure of the mechanism in the light of general physical
knowledge. It is quite easy to visualize a probability mechanism
with fluctuating probabilities. For instance, suppose that, with
the help of a simple motor, we periodically extend and contract
the red area of such a roulette wheel. Then the mechanism will
have different probabilities at different moments. Again, such an
idea is not alien to common sense experiences. There are people
who quite regularly are cross in the morning, most even-tempered
after lunch, and then cross again later in the afternoon as the
cares of the day wear them out.

Hereafter, then, it will be meaningful to say that, at a
particular moment, an individual has a probability, p, of responding positively to a given question. This will mean that, with
superior psycho-physiological knowledge, we would be willing to
assert the following: If the structure involved in answering such
a question remained constant, then, upon many repeated interviews, the proportion of positive answers given by the individual
would be p per cent. Even then, we would not be able to predict
what answer he might give at a next interview. The statement
refers to two facts simultaneously. On the one hand, it characterizes the mechanism supposedly implied in answering such a
question; on the other hand, it predicts the outcome of repeated
tests if these are possible. We shall not be concerned in any
way with how such probabilities might be determined in a concrete
case; it is enough to see that they can be talked about in meaningful operational terms.

3. COLLECTION OF INFORMATION
FROM AND ABOUT PEOPLE

Now we can attend better to our main purpose. We want to clarify the assumptions implied in a specific kind of measurement. This measurement consists of the use of an itemized test to classify people according to some "underlying" characteristic, x. We work with items of observation because we expect that, in some way which is still not specified, they are *indicative* of what we really want to get at. In other words, there is always the assumption that an individual's propensity to give a positive answer to a particular question is somehow related to his underlying characteristic.

But we know that no items are completely indicative of the underlying characteristic. We may observe that a man refuses to give money to a beggar. But we cannot be sure whether this behavior is indicative of his miserly nature or of the fact that he has forgotten his wallet. We may observe that another man agrees with a statement that is read to him. But we cannot be sure that he does so because he approves of the content of the statement or because he wants to be polite. Thus, the expressive value of a single item or observation will always be somewhat in doubt. Common sense tells us that a larger number of items will improve our inferences. Consequently, we make use of a *test,* consisting of a series of observations.

The model of latent structure analysis permits us to be more precise about how these inferences are made; it brings out the assumptions implied in various measurement procedures. In developing the model, we shall find it useful to incorporate the notion of probability mechanisms into a more elaborate scheme. In order to do this, we shall construct a world similar to that found in science fiction stories. This world is not peopled by ordinary human beings. Instead, its inhabitants are monsters who have roulette wheels, like those described in the previous section, which provide answers to questions put to them. There is a separate wheel corresponding to each question that might be asked. The "setting" of these wheels might be thought of as analogous to the mental "set" of an individual in the world with which we are more familiar.[12] Furthermore, the settings of the wheels vary in two ways. Within an individual monster, the wheel settings associated with different questions are likely to vary. That is, an individual may respond positively to a first item with a probability of .67, to a second item with a probability of .90, to a third item with a probability of .50, and so on. But, in addition, the probability mechanisms associated with a particular question are likely to vary from individual to individual. Considering one question alone, we expect to find that some individuals have a high probability of answering positively, and others a low probability.

Now let us see how such a "model" reproduces the essential elements of the interview situation.

Interviewing is a familiar way of collecting information. And interviewing procedures have corresponding operations in this mechanistic system:

Interview procedures	*Mechanical procedures*
(1) Asking a question	(1) Starting the motion of the appropriate roulette wheel
(2) Answering a question	(2) Waiting for the roulette wheel to come to rest
(3) Recording a "yes" or "no" response	(3) Examining the wheel to see whether the ball has come to rest in a red or black compartment

But we are talking of the way one collects information for a *test*. This means that several questions are asked, or, in other words, that several roulette wheels are set in motion and their outcomes separately determined.

How are the several items selected? We must return to our opening discussion in order to answer this question. Specific items are chosen because, it is assumed, they express some underlying attitude or characteristic which can be designated x. That is, a test is not made up of a random collection of items; instead, it includes only those questions which the investigator believes will reveal whatever it is he is trying to measure. In our science fiction world, different levels of this characteristic might be represented by electrical currents of different strengths. Those individuals with a great amount of the characteristic ("prudence," or "courage," for example) will have high electrical charges; those with a small amount of the characteristic will have only weak electrical impulses.

If the items which were selected actually do express an underlying trait, the *probability* of answering any one of them positively (*not* the actual answer on a specific occasion) will be predetermined by the trait. In our mechanistic scheme this means that the settings of the different roulette wheels will be centrally controlled. Through transmission devices in each wheel, the electrical charge characteristic of the monster adjusts the wheel so that it is set to yield in the long run an appropriate proportion of positive responses. These transmission devices, which establish the proper probability mechanisms, are an important feature of the model.

The fact that the wheel settings are centrally controlled does not mean that they will be identical for all wheels within any given individual. As we have said before, a person may have a high probability of giving a positive response to one item and a low probability of giving a positive response to a second question. All that we mean to imply is that the wheel settings are determined by the strength of the electrical charge, the central characteristic of the individual.

Usually there will be more than one person with a specified electrical charge, x. We shall speak of them as a "class" with the trait value, x. There may be a finite number of classes, or, as in the case of electrical current, an infinite number, a continuum.

In such a class, x, there is an additional kind of observation that can be made. Suppose that there are v^x people in the class. Suppose, further, that the test has been administered once to each member of the class. Now consider the test item, i. In spite of the fact that each monster in the class has the same wheel setting for this item, in a specific trial some will have given a positive response and others will have given a negative answer. After the test has been administered once, then, it is possible to count the proportion of individuals in Class x who gave positive responses to Item i. If the class is a fairly large one, this proportion will approximate p_i^x, the probability of the wheel setting characteristic of this class. Thus, p_i^x has *two meanings:* (a) it is the wheel setting for Item i for all individuals in Class x; and (b) if the class contains a large enough number of people, it is the approximate number of positive responses given by the whole of Class x after one administration of Item i.

One final assumption about the different latent classes is that they can be ranked or ordered according to the trait value characteristic of each. This is an assumption that cannot always be made. There are some cases in which it is necessary to talk about classes which are not ordered, when, for example, we deal with latent continua which have more than one dimension. But, in the following discussion, we shall restrict ourselves to the simplest model.

4. THE NOTION OF TRACE-LINES

This glimpse into a science fiction world has, we hope, provided a vivid picture of the way in which information is collected and observations made. This model can be translated into more systematic algebraic form. It is represented by the following scheme.

	Latent Classes			
	x^1	x^2	$x^3 ...$	x^j
Item 1	p_1^1	p_1^2	$p_1^3...$	p_1^j
"Questions" Item 2	p_2^1	p_2^2	$p_2^3...$	p_2^j
or other observations Item 3	p_3^1	p_3^2	$p_3^3...$	p_3^j
.	.	.	.	.
.	.	.	.	.
.	.	.	.	.
Item i	p_i^1	p_i^2	$p_i^3...$	p_i^j
Class frequency	v^1	v^2	$v^3...$	v^j

Probabilities of positive responses to different items in various latent classes.

Different individuals or classes of individuals are ranked along the horizontal axis of this scheme. Along the vertical axis we find the separate test items. The basic entries in the scheme are the probabilities, derived from probability mechanisms, associated with each class *and* each test item. In contrast with when we were talking about the science fiction model, however, these probability mechanisms are not now specified; but, as we explained in Section 2, any "equivalent" mechanism with probability p_i will do. Thus, p_2^3 represents the probability that an individual or members of a class with the latent characteristic, x^3, will give a positive response to the second item. (Superscripts denote different individuals or classes; subscripts denote different items or observations.) It is important to recognize that these entries do *not* represent manifest observations. They are the latent probabilities about which we are trying to make inferences.

What do we learn when we look down the columns of this scheme? We find out the total set of probabilities characterizing a particular individual or class. In terms of our mechanical example, we learn about the settings of all the roulette wheels used in this particular test. Thus we have a *profile* for each class, which corresponds to the profile one obtains, for example, from a Graduate Record Examination.

This notion of profiles, implicit in our earlier discussion, does not add materially to what we already know about the model. But we do gain new insights when we look across the rows of the scheme. Before discussing or exemplifying these insights, let us consider for a moment exactly what is to be found in each row. Each row contains an *ordered sequence of the latent probabilities associated with a particular test item*. (If there are a finite number of classes, the row is called a *"structor."* if there are an infinite number of classes, the row is called a *"truce-line."*)

This information is extremely valuable. With it, we can study how the probability of a positive response to a particular item is related to an underlying variable. Consider the following hypothetical example. Suppose that we had wanted to study the "ethnocentrism" of the American public during the last war. That is, we wanted to study the extent to which these people thought that the success of the war depended solely on the contributions and efforts of the United States. Then we might have set up a test consisting of the following three items:

1. I believe that our European allies are much superior to us in strategy and fighting morale.
   Yes_____ No_____

2. The majority of all equipment used by all the allies comes from American lend-lease shipment.
   True_____ False_____

3. Neither we nor our allies could win the war if we didn't have each other's help.
   Agree_____ Disagree_____

All three items were included in the test because they are related, but also because we hope each is a partial expression of the kind of ethnocentrism we had in mind to start with. This

assumption can be formulated more precisely: We assume that
the probability, p_i, that respondents select the first alternative of
the ith item is a function, f_i (x), of their position on the continuum
x, their degree of ethnocentrism. This formulation can then be
represented graphically by the trace-line of each item. The trace-
lines which we would expect to find had we carried out this three-
item test are shown in Figure 2.

Figure 2

TRACE-LINES OF THREE ITEMS IN A TEST
OF "ETHNOCENTRISM"

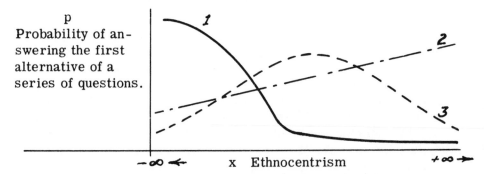

p
Probability of an-
swering the first
alternative of a
series of questions.

−∞ ⟵   x   Ethnocentrism   +∞ ⟶

The shapes of the trace-lines, in turn, permit us to say
something about the nature of the items used in the test. According to Figure 2, the first item is likely to be answered positively
only by individuals with a very small amount of ethnocentrism. Or,
to put it differently, people who show even some traces of ethnocentrism are not likely to agree that our allies in the last war were
superior to us. From its trace-line, we see that, the more ethnocentric an individual is, the more likely he is to accept the second
statement in our test as true. While the slope of the line is not
steep, it contains no special break, as did the trace-line for the
first item; in this second case, the probability of a positive response increases uniformly with x and the trace-line can be expressed by the equation, $p = a + bx$. The trace-line for the third
item shows it to be quite different from the other two. It is what
might be called the typical "middle item" of any attitude test, for
the probability of agreeing with this statement is highest in the
middle range of the x-continuum. Trace-lines of this type can obviously vary greatly in the steepness of their peaks.

     In sum, then, the *projective or expressive function of each
item is reflected in its trace-line*.

5. RESPONSE PATTERNS AND THEIR FREQUENCIES

It is now important to realize in what respects these trace-lines are to be considered a mathematical model. Neither the class frequencies nor the various probabilities in the preceding scheme are known to us. They are a construction by which we formalize the purposes for which tests or other combinations of items are developed. We do want to *find* the tracelines from our empirical observations. It is here that section 4 of this paper and section 1 must be joined. In section 1 we traced various efforts to relate overt behavior to an underlying classification. Now we have developed one formal way by which this can be done: by assuming (a) that the classes of the intended ("underlying") system (and thereby the people in them) are characterized by different response probabilities; and (b) that a specific response of an individual to a specific item is a "manifestation" of this probability, like the specific cast of a coin or a die is related to the probability of get-ting a particular throw. At the end of the first section we decided to refer to our overt observations as "manifest" and the parameters of the intended classification "latent". This permits us to formu-late conveniently the decisive question to be raised now: Can we, and if so *how can we compute from manifest data the parameters of the underlying structure,* to wit, the latent class frequencies v^x and the latent probabilities p_i^x? In order to answer this question we have to examine more carefully the kind of manifest data with which we are dealing.

In the realm of itemized tests of the kind with which we are dealing here, our manifest data consist of what is sometimes called a dichotomous system. (It is well to remember that such restric-tions to dichotomies are useful for expository purposes, but are not logically necessary.) There are two elements of special impor-tance in such a dichotomous system. There is, first of all, the single respondent, the person about whom we collect information. He is represented by a *response pattern*. In order to see what this means, let us think of the test through which we collect information. It consists of a set of observations about the individual -- his pro-perties, his answers to questions, or any other manifest character-istics which he might possess. We shall assume that the different observations are recorded in an arbitrary but fixed order. Then, a given person is represented by the sequence of positive and negative "responses" for example -- { - + + + - }, -- that have been elicited from him in a particular case. This pattern of obser-vations will be called the response pattern. In the course of a specific investigation, a concrete person and a specific response pattern are identical.

The number of possible response patterns varies with the number of items used in the test. If the list consists of k dichotomous items, then there will be 2^k possible response patterns. In a test using 5 items, for example, there are 32 response patterns, and the number increases rapidly as the list of items grows.

But there is another feature of such dichotomous systems. Ordinarily we do not collect information from a single individual; instead, the test is usually given to a large number. It is quite likely, therefore, that several of them will have the same response pattern. This leads to the notion of a *pattern frequency*, the proportion of individuals in the sample who have given the same sequence of responses. The number of pattern frequencies is, of course, identical with the number of response patterns.

We shall need a symbol by which pattern frequencies can be designated. Of the many which might be used, we have chosen the following. The proportion of individuals who have given positive responses to Items 2, 3, and 4 and negative responses to Items 1 and 5 will be designated $p_{234/15}$. In other words, items answered positively are listed to the left of the slash; items answered negatively are listed to the right of the slash.

Pattern frequencies are closely allied to response patterns, but there are important differences between them. First of all, the response pattern characterizes a specific person, while the frequency of a response pattern characterizes a total group. Secondly, the response pattern is a qualitative piece of information; the pattern frequency, on the other hand, is expressed as a proportion varying between 0 and 1.0 and therefore leads to quantitative results.

Pattern frequencies are not the only way in which a dichotomous system may be described. It can be shown, for example, that the so-called "joint positive frequencies" form what is called a fundamental system.[13] Here, briefly, is the idea. We can ascertain the frequency p_i in which any item is positively responded to. We can then move to p_{ij}, the proportion of positive responses to any two items i and j. Correspondingly we can form p_{ijk}, p_{ijkl} and so on. From these values all the pattern frequencies can be computed; this theorem is of great practical use in latent structure analysis but does not add to the discussion of conceptual foundations.

Of considerable logical importance, however, is another representation of a dichotomous system. Let us again remember that the items of such a system have been selected because, supposedly, they each, colloquially speaking, express in some way an underlying characteristic. They will not be statistically independent; this means that people who make a positive response to item i are more likely than not to make a positive response also to item j. As is well known[14], this means that in general $p_{ij} - p_i p_j > 0$ will hold for any two items. The algebraically un-trained reader is urged to give this inequality serious thought. He should familiarize himself clearly with the fact that $p_i p_j$ would be the positive response frequency to two items which are independent of each other. The inequality implies that the two items "hang to-gether"; it is the algebraic expression for the idea that our items were chosen as indicators of the characteristic we "really" want to measure.

In the algebra of latent structure analysis the excess of p_{ij} over $p_i p_j$ is symbolized by $[i \ j] = p_{ij} - p_i p_j$, a form which is also known as the crossproduct of a fourfold table; we shall give a numerical example of it in the next section. For the moment, we need to add that such cross-products can be formed on various levels. We can, for example, sort out the people with positive re-sponse to item k and then compute how two other items are related for them. This would give us the symbol $[ij;k] = p_{ijk} - p_{ik} p_{jk}$. An important theorem of latent structure analysis shows that from the "zero-order marginals" p_i and a number of these various cross-products we are also in a position to compute all the pattern frequencies. It happens that these cross-products and their gen-eralizations are the main device for computing latent parameters from manifest data. It is to this crucial problem that we now turn.

6. THE ACCOUNTING EQUATIONS

Perhaps it will be easier to understand how a pattern fre-quency can be predicted from latent probabilities if we leave the world of algebra for a moment and return to our science fiction world. Let us recall how, according to this model, information is collected. A response pattern comes about by the spinning of sev-eral roulette wheels in sequence. It takes little more than common sense to persuade ourselves that the outcome of the spin of one wheel does not affect the outcome of the spin of another wheel. In more technical language, the events are *independent* of each other.

This principle corresponds to our general notion of "brain washing". Just as a subject does not remember at one trial what he said at a previous interview, he also does not know when he is asked for one question how he responded to another. For a single person, then, defined by his belonging to class x, we presume that

$$p_{ij}^x = p_i^x p_j^x. \tag{1}$$

At this point we should remember what was pointed out on page 361. From Equation 1 we can now also deduce what *proportion* of people *within* class x would give a positive response to both i and j. This idea can easily be generalized to many items and to positive, as well as to negative responses. Suppose that an omniscient observer was able to segregate all the individuals who belong to the same latent class, Class x. These are all the people who have the same electrical charge and therefore share the same profile of wheel settings, p_i^x, for the several test items. If, after administering the test once to all of these people, our observer looks at their response patterns, he will find that they have given a large variety of answer sequences. If he is expecially interested in one, let us say $\{ - + + + - \}$, he can determine its pattern frequency by simple counting. Let us denote what he finds by the obvious symbol $p_{234/15}^x$.

With the help of what the statistician calls an expected value, we can predict to a certain extent what value the observer will find. That is, we can predict, within limits, what $p_{234/15}^x$ will be. Our expectation is that the joint frequency[15] will be approximately equal to the product of the separate frequencies. Stated as an equation:

$$p_{234/15}^x = p_2^x p_3^x p_4^x q_1^x q_5^x \tag{1a}$$

Here the symbol q_i has been used in a familiar way to signify the proportion of people who do not give a positive reply to Item i, but who instead answer negatively:

$$q_i = 1 - p_i$$

Equation (1a) expresses general assumptions of probability theory which can be checked in any elementary text. It summarizes the two basic assumptions implied in our model. These are, first of all, that, within a homogeneous latent class, x, the frequency of positive answers to each item approaches its latent probability, p_i^x, and, secondly, that, within such a homogeneous class, the answer to one question is independent of the answer to any other question.

It is important to recognize that local independence is a property of a latent class, and does not mean that there will be independence in the manifest data for the whole group. In other words, even though answers to two questions may be unrelated in separate latent classes, they are almost certain to be related in the entire sample. This is not as much of a paradox as it might seem. We can show how it happens through a constructed numerical example. Returning to our test of ethnocentrism, let us choose two of the items, each asked in a dichotomous form:

1. I believe that our European allies are much superior to us in strategy and fighting morale.

2. The majority of all equipment used by all the allies comes from American lend-lease shipment.

Disagreement with the first statement is indicative of ethnocentrism, and therefore will be taken as the "positive" response. Agreement with the second statement will be taken as the 'positive" response in that case.

Suppose, further, that we have been able to distinguish three latent classes, one with high ethnocentrism, one with a moderate amount, and one which possesses very little ethnocentric sentiment. Then, according to our assumption, there will be local independence (i.e., independence within each of the latent classes). This means that, if we cross-tabulate responses to the two items, we will find something like the following:

	Class 1 (High Ethnocentrism)				Class 2 (Moderate Ethnocentrism)				Class 3 (Low Ethnocentrism)		
Equipment is American:	Allies superior				Allies superior				Allies superior		
	No	Yes			No	Yes			No	Yes	
Yes	9	3	12	Yes	2	2	4	Yes	1	3	4
No	3	1	4	No	2	2	4	No	3	9	12
	12	4	16		4	4	8		4	12	16

There are several points to note in these tables. First of all, we can see quite clearly that the classes, as a whole, answered the two questions differently. In Class 1, that with the highest degree of ethnocentrism, the great majority disagreed that our allies in the last war were superior to us; they also agreed, in the great majority of cases, that most of the equipment used in the war came from the United States. At the other extreme, the persons with little ethnocentrism, in Class 3, denied both our superiority to our allies and the notion that we had supplied most of the equipment. In the middle group, Class 2, opinion on these two items was evenly distributed.

But the second, and more important, aspect of these tables is that, within each of them, answers to the two items are independent. The reader can easily verify this for himself. Within each class we find that the probability of answering the second item positively is the same regardless of what the answer to the first item had been. For example, in Class I, among those who answered the first item "positively," 9 out of 12, or 75 per cent, answered the second item positively; among those who gave a "negative" (not ethnocentric) response to the question about our allies' superiority, 3 out of 4, also 75 per cent, answered the second item positively. Or, in terms of Equation (1) above:

$$p_{12}^x = p_1^x p_2^x$$

which, for Class 1, gives

$$9/16 = (12/16)\,(12/16) = (3/4)\,(3/4).$$

Inspection of the other four-fold tables will show that the same independence exists also in these other latent classes.

But what happens when we add the corresponding cells of the different tables, when, for example, we sum, over all latent classes, those who answered both items "positively"? If we do this for all cells in the tables, we obtain the relationship found in the manifest data. In our numerical example, this yields the following four-fold table:

TOTAL SAMPLE

Equipment is American:	Allies superior		
	No	Yes	
Yes	12	8	20
No	8	12	20
	20	20	40

The independence evident in the separate classes is now replaced by a distinct positive relationship. Now we find that those who answered Item 1 "positively" had a higher probability to answer Item 2 positively than was the case among those who answered Item 1 negatively. In the first group, 12 out of 20, or 60 per cent, answered Item 2 positively, while this was true for only 8 out of 20, or 40 per cent, in the second group. Put differently,

$$[12] = p_{12} - p_1 p_2 > 0$$

The sudden appearance of a relationship where none existed before is not accomplished by any sleight of hand. Instead, it is a result of the fact that the probability of answering each item positively varies substantially and in parallel fashion from class to class; *it is the class-wise variations of these probabilities for both questions which produce the relationship observed in the total sample.*[16]

The same kind of situation is familiar in much empirical social research. We find, for example, that there is a positive relationship between listening to political speeches and doing volunteer work for a political candidate. We wonder whether we might not "account" for this relationship by introducing the concept of "political interest." Accordingly, we classify individuals by the amount of interest they claim to have in political matters, and then examine their behavior to see whether, within any one of the homogeneous interest classes, there is still any relationship between listening to speeches and working for a candidate. If we now find that the two types of behavior are independent of each other in homogeneous interest classes, we say that interest "accounts" for the original relationship.[17]

Much the same kind of logic also applies to latent structure analysis. In essence, the latent characteristic explains interrelationships between the manifest responses and observations. Or, to put it more precisely, these interrelationships between the manifest data *define* the latent characteristic. It is a hypothetical classification which, if carried out, would account for manifest relationships in the sense mentioned above. Unlike other research situations, however, where it is possible to ask people how interested they are in political affairs, this latent characteristic does not exist in any tangible sense. *It is a construct whose existence is inferred from the manifest data.*

We have come full circle and have returned to the distinction between manifest and latent data originally introduced at the end of section 1. We now recognize that when Weber, James, and others talk of making inferences about underlying concepts, they imply an examination of the interrelationships between manifest observations. We also have developed all of the basic ideas which, according to the model of latent structure analysis, permit these inferences.

We have not yet considered, however, the actual procedures by which these inferences are made. Although it will not be possible in this paper to discuss the required computations, we can discuss the *"accounting equations,"* as they are called, which permit the computations.

Let us assume that our omniscient observer has carried out all of his counts in separate latent classes. Could he derive from these counts what a real observer would find in the total sample? The answer is, of course, yes. The total sample consists of an aggregate of all the people in the various latent classes. Therefore, the proportion of people in the total sample giving a certain response pattern is the sum of all these response patterns from all latent classes. Before stating this algebraically, we must add a symbol to denote the size of each latent class. As we indicated incidentally in an earlier section, the proportion of the whole sample belonging to each latent class will be signified by v^x We can then state very easily *how the proportion of respondents in the total sample is related to the corresponding proportions in all latent classes:*

$$p_{234/15} = \Sigma_x v^x p_2^x p_3^x p_4^x q_1^x q_5^x \qquad (2)$$

The reader is asked to focus his attention first on the mere external differences between Equations (1a) and (2). In Equation (2), we do not have the superscript, x, on the left-hand side. This means that the proportion pertains to the whole sample and, further, that it is empirically observed. On the right-hand side of Equation (2) there is a summation sign; this means that we have summed over all latent classes what in Equation (1a) was indicated only for a specific class, x. Equation (2) therefore says this: The manifest proportion giving a certain response pattern in the empirically observed sample can be expressed as the sum, over all latent classes, of a product which is formed in each latent class separately. This product is built up from the latent probabilities which belong to each item in each latent class.

Equation (2) is typical of the many accounting equations that develop in any latent structure analysis. (There are as many such equations as there are different response patterns.) The main task of latent structure analysis, and the point at which the whole problem becomes most difficult, is finding solutions for a total system of these equations. It is obviously not the purpose of the present paper to enter into this mathematical realm. But it is important to get a general idea of what the solutions, once found, are like and how they may be used.

Accounting equations of the kind indicated in Equation (2) have two essentially different uses. First, and most important, they are used to determine the latent parameters. That is, from our knowledge of the manifest proportions, we work back to the underlying p_i^x. There is a second, and perhaps not so obvious, use of the accounting equations. Once we have determined the latent parameters, we can use them to work out what manifest proportions can be expected. This, in turn, serves two functions. It permits us, first of all, to determine how well the model which we have been using *fits* the manifest data; secondly, by working from the latent parameters to expected manifest observations, we have a means of *scoring* tests.

These two uses of the latent probabilities will be discussed and exemplified in the next two sections. Our motives are twofold. The testing of latent structures and the scoring of tests are important problems in their own right. And, in presenting them, we shall go over some of the ground which we have just covered. It is hoped that by doing this with concrete material in mind, many of the general ideas which we have just discussed will be clarified.

7. THE TESTING OF LATENT STRUCTURES

How does one decide whether or not a particular model fits the data we are dealing with? Let us consider a concrete example. The material we have chosen comes from *The American Soldier*.[18] During the last war, the Research Branch made numerous efforts to gauge the adjustment of soldiers. Four questions which seemed to Stouffer and his associates characteristic indices of morale, and which they therefore used extensively, read as follows:

(1) In general, how would you say you feel most of the time, in good spirits or low spirits?

(Positive response: I am usually in good spirits.)

(2) If it were up to you to choose, do you think you would do more for your country as a soldier or as a worker in a war job?

(Positive response: As a soldier.)

(3) On the whole, do you think the army is giving you a chance to show what you can do?

(Positive response: "A very good chance" and "A fairly good chance.")

(4) In general, how well do you think the army is run?

(Positive response: "It is run very well" and "It is run pretty well.")

A positive response to any of these questions was taken as an indication of high morale. Note that the first two questions were "cut" at different points than the last two. In the last two questions, the positive response included an intermediate as well as an extreme statement, while in the first two questions only the extreme position was taken as a positive response.

Making use of the total system of accounting equations, the full response patterns for these four questions were analyzed and a latent class structure obtained. This is reported in Table 1.

TABLE 1

LATENT CLASS STRUCTURE OF FOUR MORALE ITEMS

	LATENT CLASS		
	1	2	3
Item 1: Good spirits	.66	.14	.14
Item 2: Do more as a soldier	.63	.18	.18
Item 3: Army gives a chance	.86	.86	.30
Item 4: Army run well	.90	.90	.52
Number in each latent class	1,155.4	388.1	1,116.5

Table 1 corresponds to the scheme presented earlier (see p. 362, only now we have worked out the probabilities belonging to each class and each item. (The fact that, for each of the items,

two of the three latent classes have the same probability is a computational artifact resulting from the small number of items available for this analysis.)

The structors for Items 1 and 2 resemble each other, as do
those for Items 3 and 4. Treating these as trace-lines, that is,
assuming that we have an infinite, rather than a finite, number of
classes, we obtain the following schematic picture of the way in
which the two sets of items are related to the underlying characteristic, morale:

FIGURE 3

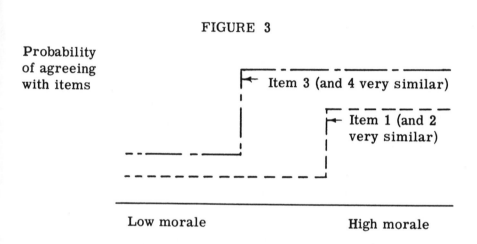

There are two things to be noted about these trace-lines.
First of all, Items 1 and 2 are "stricter" than are Items 3 and 4, in
the sense that only those with high morale agree with them. As we
move from the low to the high end of the x-axis, we find that the
trace-lines for Items 3 and 4 soon go up. Soldiers with even minimum morale concede that the army is rather fair and pretty well
run. But it takes a great deal more underlying morale for a soldier to say that he is usually in good spirits and that he is more
useful as a soldier than as a civilian.

Secondly, the trace-lines for Items 3 and 4 suggest that answers to these questions reflect something more than appraisal of
morale. It will be noted that, in every latent class, agreement with
these items is higher than is agreement with the first two. In fact,
there is more than a 50-50 chance that members of the class with
lowest morale, Class 3, will agree with the fourth item. Careful
reading of the third and fourth questions provides some clue to what
this additional element might be. While the first two items dealt

specifically with the soldier's personal affairs, the last two questions ask also for evaluations of the army as an institution.   In other words, their judgments about "reality" are superimposed on the soldiers' subjective expression of their morale.

But how do we know that the model which we have used here is defensible in the light of the empirical data?

The best way of answering this question is to see what conclusions can be drawn from the model, and then to determine how closely these conclusions correspond with what was observed originally.   On the basis of Table 1 we can work out the number in each class who can be expected to have exhibited a particular response pattern. How closely do these expectations come to the actual situation?

In making our calculations, we use Equation (1). Let us consider the number in Class 1 who can be expected to furnish the pattern $\{+ - + - \}$, positive on Questions 1 and 3, negative on Questions 2 and 4. We shall build up our answer step by step. According to our calculations, there are 1155 soldiers in this latent class. They have a probability of .66 of answering Item 1 positively. This gives $v^1 p_1^1 = 762$ soldiers. It is probable that, of these, a certain number will answer the second item negatively; we know furthermore, that the probability of such a negative response is $q_2^1 = 1 - p_2^1 = .37$. Calling now on our assumption that, within any latent class, replies to different items are made independently, we can determine how many men can be expected to answer the first question positively and the second question negatively, revealing, in other words, a $\{ + - .. \}$ response pattern. This is $(v^1 p_1^1) q_2^1 = 281$. In order to find out how many of these men also answer the third item positively, we must multiply this figure of 281 by p_3^1; when we do this, we find that 247 soldiers remain. Finally, by multiplying this last figure by $q_4^1 = .10$, we find that, in Class 1, 25 soldiers have the response pattern $\{ + - + - \}$. In other words, in order to determine how many men answered with this particular response pattern, we multiplied $v^1 p_1^1 q_2^1 p_3^1 q_4^1$ down the first column of Table 1.

This leads to a simple rule, deriving from Equation (1) above: In order to compute the frequency of a specific response pattern in a given latent class, we multiply the appropriate probabilities, p and q, and the class-frequency in a column like those found in Table 1. If we want to find out how many persons *in the total sample* can be expected to have furnished a particular response pattern, we sum this pattern across all latent classes, as indicated by Equation (2).

In Table 2 these computations have been carried out for each of the 16 possible response patterns in all three latent classes. The different response patterns are listed down the side of the page, and, in each, responses to the four questionnaire items are listed from left to right. Each figure therefore represents the number of soldiers in a particular latent class who can be expected to have manifested a given response pattern.[19] In another column, entitled "Generated Frequencies," the pattern frequency in each latent class has been summed over all of the classes to obtain the pattern frequency for the total sample.

A total scheme like that of Table 2 (with the exception of the last column) will be called a system of *generated data*. They resemble manifest data, but they are not obtained through direct observation. Instead, they are derived from a pre-existing latent structure.

With these generated data, we can determine how well the particular model which we have used corresponds to the manifest observations. We can do this by comparing the generated frequencies of the several response patterns with those actually observed. In the last column of Table 2, we report the numbers of soldiers who actually exhibited the different response patterns. We find, for example, that while 385 soldiers actually gave positive answers to all four test items -- the { + + + + } pattern -- our latent structure analysis would lead us to expect 388.3 individuals with this pattern of response. Similar comparison of the two columns will reveal that there is generally a close correspondence between the generated and observed frequencies. There are some deviations, but, by and large, these are small.[20] We have a high degree of confidence, therefore, that the particular model which we have chosen to apply to these four morale questions does indeed correspond to the manifest situation. The conclusions which we draw from this model are not widely at variance with what actually happened.

8. THE ORDERING AND SCORING OF RESPONSE PATTERNS

Generated data of the kind reported in Table 2 are thus useful in helping us to decide whether the mathematical model which we have been using is actually applicable to a given set of manifest data. But they also serve another important function.

As we stated earlier, the latent structure model assumes that each individual in the sample belongs to a particular latent

TABLE 2

THE COMPLETE LATENT STRUCTURE
(GENERATED DATA)
OF THE SOLDIER MORALE TEST

Response Pattern	Latent Classes			Generated Frequencies	Observed Frequencies
	1	2	3		
++++	376.9	7.8	3.6	388.3	385
+-++	217.2	35.3	16.5	269.0	267
-+++	193.4	46.6	21.9	261.9	252
+++-	40.0	.8	3.3	44.1	42
++-+	60.9	1.2	11.3	73.4	71
--++	111.5	212.5	99.7	423.7	439
+---	3.7	.6	47.1	51.4	54
-+--	3.4	.8	62.2	66.4	59
--+-	11.8	22.6	91.0	125.4	123
---+	18.0	34.4	310.5	362.9	353
----	2.0	3.6	283.6	289.2	286
++--	6.5	.1	10.4	17.0	25
+-+-	23.1	3.7	15.2	42.0	36
+--+	35.1	5.7	51.6	92.4	98
-++-	20.6	4.9	20.0	45.5	56
-+-+	31.3	7.5	68.6	107.4	114
TOTALS	1155.4	388.1	1116.5	2660.0	2660

2660.0

class. Since there is no way to determine directly in which class he belongs, we must make inferences. In this connection, the generated system proves useful once more.

Let us start out with the notion of *recruitment*. So far we have made use of our model to determine how many people in each of the several latent classes will answer the test items with a particular response pattern. We have seen that it is possible to generate data, on the basis of the latent probabilities, through which this question can be answered.

Now let us turn the question around and ask how many, out of the total number of individuals with a particular response pattern, come from each of the several latent classes. In other words, we want to know how the various response patterns are recruited.

This we can find out by looking across the rows in Table 2. We find that, according to the generated data, 269 respondents answer the four morale items with the response pattern { + - + + }. Of these, 81 per cent come from Class 1, 13 per cent from Class 2, and 6 per cent from Class 3. Comparable statements can be made about the other response patterns.

The arrangement of the 16 response patterns in Table 2 is not accidental. We have grouped them into four clusters according to their recruitment pattern. The first group contains those response patterns which recruit most of their respondents from the high morale class, Class 1. It will be noted that this group includes all of the patterns in which at least three of the four items were answered positively. The third group consists of response patterns which draw the bulk of their recruits from the class with low morale, Class 3. Here, too, the response patterns making up this group have distinctive character. In all of them, there are at least three negative responses to the four items. There is only one response pattern, { - - + + }, which recruits the majority of its respondents from the middle latent class, Class 2. (The remaining response patterns, those making up the fourth group, will be discussed presently.)

This kind of information enables us to make inferences about the latent class from which a particular individual comes. From the manifest data, we know what response pattern the individual had; from the data generated by the latent parameters, we know the recruitment pattern of his sequence of answers. We thus have a means of assigning him to one or another of the latent classes. We do this by placing him in the class from which the *majority* of respondents with that response pattern have come. That is, we assign him to the *modal* class.

It is important to recognize that these inferences about the
class position of given respondents are made only with a certain
degree of probability. We can say that a soldier with the response
pattern $\{+ + + +\}$ has a probability of .81 of belonging in Class
1, and that another with the response pattern $\{- - - -\}$ has a
probability of .98 of belonging in Class 3. But Table 2 indicates
that there are a few people with the "best" response pattern who
come from Class 3, and conversely, a few with the "worst" response pattern who are recruited from Class 1.

This procedure of assigning individuals to the modal class
of their response pattern is thus a rather gross method of ordering response patterns. We inevitably make a large number of
errors, some of them more serious than others. Consider the response pattern $\{- - + +\}$, for example. According to the generated data, exactly 50 per cent of the respondents with this pattern come from Class 2. If we assigned all individuals with this
particular sequence of answers to the second class, therefore, we
would misclassify about 50 per cent of them. Similar errors will
be made in connection with all of the other response patterns.

But an even more serious problem arises in connection with
several response patterns which have not been considered yet.
This is the group listed at the bottom of Table 2 which consist, in
every case, of two positive and two negative replies to the four
items. In every one of these instances, the response sequences
show a pattern of bi-modal recruitment. This is, the respondents
are more likely to have come from Class 1 or from Class 3 than
from Class 2. This makes it very difficult, if it is possible at all,
to decide which is the modal class to which the individuals should
be assigned. Take the response pattern $\{+ - - +\}$, for example.
According to the generated data, there are 92 persons with this
response pattern, 38 per cent of them from Class 1, 55 per cent
from Class 3, and 7 per cent from Class 2. It is true that a bare
majority comes from the class with lowest morale, but more than
one-third come from the other end of the established order of
latent classes. By assigning all persons with the $\{+ - - +\}$ response pattern to Class 3, then, we would make large errors. Not
only would we misclassify nearly half of these individuals, but in
a large number of cases the misclassification would be serious.
It therefore seems unwise to classify people whose response patterns show this bi-modal recruitment. Because a bi-modal response pattern quite clearly includes two distinct types of respondents, the safest procedure might be to refrain from labelling
either of them as being the modal class.

The attribution to latent classes which we have discussed so far has still another disadvantage as a device for ordering response patterns. It divides the response patterns into a limited number of groups only. In the present example, where we have three latent classes, it is possible to order the 16 patterns into 3 groups alone. Could we not find a more sensitive method through which finer distinctions can be made?

If we could assign values to the latent classes we would have a simple procedure for doing this. These values might be arbitrary, but they need not always be so.[21] Thus, we might assign a value of plus one to the highest morale class (1), a value of minus one to Class 3, and a value of 0 to Class 2. Each response pattern can then be scored by averaging the score value of its latent recruitment. For example, the position score for the response pattern $\{ + - + + \}$ would be established in the following way:

TABLE 3

THE COMPUTATION OF A POSITION SCORE

Class No.	Class Value	No. of Cases	Total Value
1	+ 1	217.2	217.2
2	0	35.3	0
3	- 1	16.5	-16.5
		269.0	200.7

The average class value for this pattern would therefore be $200.7/269 = .78$. In this way, we get a series of mean scores for all of the response patterns. These are reproduced in Column B of Table 4.

In this sense, then, *a score value is the average latent class position of the respondents who exhibit a given response pattern.* Or, in statistical terms, it is the expected class position of a single person who furnishes a given response pattern.

This method has one important advantage over the usual scoring procedure. We do not order response patterns only by

TABLE 4

THE POSITION SCORES FOR ALL 16 RESPONSE
PATTERNS OF A MILITARY MORALE TEST

A Response Pattern	B Mean Score	C Score Dispersion
++++	.96	.06
+++-	.83	.29
+-++	.78	.32
++-+	.68	.53
-+++	.66	.38
--++	.03	.50
+-+-	-.19	.55
-++-	-.01	.90
+--+	-.18	.62
++--	-.23	.95
-+-+	-.34	.81
--+-	-.63	.42
---+	-.83	.22
+---	-.84	.28
-+--	-.89	.20
----	-.97	.05

the number of positive replies. If we did, we would not distinguish between, let us say, $\{ + - + + \}$ and $\{ - + + + \}$. But Table 4 shows that the first pattern is nearer the top of the order. By using the mean latent position we can thus make finer distinctions.

But we need not stop here. Once we know how people are distributed over the latent classes, we can use other indices of this distribution to characterize a response pattern further. An obvious extension would be to compute a *measure of dispersion,* for example, the variance or standard deviation of class position.

Column C of Table 4 lists the variances as computed from Table 2. This makes it possible to distinguish the different kinds of middle patterns which we have discussed before. From knowledge of the average alone, it is hardly possible to distinguish the two patterns $\{ - - + + \}$ and $\{ - + + - \}$; the former has a score of .03 and the latter a score of -.01. But they differ significantly in their dispersion. The true middle pattern, $\{ - - + + \}$, has a variance of .50; the bi-modal pattern, $\{ - + + - \}$, has a variance of .90.

This extension of the notion of test scores might have considerable practical importance in future empirical investigation. There should be quite a number of problems where the latent dispersion of a response pattern is a more important index than its latent average. Patterns with high dispersion might be considered to be recruited from such heterogeneous groups that little can be predicted about them. Be that as it may, the main point to keep in mind is this: The latent structure scheme redefines the usual test score as one of the parameters of a distribution over latent classes; by doing so, it permits an extension of scoring to the notion of latent dispersion of a response pattern, a concept which cannot be derived from a mere inspection of manifest data.[22]

9. THE VARIETY OF LATENT STRUCTURES

General accounting equations of the kind introduced at the end of Section 6 cannot be solved without specific assumptions. We might stipulate, for instance, that the trace-lines be polynomials of a certain degree. Or we might say that, for practical purposes, we shall be satisfied with the assumption that the distribution of the population over the latent continuum is described by a relatively simple type of distribution function. If such assumptions are introduced, then it is possible to compute the actual coefficients of the trace-lines or the parameters of the latent distribution curve. We must keep in mind the fact that the validity of a specific set of assumptions can always be tested. Section 7 contained some general ideas as to how a latent model is checked against manifest data.

In a general way latent structure analysis proceeds in the following steps:
1. We obtain manifest data, the response patterns of a group of people to a set of items.
2. (a) In some way, we form an estimate as to what model is likely to fit these data or,

(b) we have systematic reasons to be interested in one specific model; if so we proceed immediately to Step **3**.
3. We compute the latent parameters of this model.
4. We generate from the latent structure the response patterns which should be found if the model fits the data perfectly.
5. By comparing the generated and original data, we decide whether our choice of model was justified.
6. If it was justified, then our task is completed. If it was not, we proceed in one of two ways: 7 (a) or 7 (b).
7. (a) We were originally just groping for a helpful latent structure, mainly guided by the data rather than by systematic considerations. We then might try another model and see whether it fits better.

(b) Our choice of model was originally guided by strong theoretical considerations; then we try to understand in the light of the content of our data why the model does not fit. We finally decide that there was something wrong either with our theory or with the indices chosen for empirical work.

At the moment of this writing the models fall into two main groups. On the one side we have the discrete class models, of which section 7 has given a simple example. Their accounting equations have been solved in full generality. As a matter of fact, several solutions are available, each serving well for different purposes. We shall see presently that these models bear a close relationship to factor analysis. They are, for example, appropriate to the following kind of problem. Suppose that a sample of subjects is shown a list of radio programs and is asked to check whether or not they listen to each program. W.A.Gibson has shown that it is possible to derive a typology of listeners from data of this kind.[23] Lee Wiggins has made interesting applications of this model to problems of item reliability in interviewing procedures.[24]

It is worthwhile to mention that the idea of discrete latent classes is not necessarily only an approximation to reality. A good example of how such discrete classes correspond to a realistic situation is found in lie-detector experiments. Suppose a group of people is asked to write down either an odd or an even number, and then all of them are instructed to claim that they wrote even numbers. Those, then, that wrote down odd numbers are "liars;" if we test them with a set of lie detectors, they should show positive reactions. Suppose that 4 or 5 different lie detectors are used with

each person, some based on blood pressure, others on skin re-
flexes, and so on. Not all of the detectors will be infallible. Some
"liars" will not be detected and some "innocent" respondents will
appear to be lying. The reader is invited to think about this situation carefully. Our manifest data will be the reactions registered
on the lie detectors. From these manifest data we can compute two
latent classes, those who presumably wrote odd numbers and those
who presumable wrote even numbers. After this computation has
been carried through, we can then actually check whether our latent structure analysis was correct. This is possible because we
can find out in which of the two classes each person really belongs.
In actual applications of latent structure analysis this knowledge is
not available, of course; but it is useful to see that situations can
be created where the validity of a latent structure model can be
checked.

We are now turning to the second group, the continuous
models, for which a general description was given in section 4.
The cases which so far have been analyzed in detail are all deriv-
ative of the trace-line $p(x) = y = a + b(x - c)^d$. By putting restrictions on the coefficients of this equation, various practically
useful models can be completely solved.[25] Two of these cases have
proven applicable to a considerable amount of empirical data. One
is the latent distance scale.[26] A special case of a latent distance
scale is the Guttman scale. Its trace-lines have probabilities of
either zero or one, meaning that at any point on the latent continuum
either all members of a latent class or none of them gives a positive response to the item in question. Harvard is at this moment
doing extensive work on this type of model, under the direction of
S. A. Stouffer.[27] Another important model is characterized by
linear trace-lines. It is likely to become especially useful for projective tests; for the psychological significance of such trace-lines
is that the items used in the test do not permit the respondent to
see what position his answer indicates.[28] More recently the
Harvard group has developed an H-scale which is a combination of
a latent distance scale and a latent dichotomy model.[29]

This brief survey of actual work in progress should not be
left without mentioning the status of the sampling problem. T. W.
Anderson has developed the first steps of a sampling theory; this
is presented in a recent RAND memorandum. The Computing Division of the Santa Monica RAND office has carried out elaborate
experiments with random numbers, along lines developed by
Mosteller.[30] The findings bear out Anderson's approach and turned
out to be very helpful in facilitating practical computations.

It seems appropriate, finally, to point out how latent structure analysis is related to the work of other students concerned
with similar problems.

Our manifest materials are itemized tests. Measurements
can be developed from other kinds of manifest data, for instance,
from rank orders or paired comparisons. There, too, models must
be developed to relate manifest and latent data. But the models
are usually rather different, and therefore the algebra, the practical applications and many other aspects of model construction
also differ. It will be interesting in the future to see how these
various models are related to each other. In the present context,
the main point to keep in mind is that different kinds of manifest
data require different latent models.

When the manifest data are the same, it should be possible
to relate any kind of statistical treatment to latent structure analysis. A good example in point is the well-known Thurstone-Chave
attitude scale. This also consists of a list of items, but "judges"
are introduced into the development of the measuring instrument.
The judges divide the items among 11 piles, and therefrom a weight
for each item is derived. These weights, then, are applied when
the response patterns of the subjects (to be distinguished from the
judges) are scored

Thurstone and Chave, in their original publication, make the
following remark:

> "Ideally, the scale should perhaps be constructed by means of
> voting only. It may be possible to formulate the problem so that
> *the scale values of the statements may be extracted from the
> records of actual voting.* If that should be possible, then the pres-
> ent procedure of establishing the scale-values by sorting will be
> superseded."[31]

It can be shown that latent structure analysis performs this
task. The latent classes are derived from the "votes" of the subjects, but they correspond to the piles used by the judges. It would
be too involved to prove this interrelationship here.

There are other measuring devices which use a different
terminology, but which are logically equivalent to itemized tests.
Lloyd Warner, for instance, has developed a rating of social stratification which divides people into six social classes, beginning
with "upper-upper" and ending with "lower-lower." These six
classes are logically equivalent to Thurstone's piles. Peter Rossi
has shown that, step by step, the Warner procedure can be translated into a latent structure analysis. As a matter of fact, such a

translation clarifies quite a number of controversial points in the Warner technique.[32]

The Guttman scale and the Bogardus social distance scale also make use of itemized tests. They can be reinterpreted quite directly in terms of latent structure analysis; both turn out to be special cases of latent distance scales. The matter is not so simple for Guttman's theory of principal components. Whether there is any relationship between this theory and latent structure analysis is a challenging topic for future investigation.

The relationship to factor analysis is very interesting. Many authors have pointed to the need for a method of factor analysis applicable to qualitative data. There is general agreement on a negative point: It is not justifiable to apply arbitarary coefficients to four-fold tables, and then to submit these coefficients to a factor analysis. As has been mentioned before, the model of unordered, discrete latent classes is certainly one way in which the basic logic of factor analysis can be applied to qualitative data. But there are probably other ways, as well. One further relationship has been pointed out by Bert Green, Jr.[33] W. A. Gibson has also shown many parallels in the algebra of factor analysis and latent structure analysis, as has been mentioned before. There is certainly one logical feature which the two approaches have in common. Most authors agree that there are two basically different ways of treating empirical data: We can either work with an outside criterion, or we can confine ourselves to an intrinsic analysis of the data. The approach presented in this paper obviously makes use of the second technique.

There can be little doubt that, as work continues, further interrelationships will appear. T. W. Anderson, for instance, has shown that latent structure analysis has its place in the application of stochastic processes to the treatment of time series, the elements of which are attitudes. It is not unlikely that the economist concerned with the measurement of utility will find the logical machinery of latent structure analysis useful. Some work in medical statistics is also pertinent, as, for instance, when the results of different diagnostic tests have to be reconciled. It is the conviction of this writer that a mathematical model in the social sciences benefits, rather than suffers, by being just one further step in an intellectual development of which many other workers in the field have been aware.

8. *Some Strategic Considerations in the Construction of Social Science Models* [1]

By **HERBERT A. SIMON**

Carnegie Institute of Technology

Section I. MODELS OF OPTIMIZATION

It is my aim in this paper to discuss some problems of strategy in theory construction in the social sciences. To put the matter more modestly, I should like to set forth, illustrate, and discuss some of the basic strategic considerations that have guided my own work in the formulation of theories -- and particularly mathematical theories -- of various aspects of human behavior.

The undertaking requires some preface. First, I should like to rule out of bounds the question of whether mathematics has any business in the social sciences. I will simply assert, with J. Willard Gibbs, that mathematics is a language; it is a language that sometimes makes things clearer to me than do other languages, and that sometimes helps me discover things that I have been unable to discover with the use of other languages. What the contribution of mathematics will be to the social sciences can perhaps be more fruitfully evaluated some generations hence when that contribution -- if any -- has been made.

Second, we shall be concerned with *applied* mathematics, and hence we shall be as concerned with the field of application as with mathematics itself. The strategy of mathematical theorizing must come primarily from the field about which the theorizing is to be done. The aim of a language is to say something -- and not merely to say something about the language itself. Mathematical social science is, first and foremost, social science. If it is bad social science (i.e., empirically false), the fact that it is good mathematics (i.e., logically consistent) should provide little comfort.

In the first section, I should like to comment, in a completely unmathematical fashion, upon certain current trends in social science research that have an important bearing upon the strategy of theory construction. In succeeding sections of this and the following chapter I shall attempt to draw out more specifically the implications of these basic trends, illustrating the discussion with a few of the relatively primitive mathematical social science models that are now in existence.[2]

THE REINTEGRATION OF THE SOCIAL SCIENCES

The social sciences -- weakened by a half-century of schisms among economists, political scientists, sociologists, anthropologists, and social psychologists -- are undergoing at present a very rapid process of reintegration. This development is so rapid, and so obvious from even a casual survey of the journals and new books in these fields, that it hardly requires documentation.[3] The common diplomatic language for the scientists participating in the process is the language of sociology and social psychology, and the common core of theory -- the rules of international law, if you like -- is theory drawn primarily from those two fields.

An important cause of this development is that, in attempting to understand and analyse the large events in the political and economic scene -- the wars, elections, and depressions -- the social scientist has been forced to a recognition that all such events are aggregated from the interrelated behavior of human beings. The theoretical models, and the predictions based on models, of the larger scene have required him to make assumptions (explicit or implicit) about the motives, understandings, and abilities of these human beings. Critical attention to these assumptions, and a desire to validate them in a scientifically respectable manner, has gradually and inexorably driven social science back to the molecular phenomena of human behavior in a social environment.

Of course, psychological postulates -- generally contrived in the comfort of the armchair -- have long been a part of social science theory. What is new in the present situation is that the student of aggregative phenomena is now confronted with a growing body of social psychological and sociological theory and empirical verification that places a check on his free imagination and requires him to reconcile his postulates with this theory and these data. To state the matter in a more constructive way, social psychology and sociology are, perhaps for the first time, reaching a stage of development where they can make a positive contribution toward the foundations on which the more aggregative theories are built.

MODELS OF EXISTING SOCIO-PSYCHOLOGICAL THEORY

It is from these important trends that I would derive a first canon of strategy. If mathematics is to play an important role in the development of social science theory, then a great deal of experience must be gained as to what kinds of mathematics are likely to be useful, and as to what are some of the promising ways of imbedding fundamental psychological and sociological concepts and phenomena in mathematical models. What form shall human motives take in such models, how shall the rational and the non-rational aspects of human behavior be represented, what kind of mathematical schemes will conveniently represent the interactions of human groups, and so on?

The starting point, if this strategy is adopted, is the task of translating into the language of mathematics some of the concepts and some of the propositions that appear promising and fundamental in the growing body of social-psychological theory. In one sense, such translations will not say anything that is not already known -- they will merely say it in another language. In another sense it is improbable that any great amount of translation of verbal theories into mathematical language can take place without significant advances in the clarity of the concepts imbedded in the theory.

The few areas where any considerable amount of activity of this sort has already been undertaken will suggest what might be accomplished. The most important of these is economics, where, to cite one example from many, the attempt to construct mathematical models of utility theory has rubbed off a great deal of fuzziness from the concept of "rational behavior," and has laid bare some of the basic methodological problems in the operational definition and measurement of "utility."[4] Perhaps these advances could have been made without mathematics, but the fact is that they weren't.

A widespread effort to translate into mathematical language the core of existing social science theories will make another, and very direct, contribution to the reintegration of the social sciences. By translating from the specialized languages of the several social sciences to the common language of mathematics, unsuspected relationships will be discovered among theories that have been developed independently in these several sciences. In later sections of this paper I shall cite some examples of this -- notably an example of two closely related theories, one drawn from the

economist's theory of the firm, the other from the notion of organizational equilibrium discussed by administrative theorists.

NEED FOR A PLURALITY OF MODELS

A second canon of strategy is suggested by the magnitude of
the task proposed. In social psychology today -- much less the
other social sciences -- we do not have a theory, but theories --
disconcertingly many of of them. *Realism would suggest that we
attempt to construct, not a mathematical model, but a plurality of
mathematical models.* Once we have learned to imbed particular
pieces of social reality in particular pieces of theoretical models,
the interconnections among these will begin to suggest themselves.
This has been the path of development of even the most successful
of the sciences.

In the succeeding sections of this paper I shall suggest a
number of central concepts that, I believe, should receive the attention of model builders and I shall survey some of the approaches
that have been employed already to incorporate these concepts in
models.

MODELS OF RATIONAL BEHAVIOR

As far as economic and administrative theory are concerned,
man has been conceived primarily as a rational animal. The concept of rationality has played a prominent, but much less central,
role in the other social sciences. Since economics, of all the social sciences, has had by far the greatest assistance from mathematics, it is not surprising that models of rational behavior are
far more advanced than mathematical models of other aspects of
behavior.

The most advanced theories, both verbal and mathematical,
of rational behavior are those that employ as their central concepts the notions of: (1) a set of alternative courses of action presented to the individual's choice; (2) knowledge and information
that permit the individual to predict the consequences of choosing
any alternative; and (3) a criterion for determining which set of
consequences he prefers. [5] In these theories rationality consists
in selecting that course of action which leads to the set of consequences most preferred. (At a later point of our discussion we will
see that this definition of rationality is somewhat too restrictive,
but we may accept it temporarily as a starting point for analysis.)

Practically the whole of classical economic theory is constructed within the framework of this model. As an example of a
mathematical version of it, which will serve to indicate how a verbal theory can be mathematized, we may take a very simple model
of the theory of the firm. In this simple example there is a single
rational human being, an "entrepreneur" who is operating a firm
that manufactures a single product from a single raw material.
(1) The alternatives open to the entrepreneur are to employ more
or less of the raw material. (2) The consequences of a given course
of action are that he will incur a cost (determined by the price of
the raw material, and the quantity used), and he will receive a revenue (determined by the price of the product, and the quantity produced with the given amount of raw material). We assume that he
knows the price at which any specified amount of raw material can
be bought, the price at which any specified amount of product can
be sold, and the maximum amount of product that can be produced
from a given amount of raw material. That is, he knows his "supply curve, " his "demand curve," and his "production function."
(In this model, the supplier and the consumer need not be regarded
as rational human beings, their behavior being specified and known.)
(3) The entrepreneur's criterion is that he wishes the largest possible profit -- the largest attainable difference between total
revenue and cost of production.

THE MATHEMATICAL TRANSLATION

In the language of mathematics, let y be the quantity of product made, and x the quantity of raw material bought. Let $p = p(y)$
be the price of the product, which is assumed to depend on the quantity sold; and $P = P(x)$ be the price of the raw material, assumed to
depend on the quantity bought. Let the quantity of product obtain-
able from a given quantity of raw material be given by $y = f(x)$.
Then the entrepreneur's alternatives are a range of values of x.
The revenue, $yp(y) = f(x)p(f(x))$, and the cost $xP(x)$, are the consequences which can be calculated when x is known. The criterion is
to maximize the profit, $\pi = yp(y) - xP(x)$, regarded as function of x.
The rational behavior is given by the well-known "marginal"
condition,

$$\frac{d\pi}{dx} = \frac{df}{dx} p[f(x)] + f(x) \frac{dp}{dy} \frac{df(x)}{dx} - P(x) - x\frac{dP}{dx} = 0 \qquad (1)$$

Translating this equation back into English, it says that the rational entrepreneur will fix his output at the point where marginal cost equals marginal revenue.

Several features of this model deserve notice, as generally characteristic of models of rational behavior. Certain variables -- in this case x -- are regarded as "strategic" variables, controllable by a rational being. Other variables -- in this case π -- are the criterion, and measure of the goal he is seeking. The limits of attainment are set by conditions outside his control -- relationships he must accept -- which determine the value of the criterion as a function of the strategic variable. The problem of rationality then becomes a problem in maximization -- to find the greatest value of the criterion, regarded as a function of the strategic variables.

SIGNIFICANCE OF THE LIMITS OF RATIONALITY

If we regard this model as a description of the actual behavior of some entrepreneur, we see that if we are to predict his behavior, the knowledge that he is rational is only a small part -- almost an insignificant part -- of the information that we require. His intention to be rational leads to particular behavior only in the context of conditions in which his behavior takes place. These conditions include both (1) the limits expressed by the demand curve, the supply curve, and the production function -- we might regard these as the limits of his "abilities" in the situation -- and (2) the limits expressed by the criterion function. The criterion (regarded as a "final end") is itself not an object of rational calculation, but a given. The model would be equally a model of rational behavior if the entrepreneur chose to maximize his losses, or his gross revenue instead of his profit.

Indeed, our principal use for such models is in predicting how the entrepreneur's behavior will be affected by a change in the environment that conditions or "bounds" his rationality. For example, we may wish to predict how the price and output of the product will be altered, assuming the entrepreneur always to behave rationally, if there occurs a shift in the demand function. To do this, we can regard the price of the product, p, as depending both on the quantity sold, y, and upon a parameter (i.e., a coefficient regarded as constant in the short run, but as possibly varying in the long run), a, which may vary, for example, with changes in consumers' tastes: $p = p(y,a)$. Each change in a shifts the whole demand curve -- relating p to y -- to right or left. If we follow the maximizing procedure previously described for finding

the optimal value of x, this value will now depend on a --
that is, a will in general appear in equation (1). Hence, we can
regard equation (1) as a statement of relationship between x
and a -- a statement of how production, under the assumption
of the entrepreneur's rationality, will vary with shifts in
demand.[6]

We may summarize our discussion to this point by saying:
that a simple model of rational behavior leads quite naturally to
maximizing procedures and, in mathematical translation, to the
methods of the differential calculus; and that the specific features
of interest in any particular model arise primarily from the particular conditions under which rationality is exercised. This second point perhaps deserves to be dignified as a third canon of
strategy: *In mathematical models incorporating rational and non-*
rational aspects of behavior, the non-rational aspects can be im-
bedded in the model as the limiting conditions that "bound" the
area of rational adjustment.[7]

QUALIFICATIONS ON THE MODEL
OF RATIONAL BEHAVIOR

The previous paragraph registers my conviction that im-
provement in the model of rational behavior will come primarily
through careful attention to the boundaries of the area of rationality. In the remaining sections of this paper, I shall try to make
this recommendation more explicit. We can begin our examination
of these boundaries by looking at some of the extensions and
amendments to the rational model that economists have been led to
by their attempts to extend that model to broader and broader
classes of phenomena.

RATIONALITY OF MORE THAN ONE

The rationality of the classical maximizing procedures is
essentially the rationality of Robinson Crusoe. For each rational
individual in the model must take as fixed "givens" the patterns of
behavior of the other individuals -- he must regard these others
not as rational beings, but as some kind of responsive or unrespon-
sive mechanism. The classical theory found three paths that gave
promise of leading out of this wilderness:

(1) *Perfect Competition.* In the theory of perfect competition, each participant assumes that what he does is such an

insignificant part of the total picture that it will have no effect on the others. Hence, if he can predict the behavior of the others, and adjust his own behavior to the prediction, his adjustment will not have repercussions that would disturb the prediction.

(2) *Imperfect Competition.* If the participants will adjust their behavior to each other, but each participant can predict what the adjustments of the others to his behavior will be, then he can determine which of his own behavior alternatives will be optimal in the light of the prediction. This was our procedure in the simple model used in the previous section. The demand curve and the supply curve each constitutes a prediction of the price that the customer or supplier, respectively, will pay or require for the quantity of product or raw material the entrepreneur decides upon. The customer and supplier are supposed to regard the price as something given -- as something they cannot influence.

(3) *Cournot's Oligopoly Theory.* If the customer and the supplier in the previous case were just one whit cleverer, the solution there given would be untenable. If the entrepreneur assumes they are going to adjust to his behavior, and acts in anticipation of that adjustment, why do not they, in turn, assume that he is going to adjust to their behavior and act in anticipation of that adjustment? The imperfect competition model admits rationality of all participants, but does not permit the same level of cleverness in the customer or supplier as in the entrepreneur. The limits on his rationality, as it is postulated, are broader and less restricting than the limits on theirs -- he tries to outguess them, but they do not try to outguess him.

Cournot sought a way out of this difficulty by permitting *each* participant, in a two-person model, to guess at the reaction of the other, and to behave accordingly. Equality of cleverness was restored, and if dynamic stability was present the actual behaviors would in fact conform to the predicted behavior. (At the equilibrium point, the participants would predict correctly on a wrong basis.) But the Cournot model, while consistent with the assumptions of rationality, is not a model of unlimited cleverness. For either participant, if he knew the other was following the Cournot procedure, could form some new, and more accurate, expectations of that other's reactions to his choices, and use this new prediction to better his position. This way lies madness, for it leads to an infinite regress of prediction in which A predicts what B will predict as to A's prediction of B's reaction to A's behavior -- and so on, ad infinitum. [8]

The conclusion we reach from our examination of models of rationality involving the behavior of more than one person is that

we must adopt one of two alternatives: (a) on the one hand, we can
assume that not more than one participant is unlimitedly clever in
predicting the reactions of the other participants to his behavior;
(b) on the other hand, we can seek a new definition of rationality
that does not identify rationality with a simple maximization process. The first approach -- assumptions of rationality and maximization, but limited cleverness -- is the one involved in all three
paths described above: perfect competition, imperfect competition,
and oligopoly theory. The second approach, abandonment of simple
maximization, was adoped by von Neumann and Morgenstern in
their pioneering work on the theory of games.[9] By replacing the
maximum, in the definition of rationality, with a more sophisticated
mathematical concept, the minimax, the difficulty is avoided[10]--
at the expense of attributing to human beings a cleverness they
have perhaps not often exhibited outside the more successful poker-
playing circles.

No attempt will be made here to evaluate the respective merits of the two approaches to rationality. The von Neumann model
may be the more useful appraoch to the question of optimal be-
vior -- i.e., for a book on how to play successful poker. The model
of limited cleverness may be more useful in the description of
actual rational behavior -- at least until such time as most people
have learned to minimax rather than to maximize.

REACTION TIME--RATIONALITY AND DYNAMICS

The outguessing difficulty is only one of the problems that
can be raised in connection with the classical model. Another is
the question of speed of adjustment. In our simple model of the
theory of the firm, the entrepreneur is assumed to know not only
the shape of the demand curve, but also its position at any given
time -- i.e., the value of the parameter a. For many situations a
more realistic assumption would be that he does not have this detailed knowledge, but only discovers his optimal position by experimenting and learning on the basis of his experience and his
mistakes. For example, he might have some information about
marginal costs and marginal revenue, but only in the neighborhood
of the position in which he is actually operating. He might then
adopt the rule of behavior that he will continue to increase his output so long as his marginal revenue is in excess of marginal cost,
and decrease it whenever he finds marginal cost in excess of marginal revenue. In equations, the assumption is:

$$\frac{dx}{dt} = b \left\{ \frac{df}{dx} p\,[f(x)] + f(x)\,\frac{dp}{dy}\,\frac{df(x)}{dx} - P(x) - x\,\frac{dP}{dx} \right\},\ (b > 0). \quad (2)$$

Now if "other conditions" like the parameter a remain reasonably steady, and if the system satisfies certain other stability
requirements, it turns out that the optimal solution, in the sense
of equation (1), is actually the stable equilibrium position of the
time path described by equation (2)[11]. When this is true, equation
(2) may be taken as a definition of rational behavior under the restrictions of information that have been assumed. *How* rational
it is, will depend, of course, on the size of the coefficient b, which
measures the adjustment rate, for if this coefficient is large the
adjustment and the approach to the equilibrium will be rapid,
while if b is small, the approach will be slow. If, now, a fluctu-
ates moderately (there are shifts from time to time in demand), a
large b will prevent the entrepreneur from ever departing very
widely from the optimal output, while a small b may permit very
wide departures, and consequent loss of profit.

The difference between the kind of rationality depicted in
equation (1) and the kind depicted in equation (2) might be described as follows. Two popcorn men are vending their wares on a very
large county fair ground. Their profits will depend on keeping
their wagons in the part of the fair ground where as dense a crowd
as possible has assembled. The crowd is in continual motion. The
first popcorn man has radio equipment on his wagon on which he
has arranged to receive from all parts of the fair ground frequent
reports on the size of the crowd. As soon as he learns where it is
densest, he speeds to that part of the ground. The second popcorn
man has less modern equipment. He keeps his cart in motion in
the direction of increasing density of the crowd, and away from the
direction of decreasing density.

Amount of Information and Speed of Adjustment. Now if one is
willing to include amount of information and speed of adjustment
among the boundaries of rationality, a large number of interesting
possibilities offer themselves. In the first place, while it seems
to be almost always possible to construct a stable dynamic system
whose equilibrium position corresponds to the maximum of a given
static system, it is often possible to construct more than one such
dynamic system. In terms of our "dynamic" definition of rationality, it would then occur that there would be more than one rational
pattern of behavior in a given situation.

For example, in the usual dynamization of the theory of markets -- leading to the well-known cobweb phenomena -- it is assumed that when supply is out of balance with demand, a price adjustment will take place in the short-run to "clear the market,"
while in the long run, an adjustment in the quantity supplied will

restore the suppliers to their position of profit maximization. An alternative dynamic mechanism can be constructed in which a lack of balance between supply and demand leads to an adjustment in the quantity supplied, while if the current price does not provide suppliers with a "reasonable" profit, a price adjustment takes place. With suitable assumptions, this second model has the same position of equilibrium, and virtually the same stability conditions as the first.

To predict an individual's behavior under these circumstances, we would have to know, not only that he was being rational, but also whether he was exhibiting rationality of species A (corresponding to one dynamic system) or rationality of species B (corresponding to another). In the long run -- in equilibrium -- it would not make any difference, but as Keynes has pointed out, in the long run we are all dead.

Optimizing versus Adaptive Behavior. As we move from the static model to the dynamic, our original definition of rationality (selection of that course of action which leads to the set of consequences most preferred) becomes somewhat too restrictive. On the one hand, we may build the concept of rationality, as in the earlier models, upon the ability of the individual to discover a "best" situation and to move toward it, either instantaneously (as in the static models) or gradually (as in the dynamic). On the other hand, we can base an alternative notion of rationality on the ability of the individual to distinguish "better" (or "preferred") from "worse" directions of change in his behavior and to adjust continually in the direction of the "better." A rational process in which the choice of a "best" is central we will call optimization; a rational process in which movement toward a "better" is central we will call adaptation. Clearly, as is shown by the models of dynamic adjustment toward an optimal equilibrium, the two species of rationality are not mutually exclusive. In spite of the overlap, however, we will find the distinction useful in progressing through the whole continuum of models of rational behavior from those, on the one extreme, incorporating instantaneous optimization to those, at the other extreme, requiring only that minimum of adaptation which may be essential for survival.

Now, taking the next step along the continuum, and freeing the dynamic model we have already discussed from its ties with the corresponding static system, we may view it as follows:

An individual has a certain criterion, by means of which he judges his situation. Call the criterion θ_s. He measures his actual situation, θ_0, and its departure, $(\theta_s - \theta_0)$, from the criterion.

He then adjusts his behavior at a rate that is proportional to the difference between the actual and the criterion. In the model previously discussed, for example, the criterion is that the marginal revenue should equal the marginal cost; the actual situation is described by the difference between the (actual) marginal revenue and the (actual) marginal cost. He then adjusts his behavior -- the variable x -- at a rate assumed to be proportional to this difference. In equations, the system is:

$$\theta_s = 0 \tag{3}$$

$$\theta_0 = \left\{ \frac{df}{dx} \, p \, [f(x)] \, + \, f(x) \, \frac{dp}{dy} \, \frac{df(x)}{dx} \, - \, P(x) \, - \, x \, \frac{dP}{dx} \right\} \tag{4}$$

$$\epsilon = \theta_s - \theta_0 = -\theta_0 \tag{5}$$

$$\frac{dx}{dt} = b\epsilon \tag{6}$$

An engineer looking at this model would recognize in it something he is accustomed to call a "servomechanism" or a "closed-loop control system." If we follow the engineer's terminology in calling the difference between the actual state of the system and the criterion an "error," then we may say that the system is an adaptive one in which the individual measures the error in his behavior, and adjusts the behavior seeking to eliminate the error. Norbert Wiener has argued persuasively that the servomechanism model may be a useful model for describing physiological, psychological, and sociological adaptive systems.[12]

There is yet another sense in which the notion of an adaptive system is broader than the notion of optimizing behavior. Optimization carries at least the connotation of conscious deliberation, foresight, and intention. Adaptation, on the other hand, more generally connotes appropriateness for survival, movement toward equilibrium. Now the two notions of optimization and survival are combined in the classical economic theory of pure competition in an ingenious fashion. But there is no reason why we cannot consider systems that are adaptive, in the sense of possessing a stable equilibrium position toward which the system continually moves, without postulating an optimizing mechanism (in the conscious sense) that explains the adaptation. As a matter of fact, refusal to consider such systems would make all of biology hopelessly anthropomorphic. It may be argued that a similar refusal in the social sciences would make those sciences hopelessly economomorphic.

At any rate it would appear that there is a large number of possible dynamic models of social behavior that deserve to be examined quite apart from their possible linkage to models of static optimizing behavior, and quite apart from any insistence that the "criterion" in terms of which the system adjusts need be a conscious goal of rational action. In the next chapter we shall proceed to an examination of several such models, but before we do so, some concluding comments need to be added under the present heading of "Qualifications on the Model of Rational Behavior."

INCOMPLETE INFORMATION AND UNCERTAINTY

In the previous section, we examined one way in which the model of rational behavior can be altered to take account of limits on information and speed of adjustment. In that section we were concerned primarily with the individual's information about the behavior of other individuals. He may also, of course, have incomplete information about the non-human conditions that surround his activity. We may sketch briefly a number of schemes for handling the problem:

(1) We can incorporate the individual's expectations into the behavior model. Then we require a theory of how he forms those expectations -- a theory of his forecast model. His expectations may take the form of specific predictions, or of probability distributions of the predicted variable. If we take the latter alternative, then we may wish to define rational choice as the choice that maximizes the expected value (in the statistical sense) of the criterion variable. This approach adds nothing essentially new to our optimization model. It is the approach that, in combination with the von Neumann game theory, dominates modern statistical theory -- e.g., the Neyman-Pearson theories of testing hypotheses and the sequential analysis theories of Wald.[13]

(2) We can assume that the individual adjusts to his changing situation without forecasting. This leads again to dynamic models of the servo-mechanism type.[14]

(3) We can assume that the individual balances the costs of postponing decisions against the advantages of obtaining additional information before he makes them. Then we are led to the theory of the timing of decisions. J. Marschak has shown how such an approach can be used to explain certain aspects of liquidity preference -- the preference for holding assets in relatively liquid form -- and I have shown that the same approach can be used as a basis for explaining, on rational grounds, the authority relationship

between employer and employee and the comparative advantages of an employment or a sales contract for accomplishing a particular task.[15]

PREFERENCE FIELDS

In our initial model of optimizing behavior, we assumed that a criterion function exists. In the case of the entrepreneur, the criterion function has traditionally been his profit, in the case of the consumer, his "utility." This has led to the question of whether such a function exists, and this question, in turn, to some very fruitful examinations of the whole subject of preference fields. In those cases where we are willing to admit that an unambiguous field exists -- where at the very least, each possible outcome can be judged as "better," "the same," or "worse" than each other possible outcome -- we are assuming again a very global kind of rationality. We are assuming that the individual possesses a very wide span of attention, and a single consistent system of values that he applies simultaneously to the whole range of action.

There has been only a little exploration into the possibilities of models that make less global assumptions about the consistency, comprehensiveness, and stability of the individual's preference field.[16] Yet these limits of rationality -- limits on the consistency of choice -- certainly have empirical importance in many areas of behavior. I can offer at the moment no concrete suggestions as to the way in which such limits can effectively be incorporated in a model, but simply call to the reader's attention this potentially significant area for theoretical work.

CONCLUSION

This completes our survey of the various directions that have been pursued in the construction of models of that species of rational behavior we have called optimization. We have seen that as soon as we begin to introduce limits upon the speed of adjustment and upon the range of alternatives over which choice is exercised, we begin to move from models of optimization to models of adaptation. The next section will be devoted to a further investigation of this latter class of models.

Section II. MODELS OF ADAPTIVE BEHAVIOR

Theory construction, largely the work of mathematical economists, in the area of rational human behavior has been developing, as we have just seen, in the direction of more and more explicit attention to the various limitations upon the capacity of human beings to behave in a "perfectly" rational fashion. Of the various amendments to the classical model, perhaps the most radical is the one -- leading to dynamics -- that shifts the focus from "optimal" behavior to "adaptive" behavior. In the present section I shall explore some of the implications of this shift. Rather than to speculate about the problem in the abstract, our procedure will be to exhibit several models that show how various kinds of behavior, viewed as an adaptive process, can be handled. We will begin with a model of individual behavior, and proceed to some models of behavior in groups.

MOTIVATION AND LEARNING

In psychological formulations of adaptive human behavior, the concepts of motivation and learning are central.[17] The notion of motivation is closely connected with the "criterion" in the models of optimization, while learning is connected with changes in such limitations on rationality as "state of information" and "technology." In the present model we shall not attempt any further exact translation from the previous concepts, but will start afresh.

THE "BERLITZ" MODEL

We suppose that there is an activity in which an individual engages from time to time, and that he can engage in varying amounts of it each day. As he engages in it, it becomes progressively easier for him (this is our "learning" assumption). To the extent that he finds it pleasant, he engages in it more frequently; to the extent he finds it unpleasant, he engages in it less frequently. Its pleasantness depends on how easy it is for him. (The latter two statements comprise our "motivation" assumption.)

As a concrete example, we may suppose that our individual has subscribed to a correspondence course to learn French by the Berlitz method. Each day he spends a certain amount of time in practice. As he practices, the language becomes easier; so long as the difficulty is greater than a certain level, he finds the work unpleasant, and tends to shorten his practice sessions. (We assume our student to be a kind of hedonist.) If he reaches a certain level of skill, however, the work becomes pleasant, and he will tend to practice for a longer period.[18]

Let x be the rate (say, in hours per day) at which the activity is performed. Let D be the level of difficulty, and let us assume (learning) that the difficulty decreases logarithmically with practice:

$$dD/dt = -aDx \qquad (7)$$

Let us assume that at any given level of difficulty, practice is pleasurable up to a certain point, and unpleasant beyond that point, and that $x = \bar{x}(D)$ is this satiation level of activity. We assume then (motivation) that:

$$dx/dt = -b(x - \bar{x}) \qquad (8)$$

The two equations for dD/dt and dx/dt permit us to predict the time paths of D and x if we know their initial values, D_0 and x_0 at time t_0. Several representative time paths are shown in Figure 1.

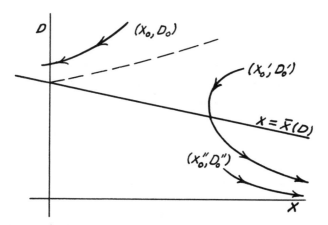

Figure 1.

The figure shows that whether our student eventually becomes discouraged and fails to complete his course, or whether he is successful in learning French depends on his starting point (and, of course, on the relative magnitudes of a and b and the shape of $\overline{x}(D)$). The value of D_0 represents the difficulty of the language to him at the outset, and x_0 the amount of time he initially devotes to practice. If the point (x_0, D_0) lies above the dotted line, he will ultimately become discouraged and give up his lessons; if, instead, he begins at (x_0', D_0'), between the dotted line and the line $x = \overline{x}(D)$, he will suffer some discouragement at the outset, but practice will ultimately become pleasant and he will learn the language. If he begins at (x_0'', D_0''), practice will be pleasant from the outset, and he will learn.

Clearly one would want to refine this model before trying to verify it from actual situations, but even in its highly simple form it exhibits some of the qualitative features we would expect to find in such situations, and illustrates in what a natural manner differential equations can be employed in a model of adaptive behavior.

Prediction and Verification. One interesting feature of a model of this sort is that it permits qualitative predictions to be made that are very easy to test empirically. We do not need to trace out in detail the time path of the system, but merely to observe whether the activity terminates before learning was completed, or whether it ends in mastery of the language. With such observations we can test, over a sample of cases, a prediction like: the activity is likely to persist until learning has been achieved only if the initial rate of practice is above a certain critical level.

Multiple Equilibria. Another feature of importance is that the model allows us to deal with behavioral or social systems in which both intermittent forces, which act for a brief period, and continuously acting forces are at play. The intermittent force in this case would be the individual's decision to subscribe to the language course and devote a certain amount of time to practice (i.e., the determinants of the initial position). The continuous forces would be the process of learning and the varying motivation as the resolution was actually carried out (i.e., the forces determining the path from the initial position). A Spencer would say that the final outcome is determined by the continuous interplay of forces immanent in the behavioral interaction itself; a Bentham would say that the outcome is determined by the intermittent intervention -- the determination of the initial conditions.[19] The two views are in fact not contradictory provided the system has more than one position of final equilibrium. In this case an intervention can "jar" the system from one position of equilibrium to another.

A possible application of this notion is to the theory of political and social "reform" movements. It is notorious that such movements are short-lived, at least in their active and influential phases. If they are effective, it must be through disturbance of a system of forces previously in equilibrium, and a sufficient shift in initial conditions to permit the system to move toward a new equilibrium with a different stable constellation of forces.

There would seem to be a wide class of social phenomena that could be studied in terms of a model embodying this feature of multiple equilibria. Gunnar Myrdal's theory of social change appears to be of this sort, as do most theories of revolution.[20] The relationship between "formal" organization (which operates in considerable part through intermittent pressures) and "informal" organization might also be expressed in these terms.[21]

A Social Interpretation of the "Berlitz" Model. It might appear that we are not justified in discussing the applicability to social systems of a model that represents, after all, the behavior of a single human being. In fact, however, the writer was originally led to construct this model in order to represent a social situation. In an organization where accountants were given the task of providing accounting information to operating executives, it was found that if understanding between accountants and operators was good, they tended to communicate frequently with each other; when it was bad, less frequently. Moreover, frequent communication, by helping them understand each others' languages, made communication easier. By renaming the variable x "frequency of communication between accountants and operators," and the variable D "difficulty of communication between accountants and operators," we obtain in the model a clear representation of this social system.

FURTHER COMMENTS ON MOTIVATION

If we compare the notion of motivation in the present model with the notion of a preference field, discussed earlier, we find one important difference that has not been mentioned. In a preference field we can say that one alternative is preferable or "more pleasant" than another, but there is no natural zero-point for pleasantness: we can distinguish more or less of pleasantness, but cannot speak of pleasantness and unpleasantness in any absolute sense. In the "Berlitz" model, the function $\bar{x}(D)$ does define such a dividing line, or zero separating pleasantness from unpleasantness.

We can reconcile the present viewpoint with the earlier one by supposing that our student, if he does not study his language,

can engage in some other activity which, when $x > \bar{x}$, is more
pleasant than the work on his language. Then to say that an activity is "unpleasant" simply means that there is an alternative that
is preferable. The zero-point of preference for an activity is defined by what the economist would call the "opportunity cost" of
the activity.[22]

From the standpoint of psychological theory, however, it
would appear that a "natural" zero-point can be defined with respect to motivation. This zero-point arises from two related
psychological mechanisms. The first of these is the dependence
of strength of motivation upon the relationship between the level
of aspiration and the level of achievement.[23] The second of these
is the qualitative change in motivation that takes place under conditions of frustration.[24]

We take as our independent variable the difference between
the actual level of skill of an individual in performing a task and
the level of skill to which he aspires. If achievement exceeds aspiration, this variable will be positive; if the two are equal, zero;
if aspiration exceeds achievement, negative. Now the psychological evidence would appear to indicate that the strength of drive
toward the activity is related to achievement in somewhat the fashion indicated in Figure 2.

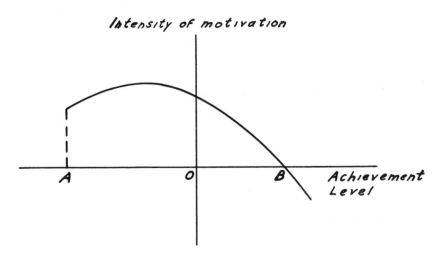

Figure 2.

As the achievement level exceeds B, the drive toward im-
provement of skill disappears. We may call this "satiation." On

the other hand, as the achievement level falls below A, the drive changes its character. Instead of engaging in rational, adaptive behavior, the individual in his frustration engages in behavior best described as non-adaptive or "neurotic."

The evidence generally indicates that frustration will not occur if there are alternative activities available that are regarded as desirable. In this case the aspiration level for the first activity will simply fall, until point B is reached. Frustration occurs when *all* alternatives are regarded by the individual as distinctly unpleasant -- when he is faced with a dilemma rather than a choice. But this distinction between dilemma and choice suggests, again, a natural zero of motivation which is distinct from the zero of satiation. The latter would seem to correspond best with the notion of zero opportunity cost.

EQUILIBRIUM IN GROUP INTERACTION

The previous section suggests that in the study of human and social adaptive systems we may be interested not only in the mechanism of adaptation, but also in the possible states of equilibrium of the system. In the present section we will examine a system of social interaction with primary emphasis on equilibrium, and will return more specifically to the question of adaptation in the next section.

THE HOMANS MODEL

The system to be examined has some intrinsic interest in that it appears to represent fairly well in a formal model some of the theoretical relations postulated by George Homans in *The Human Group*.[25] Homans' system contains four variables (his treatment of them is, of course, verbal rather than mathematical):

(1) The intensity of interaction (or communication) among the members of a group; we will designate it by $T(t)$.

(2) The amount of friendliness (or group identification) among group members; we will designate it by $I(t)$.

(3) The total amount of activity carried on by a member of the group; we will designate it by $W(t)$.

(4) The amount of activity imposed on the group by its external environment (the amount required for its survival); we will designate it by $F(t)$. (Homans also calls it the activity required for survival, the "external system.")

Each of the variables is written as a function of time, and each of the first three is supposed to be some kind of average of the levels for the individual members of the group. Homans nowhere explicitly states his postulates regarding the interrelations of these variables, but the postulates he actually employs would seem to be contained in the following statements:

"If the scheme of activities is changed, the scheme of interaction will, in general, change also, and vice versa."[26]

"Persons who interact frequently with one another tend to like one another."[27]

"If the interactions between the members of a group are frequent in the external system, sentiments of liking will grow up between them, and these sentiments will lead in turn to further interaction over and above the interactions of external system."[28]

"Persons who feel sentiments of liking for one another will express those sentiments in activities over and above the activities of the external system, and these activities may further strengthen the sentiments of liking."[29]

"The more frequently persons interact with one another, the more alike in some respects both their activities and their sentiments tend to become."[30]

A MATHEMATICAL TRANSLATION

Now these five statements can be approximately translated into three equations among our four variables. The first equation will be algebraic -- representing an "instantaneous" or very rapid adjustment. The other two will be differential equations determining paths over time.

$$T = a_1 I + a_2 W \qquad (9)$$

$$\frac{dI}{dt} = b (T - \beta I) \qquad (10)$$

$$\frac{dW}{dt} = c_1 (I - \tau W) + c_2 (F - W) \qquad (11)$$

The first equation may be translated, roughly: interaction will be produced by friendliness and/or group activity. The second: friendliness will tend to increase or decrease as the amount of interaction is disproportionately large or disproportionately small, respectively, in relation to the existing level of friendliness. (The two variables will be in adjustment when $T = \beta I$) The third:

group activity will tend to increase as the level of friendliness is high relative to the existing level of activity (the two being in equilibrium when $I = \gamma W$), and as the requirements of the external system are high relative to the existing level of activity, otherwise group activity will tend to decrease.

By studying these translations -- or better, by studying the equations themselves -- in relation to Homans' postulates, the reader can judge for himself how well we have succeeded in capturing the essential features of Homans' system in our equations. In any event it is unnecessary to concern ourselves here with the exactness of the representation or the empirical correctness of his postulates.

Now systems of the kind we have just written down (linear differential equations with constant coefficients) are well known to the mathematician, and he can provide us with a well-stocked kit of tools for analysing their behavior. Without going into details of method or result, it may be stated that he can easily find: (1) the equilibrium position of this system, (2) the conditions under which this equilibrium is stable and unstable, and (3) the precise time path the system will follow from any initial position.[31]

Social Disintegration. Among the conclusions that can be drawn from the purely mathematical properties of the system is the following:

If the system represented by equations (9) - (11) is dynamically stable, then as the system of externally imposed activities, F, decreases toward zero, the amounts of interaction, friendliness, and group activity will decrease toward zero (with a lag).

But this is precisely the hypothesis that Homans employs to explain social disintegration in Hilltown,[32] and to explain the difference in extension between the primitive and modern family.[33] Our formal model permits us to demonstrate rigorously that this is not an independent hypothesis, but follows logically from the other postulates if only the system is assumed to be dynamically stable.

Morale and "Anomie". We will cite one further example of the conclusions that mathematical reasoning permits us to draw from the model. One of Homans' empirical statements is that a social group will tend to develop a system of activities more elaborate than that needed to satisfy the requirements of the external system. In one sense we have already incorporated this statement in equation (11) -- for this equation says that W will tend to increase not only if F is greater than W, but also when I is greater than γ W.

That is, friendliness, as well as external requirements can be a source of group activity. But does it follow from this that, when the system has attained equilibrium, W will be greater than F?

Let us define a group as possessing "positive morale" if, when the group is in a state of equilibrium, W exceeds F -- the actual level of activity is higher than that required for survival. When this condition is not satisfied, we will say that the group possesses "negative morale." It can be shown from equations (9) - (11) that the group will possess positive morale if and only if $a_2 > \gamma(\beta - a_1)$. To see what the condition means we note that, in particular, it will be satisfied if a_2 is sufficiently large -- that is, if the amount of interaction required per unit of group activity is large. This can be stated in still another way: group morale will be positive if there is a sufficiently high degree of interrelation among the members' tasks, requiring much communication for their performance. But this is, in substance, the central proposition of Durkheim's theory of *anomie* -- a proposition that has received considerable empirical verification in work situations from the Hawthorne studies and their successors.[34]

RELATION TO THE EARLIER MODEL

These two examples will serve, I hope, to whet, if not to satisfy, the reader's appetite for empirically verifiable propositions derivable from our three mathematical postulates. We will leave this system with a final observation as to its possible relation to the motivation-learning model discussed in the previous section. Equations (9) and (11) may be regarded as statements of motivation: the former says that interaction is motivated by friendliness and group activity, the latter that activity is motivated by friendliness and the requirements of group survival. Equation (10) may be regarded as a learning process: Interaction develops friendliness. Hence the two systems may be interpreted as special cases of a broader class of systems in which group relationships are determined by a system of motivational and learning processes.

GROUP SURVIVAL

In the "Berlitz" model, motivation to perform a task was assumed to depend on the pleasantness of the task (i.e., the task was assumed to be pleasant if it was not too difficult). In the "Homans" model, one of our motivational assumptions was that the

necessity of group activity for group survival provided an inducement to group activity (this is incorporated, as has been pointed
out, in the last term of equation (11)). The first ("Berlitz") assumption is plausible from the standpoint of individual psychology,
but the second has no immediate explanation in these terms. To
provide a psychological basis for deriving the proposition that
"members of a group will be motivated to activity" from the proposition that "activity is essential to survival," we must postulate
that the members of the group wish it to survive. What kind of
model of the relation of the individual to the group can we construct that will make such a postulate plausible?

TWO THEORIES OF SURVIVAL

Two general paths appear to be open. On the one hand we
can adopt a "sociological" hypothesis that the values an individual
possesses are, in large part, the internalization of values the society inculcates in him. If this is so, then those societies would
tend to survive that inculcated in their members values conducive
to the society's survival. In the "selection of the fittest" among
societies, there would tend to be present among the survivors motivational forces like those expressed in equation (11).

On the other hand we can adopt the "economic" hypothesis
that each member of a group calculates, on the basis of given values, whether he prefers to remain in the group or leave it. Those
groups would then tend to survive that provided satisfaction to the
values of their individual members. Moreover, if certain members
of a group found a great advantage, from the standpoint of their
values, in the continued existence of a group, their rational effort
to secure its survival would provide a specific adaptive mechanism.

It is probable that a complete theory of group and organizational survival will have to incorporate elements of both mechanisms. The mechanism first mentioned may predominate in groups
characterized by face-to-face contact, opportunities for thorough
and long-term indoctrination of members, and a relative weakness
of individualistic values. The second mechanism may predominate
in the secondary associations of a modern society, characterized
by freedom of association and rationalistic calculation in terms of
individual values. It may be suggested, parenthetically, that the
difference between the theories of the "human relations" school in
contemporary industrial sociology and the classical theory of
"economic man" is closely related to the difference between these
two motivational mechanisms.

THE BALANCE OF INDUCEMENTS AND CONTRIBUTIONS.

Having described in the two previous sections some "sociological" models of group behavior, we return in the present section to a model in which individual values are determined outside the group process.

We postulate for each member of a group a *satisfaction function*. We assume that his satisfaction increases with the amount of inducement, y, the group provides him, and decreases with the amount of contribution, x, the group requires from him. Thus, we write for the ith member:

$$S_i = \phi(y_i) - \psi(x_i), \quad (i = 1, \ldots, n). \tag{12}$$

In a business firm, for eample, customers receive products in return for money; employees receive money in return for labor; and so forth. The organizational activity consists in taking the contributions of the several members and transforming these into the inducements that it then distributes among the same members. Since something can seldom be made out of nothing, the quantities of inducements that can be "manufactured" are limited by the quantities of contributions that can be obtained. This limitation can be stated in the form of a set of transformation functions:

$$\xi_j(x_1, \ldots, x_n; y_1, \ldots, y_m) = 0, \quad (j = 1, \ldots, k). \tag{13}$$

Let us now measure the zero of each member's satisfaction function from the point where he is just indifferent between remaining in the organization or leaving. Then the organization can survive if we can find a set of members, and a set of inducements and contributions for these members satisfying the limitations (13), such that $S_i \geq 0$ for all i. For the case of a business, this requirement can be translated: the business must be able to produce its product cheaply enough (as determined from some of the limitations (13)) so that it can sell the product at a price customers are willing to pay, and receive enough money from the sale (another limitation--the business is not generally permitted to manufacture additional money on a printing press) to pay employees for their services, and so forth.

When the organization more than satisfies this condition-- when each member receives a positive net satisfaction -- then the net satisfactions of members, taken together, can be regarded as a "surplus" which can be distributed in a variety of ways without endangering survival. This suggests elaboration of the model in a number of directions:

(1) We might wish to add to it a description of the processes whereby the surplus actually gets divided. This might take the form, for example, of a theory of bargaining between employer and employee, or between buyer and seller. As a matter of fact, it can be shown that if we assume (1) that this bargaining takes place in incremental units (rather than on an all-or-none basis of participation or non-participation), and (2) that the entire surplus is captured by the entrepreneur, then we obtain as a special case of the present organizational model the theory of imperfect competition discussed earlier in this paper. (The "surplus" in this case becomes the "profit" in the earlier model.)

(2) When a surplus exists, the organization is not committed to a single course of action -- a number of paths are compatible with survival. This situation provides one psychological basis for a theory of authority--members of an organization may be willing to accept authority over their activities provided that the exercise of this authority is limited to the area in which these members receive a net balance of inducements over contributions. Authority may be directed by its possessors toward various goals. For example, if the persons who control the organization are strongly motivated towards its survival, they may employ the range of choice permitted them in such a way as to enhance the chances of future survival and growth.

Since this model is described at length elsewhere,[35] we will not carry its analysis further here.

CONCLUSION

The main aim of these chapters has been to show how the essential elements of a wide range of postulates about human behavior, individual and social, can be translated into mathematical models; and to suggest how this translation can be employed both to clarify the similarities and differences among theories and to draw new conclusions, by mathematical means, from the postulates. In doing this, we have been guided by the canons of strategy that were set forth at the beginning of the first section. In conclusion, I should like to refer again to those canons, to see what help they give us in overall appraisal of the systems we have surveyed.

The canons were three in number:

(1) We should begin by translating into mathematics concepts and postulates that lie in the central core of existing social science theory;

(2) We should not attempt to incorporate all of these concepts and postulates in a single model, but should be satisfied at the outset with constructing a number of partial models;

(3) Significant models can be constructed by singling out for attention, and for embodiment in them, the significant limiting conditions that serve as boundaries to the area of rationality in human behavior.

Our general procedure in this paper has been to start with theories of optimizing behavior -- theories that incorporate the fewest possible limits on rationality. We have then progressively diluted the requirements of rationality -- or stated otherwise, have imposed successive limitations. In this way we have progressed from simple processes of maximization to much more complex processes of adaptive (and even of "motivated" and "learned") behavior.

With each additional limitation we have been confronted with choices - we have had to make more and more assumptions as to the characteristics of actual human behavior. Hence it is not surprising that at each step we have (at least potentially) gained realism, but lost certainty. Empirical research has not progressed to the point where we can make assured choices among alternative assumptions; and mathematical analysis of the models has not progressed to the point where we can handle simultaneously all of the complications we should like to incorporate.

What can we conclude about the present state and future prospects of this kind of model-building? We do not pretend to have surveyed all, or even most, of the existent attempts at mathematization. Many not mentioned here are discussed in other contributions to this volume. We can, however, draw several conclusions. Formalization of the systems in which highly rational and individualistic behavior is postulated has already reached a point of development where mathematical theory is displacing literary theory on the frontiers of research. Most of the things that can be said in economics can be said more easily and clearly with the language of mathematics than without it. Moreover, mathematics has already made important contributions not only to substantive theory but also to the clarification of central concepts. In particular, we have seen that the attempt to set down in mathematical form the precise assumptions of "rationality" has led to important advances in the understanding of that concept and its various possible meanings.

In areas of a more distinctly sociological or psychological character, much less has been accomplished. Even here we have seen that rather simple mathematical tools permit us to study with a high degree of clarity and rigor the assumptions underlying particular theories, the conclusions that follow from these assumptions, and the interrelations of competing theories. The tentative explorations made thus far give sufficiently good prospect of rich reward to justify further work on a much larger and more systematic scale.

Notes

Introduction

1. The two terms social and behavioral sciences will be used interchangeably in this introduction.

2. For an instructive survey of this kind of work, see Kenneth Arrow's review, "Mathematical Models in the Social Sciences," in *The Policy Sciences*, D. Lerner and H. D. Lasswell, eds., Stanford University Press, 1952, p 129-154.

3. The more detailed proofs of Anderson's original contributions will be published elsewhere.

4. Macmillan, 1951.

5. "A Mathematical Model for Simple Learning," *Psychological Review,* V. 58, 1951, p 313-323; and "A Model for Stimulus Generalization and Discrimination," *Psychological Review,* V. 58, 1951, p 413-423.

6. Both models finally take off from certain more elementary ideas; the imitation analysis is based on a neurological system which Rashevsky has developed in previous publications; the so-called "distribution of status" model is based on certain mathematical representations of pecking orders in animal societies, which have been observed and studied by animal psychologists for quite some time. This background material will not be discussed in out introduction.

7. Coleman's paper was sponsored jointly by the Behavioral Models Project of the Office of Naval Research and the Columbia University Planning Project on Advanced Training in Social Research.

8. Roland Press, 1950; especially chapters 1 to 7.

9. Dover Publications, 1948.

10. Cavin P. Leeman, "Patterns of Sociometric Choice in Small Groups: A Mathematical Model and Related Experimentation, " *Sociometry,* V. 15, 1952, p 220-243.

11. H. A. Simon, "A Formal Theory of Interaction in Social Groups," *American Sociological Review,* V. 17, 1952, p 202-211.

12. Because of the many specific bibliographical references in Marschak's lectures, there is no need for the editor to refer to additional literature at this point.

13. Volume 4 of Studies in Social Psychology in World War II, by S. A. Stouffet et.al., Princeton University Press, 1950.

14. In the present paper Guttman gives only the psychological interpretation of his mathematical model. For the mathematical formulation itself the reader will have to consult Chapter IX of *Measurement and Prediction.*

15. R. B. Cattell, *The Description and Measurement of Personality;* World Book Company, 1946.

16. Leon Festinger, "The Analysis of Sociograms using Matrix Algebra," *Human Relations,* V. 2, 1949, p 153-158.

17. Leo Katz, "A New Status Index Derived from Sociometric Analysis," *Psychometrica,* V. 18, 1953, p 39-43.

18. *Ibid.,* Chapters X and XII.

19. For a review, see C. Hempel, *Fundamentals of Concept Formation in Empirical Science,* University of Chicago Press, 1952. A survey on the present state of scaling is under preparation by a committee of the Social Science Research Council.

20. The editor wishes to thank Mr. Leo Tick who carried out this editorial work. Anderson's original paper, incidentally, contains also sections relating his work to a project on latent structure analysis, which was sponsored by the RAND Corporation. These sections are omitted from the present edition and will be published later.

21. As can be seen from Guttman's introductory remarks, he had in mind a trilogy of papers. However, his third paper was not completed at the time this volume went to press and therefore had to be omitted.

22. The editor had hoped at one time that the volume would contain a contribution on the various mathematical methods for analyzing the notion of social process; the task at the moment seems to go beyond the contribution of a single writer in a limited space.

23. The latter group is probably best represented by John Q. Stewart and Stuart Dodd.

1.

1. I am greatly indebted to Professor Paul F. Lazarsfeld for interesting me in studying attitude time series analysis and for innumerable discussions of the material in this paper. I am also indebted to Mr. Lee Wiggins for his work on the illustrations in this paper.

2. These questions are treated by Marschak and we shall not go into them deeply.

3. More sophisticated economic theory would say that the supply equation involves also costs of factors of production and that there is a demand question involving price, quantity and income of consumers. These equations are behavior equations. On the other hand, an ad hoc model might simply say that there are two equations relating price, quantity, costs and income. The second model describes the data as well, but does not analyze it into the behavior of two groups.

4. Characteristic roots are the roots of the determinental equation $|\,P - \lambda I\,| = O$, where I is the diagonal matrix with all diagonal elements 1.

5. Or we take this one individual and imagine putting him into an increasing number of similar situations.

6. The question of interpretation of this probability model for one individual is similar to the question regarding a probability model in econometrics for one set of time series. See T. Haavelmo, "The Probability Approach in Econometrics," *Econometrica, 12,* Supplement, 1944.

7. In the case of continuous variate one uses residuals from regression on the bothersome variable; the analogue for discrete variables is stratification.

8. S. S. Wilks, *Mathematical Statistics,* Princeton University Press, 1943, p 50.

9. For a description of the survey see Paul F. Lazarsfeld, Bernard Berelson, and Hazel Gaudet, *The People's Choice,* Columbia University Press, 1948.

10. T. W. Anderson. Rand Report.

11. S. S. Wilks, *op. cit.,*

12. The statistical problem here is choosing one of a number of alternative hypotheses on the basis of our data. In principle we should set up a procedure that takes explicitly into account the entire set of hypotheses and the probabilities of accepting each hypothesis when a particular one is true. Since the mathematical theory required is very complicated, this step by step procedure is suggested as a crude, but practicable method. Unfortunately we do not know very accurately the risks we are running with this procedure.

13. The steady state corresponding to this matrix is p' = (.543 .334 .123).

14. These data have been taken from the file of the Bureau of Applied Social Research.

2.

1. N. Rashevsky. *Mathematical Biophysics*. Revised edition. Chicago: University of Chicago Press, 1948.

   A. S. Householder and H. D. Landahl. *Mathematical Biophysics of the Central Nervous System*. Bloomington, Ind.: The Principia Press, 1945.

2. H. D. Landahl. "A Contribution to the Mathematical Biophysics of Psychophysical Discrimination." *Psychometrika, 3,* 107-125, 1938.

3. H. D. Landahl. "A Contribution to the Mathematical Biophysics of Psychophysical Discrimination II." *Bull. Math. Biophysics,1,* 95-118, 1939; *Ibid., 2,* 73-87, 1940.

4. H. D. Landahl. "Contributions to the Mathematical Biophysics of the Central Nervous System." *Bull. Math. Biophysics, 1,* 95-118, 1939.

5. H. G. Landau. "Note on the Effect of Imitation in Social Behavior." *Bull. Math. Biophysics, 12,* 221-235, 1950.

6. N. Rashevsky. "Mathematical Biology of Social Behavior: IV. Imitation Effects as a Function of Distance." *Bull. Math. Biophysics, 12* 177-185, 1950.

7. H. D. Landahl. "Mathematical Theory of Imitative Behavior in a Social Group with Finite Imitation Threshold." *Bull. Math. Biophysics, 12,* 207-213, 1950.

8. N. Rashevsky. *Mathematical Biology of Social Behavior*. Chicago: University of Chicago Press, 1951.

9. N. Rashevsky. "Some Bio-Sociological Aspects of the Mathematical Theory of Communication." *Bull. Math. Biophysics, 12,* 359-378, 1950.

10. W. C. Allee. *Animal Aggregations: A Study in General Sociology*. Chicago: University of Chicago Press, 1931.

11. A. Rapoport: "Outline of a Probabilistic Approach to Animal Sociology: I." *Bull. Math. Biophysics, 11,* 183-196, 1949.

12. A. Rapoport: "Outline of a Probabilistic Approach to Animal Sociology: II." *Bull. Math. Biophysics, 11,* 273-281, 1949.

13. A. Rapoport: "Outline of a Probabilistic Approach to Animal Sociology: III." *Bull. Math. Biophysics, 12,* 7-17, 1950.

14. H. G. Landau: "On Dominance Relations and the Structure of Animal Societies: I. Effect of Inherent Characteristics." *Bull. Math. Biophysics*, *13*, 1-19, 1951.

3.

1. I am indebted especially to Dr. Paul Lazarsfeld for his guidance throughout, as well as to others at Columbia University for their helpful comments.

2. *Mathematical Biology of Social Behavior*, University of Chicago Press, Chicago, 1951.

3. From our experiences with these models and those of others who have made serious efforts to study them, one of the main obstacles seems to be the lack of systematic presentation and full explanation, so that the essential characteristics of the models are found only with difficulty. This exposition is in part an attempt to overcome this obstacle.

4. The present usage of this word is not to be confused with that of some model builders, who use it to distinguish the several different structures of a single model resulting from different sets of values for the independent variables.

5. A compromise is possible, since two of the models here examined are included in their original form elsewhere in this volume. These are the models of "Imitative Behavior" and "A General Theory of Social Distributions."

6. Page references to *Mathematical Biology of Social Behavior*, will be noted in parentheses in the text, followed by an "R.", to distinguish them from references to other parts of this paper.

7. These are characteristics which Rashevsky derives from his neurological theory, but for simplicity, we shall call them "dispositions" or "tendencies" here. It is assumed that the tendency is measurable in terms of real numbers, ϵ_i.

8. These equations are introduced by Rashevsky as an approximation for a cumulative normal distribution, which is not easily handled mathematically.

9. In another paper, Rashevsky has modified the assumption that everyone's behavior acts as a stimulus, to give a model in which an individual is affected only by those within a certain area close to him. *Bull. Math. Biophysics*, V. 13, 1951, p 147-151.

10. This model was developed and first presented by one of Rashevsky's associates, H. D. Landahl, in *Bull. Math. Biophysics*, *12*, 1-6, 1950.

11. This notation may be confusing, since K seems to mean different things
    on each side of the equation. However, the equation says only
    that K is a function of s and s', meaning the same as if the no-
    tation were $K = f(s,s')$. This same convention will appear
    elsewhere.

12. Actually, x_i is not "effort", but an amount of some "object of satisfaction"
    such as pay. But effort is considered to be proportional to x_i, so
    that it is not important whether we think of x_i as the amount of pay
    or the amount of effort required to obtain it. Some terms involv-
    ing x_i in the equations are "effort terms", while others are "pay
    terms". Because of this, although x_i is defined by Rashevsky as
    the amount of some object of satisfaction, we shall call it "effort"
    here, which makes the exposition simpler. However, the two
    different roles played by different terms involving x_i should be
    kept in mind.

13. *The Policy Sciences*, Lasswell and Lerner, eds., Stanford Press, 1951.

14. When we say that a characteristic changes as time passes, we ordinarily
    mean that with passage of time something happens to the individ-
    ual to bring about a change in the characteristic. Thus the pas-
    sage of time does not directly affect the variable, but allows
    another variable to produce the change. The one major exception
    to this is age, which, since it is a direct measure of time, changes
    as a *direct* consequence of passage of time.

15. Some schemas employ the unit act as the basic element of the system
    with the act itself having characteristics, rather than considering
    the various aspects of the act as characteristics of the individual.
    In such schemas, the individual represents a particular cluster of
    such acts. See, for example, T. Parsons, *The Social System*, The
    Free Press, Glencoe, Illinois, 1951, especially pp. 25 and 26.

16. This terminology is also taken from the Lazarsfeld-Barton paper, op. cit.

17. See P. W. Bridgman, *Dimensional Analysis*, Yale University Press, 2 ed.,
    1931.

18. One of the more valuable uses is indicated in footnote 25.

19. Not all equations in a model represent processes. For instance, when in
    the model on imitative behavior, we write the equation:
    $N_0 = X + Y$, we are merely saying that the total number of people
    in the society, N_0, is equal to the number doing R_1, X, plus the
    number doing R_2, Y. Ordinarily, it is obvious what equations
    represent such identity relations as this rather than processes of
    the type we shall consider.

20. It is also possible, as we noted previously, that the equation is simply a
    definition of a new variable in terms of others. But such an
    equation does not represent a process of any sort, and it is no
    different from any other definition of a variable, except its defi-
    nition is internal to the system. This is a point at which a

distinction is not made on *mathematical* grounds, but in terms of the *content* which remains in the model. Mathematically, it is not meaningful to speak of the equation as stating a causal relationship. Mathematically, all these equations are simply definitions of one variable as a function of others.

21. There is another possible type of equation here, equivalent to (3), but with the arrow reversed. This is a real possibility only in a process in which characteristics of the individual affect some primary characteristic of the group. No such processes occur in these models, and they are of no great interest to us in this discussion.

22. There is one other such process in the model of Altruistic and Egoistic Behavior, but it is not a fully developed process, as this is.

23. In economic models, the total system is sometimes broken down into several component parts (e.g., "production," "inventory,"), forming circuits of some sort, including an input from and output to the consumer. These systems with their several component parts are structurally quite different from the systems we are examining in these models. The component parts of such economic models ordinarily stand in a fixed and continuous relationship to one another, and the primary concern is with the effect of certain characteristics of the component parts upon the rate of flow of the commodity through the circuit. The general structure of these models is similar to that of electrical circuits or systems of fluid flow, in which the problem is much the same. It is because of this structural similarity that a number of electrical analogues of economic models have been designed. Although the four models examined here, with their systems of interacting elements, are different from economic models, it would be interesting to attempt to develop an electrical analogue to one of them, or to a model of this general type.

24. It is not precisely true that this model as presented by Rashevsky is static, for he has some consideration of the time path of the system (see p. 21, R.). However, the model as presented here, and as considered by Rashevsky except at that one point, deals only with the equilibrium state of the system, and thus may be considered static for our purposes.

25. We mentioned in Part 2 that dimensional analysis had some more valuable uses than the one indicated there. Here it would have been of use in helping us guess at what the inequality condition was if it had been impossible to integrate. A "blind" use of dimensional analysis, beginning only with the basic postulates, which tell us that the condition for equilibrium may depend upon N_0, a, A, k, and σ, would have suggested that our inequality condition was: a $< AN_0 \ (k\sigma)^{1/2}$, while the actual condition is: $a < AN_0 \ \dfrac{k\sigma}{\sigma + k}$. The estimate given by dimentional analysis is not far wrong, and

in fact would have allowed most of the same qualitative deductions which can be made from the correct condition.

26. The deduction seems not to have been made as rigorously as might be necessary, for in its very beginning, a simplification has been implicitly made. Equation 4, p. 59, R., is supposed to represent the total loss of wealth per unit time for an individual with ability x and wealth W. But unless this individual meets every individual in the society exactly once during that unit time, the equation represents rather the *average* loss per unit time. That is, the model as set up seems to have this as a probability process, while the process of integrating to find the equilibrium state has made it deterministic. Also, the equation makes the assumption that his wealth, $W(x)$, will be less than that of each of these other individuals, for it is his wealth which enters the equation, rather than the other individuals'. This is true only at equilibrium.

27. These same processes which the model here includes have been dealt with in several recent systematic hypotheses or models. Merton's model of value-homophily, while it says much more than this, contains the two processes of this model as its basic structure. See R. K. Merton's Housing Study (in publication). In Simon's "Homans Model" (*American Sociological Review,* V. 17, pp. 202-211, 1952) one of the basic relationships is between "friendliness" and frequency of interaction. "Friendliness" would seem to be the intervening variable between attitude differences and their effect on frequency of interaction specified here. Another systematic discussion which includes the processes set forth here is Festinger's set of hypotheses on communication in a group *(Psychological Review* V.57, p.271-282, 1950).

4.

1. The lecture was given on 6 December 1950.

2. Such a weighted average of utilities has been called "mathematical expectation of utility" or simply "expected utility." The founders of the theory of probabilities when speculating about gamblers' choices, called this weighted average the "moral expectation" (= the mathematical expectation of "moral" as distinct from "physical," or "monetary" wealth). The term "military worth" (of a military situation or objective), encountered in military writings is presumably equivalent to "utility." It is likely that the often heard term, "calculated risk" of a military enterprise, if the term has any meaning at all, means the negative of "expected military worth," in the sense of an average of the utilities of the alternative outcomes of the enterprise, weighted with their respective probabilities.

3. Actual experiments of this kind were reported by **F.** Mosteller and
   P. Nogee in "An Experimental Measurement of Utility," *Journal
   of Political Economy,* 1951, Vol. 59, pp. 371-404.

4. "An Essay towards Solving a Problem in the Doctrine of Changes," *Phil.
   Trans. Royal Soc. of London,* 1763, pp. 370-418. (Facsimile
   edition by W. Edwards Deming, Washington, D. C.).

5. Daniel Bernoulli's "Specimen theoriae novae de mensura sortis" was
   published in the 1730-31 volume of transactions of the St. Petersburg Imperial Academy of Sciences, pp. 175-192. A German
   translation by Alfred Pringsheim, is available: "Die Grundlage
   der modernen Wertlehre. Versuch einer neuen Theorie von
   Glücksfällen." Leipzig, 1896.

6. Recent studies by Savage and by Herstein and Milnor (to be published)
   have simplified or generalized the earlier formulations of von
   Neumann and Morgenstern, and of J. Marschak.

7. Frank Plumpton Ramsey. "Truth and Probability" (1926) and "Further
   Considerations" (1928) published posthumously in *The Foundations
   of Mathematics and Other Logical Essays,* London, 1931 (re-
   published New York, The Humanities Press, 1950). De Finetti,
   Bruno. La Prevision: ses lois logiques, ses sources subjectives.
   Annales de l'Institut Henri Poincare, 1937, pp. 1-68. L. J. Savage.
   "Notes on the Foundations of Statistics" (mimeographed). Uni-
   versity of Chicago lectures. 1951.

8. David Hilbert, *Die Grundlagen der Geometry,* Leipzig....(This is more
   complete, for the problem that interests us here, than the English
   edition, Chicago 1910).

9. Note that here and in what follows we are taking a more general view of
   a "state of the world" than in our previous examples. A state of
   the world may now include more than one possibility; and each
   possibility can, in turn, be subdivided. Thus "W" is a state of
   the world, and its subdivision, the alternatives "W and V" and
   "W and $\overline{V}$" are also states of the world.

10. However the arithmetical operations leading to the statement are inde-
    pendent of this interpretation of it. They are the same as those
    used by James Bernoulli (Daniel's kin) who possibly did not think
    of probabilities as subjective.

11. A rigorous analysis on these lines is contained in an unpublished study by
    Roy Radner on "Consistent Decision Functions."

12. In our example, this assumption can be used only as an approximation
    since normal distribution applies to a continuous (and therefore
    infinite-valued) variable whereas x(cigarettes, communism) is
    discrete. Such approximations are convenient. For example, in
    Lloyd Warner's studies, the variable x is social status measured
    on a 12-point scale on the basis of neighbors' opinions; the $z^{(1)}$,
    $z^{(2)}$ ... are, respectively, income, housing conditions (again a dis-

crete variable) etc.; and "weights" α_i are estimated, as well as μ and σ, by the method of "multiple regression." With two-valued variables, this appraisal degenerates into familiar "tests of dual hypotheses" (chi-squared, analysis of variance).

13. The problem may be posed somewhat differently. Given the joint distribution of the random disturbances v of the responses of individual firms (i.e., given μ, σ and ρ), what is the distribution of the disturbance of the sum (not of the average) ? One may, for example, compare the constant ratio $\frac{\sigma}{\mu}$ (the "coefficient of variation" of v) and the ratio between the following two constants: the standard deviation of the sum of random disturbances and the expectation of this sum. This ratio converges to $\frac{\sigma}{\mu}\sqrt{\rho}$. (A more difficult problem is to estimate the coefficient of variation of the sum: it is the expectation of a random ratio, not the ratio of two constants).

14. Cf. Paul Lazarsfeld, "The logical and mathematical foundations of latent structure analysis," "The interpretation of some latent structures," *Measurement and Prediction*, Vol. 4, Studies in Psychology of World War II, Princeton University Press, 1950.

15. See, for example, A. M. Mood, *Introduction to the Theory of Statistics*, pp. 299-301. New York 1950. To quote Mood's example, "Anthropologists...make measurements x on skulls, of known age z, then estimate the age z_0 of a skull of unknown age with measurements x'."

16. The random variable $x_1 - z(= u + \lambda_1)$ corresponds thus to the expression (2.3), with n = 1 and all the α_i known. It is normally distributed (with mean $\mu = \lambda_1$), jointly with another random variable, $x_2 - z$.

17. For example, although we cannot ascertain the incomes of families who tell us their consumption of cigarettes and cereals, we may know from some other source the distribution of those incomes; e.g., if our sample is large and we have reasons to regard it as representing the whole U.S. population, then the income distribution is known from income tax statistics.

18. Remembering that λ_i, x_i, z stand for the logarithms of Λ_i, X_i, Z, this means that the unknown proportionality factor Λ_i in (2.7), can be estimated as the ratio of the geometric mean of X_i (observed in a large sample) to the (known) geometric mean of Z -- a result that is not unexpected, in view of the multiplicative character of the random deviation $(1 + U_i)$.

19. Implying that the consumption item X_i is (apart from random disturbances) proportional, not to the individual's income Z, but to some unknown power of it, Z^{β_i}.

20. If the sample is not very large, the test procedure is more delicate, since the non-fulfillment of equations such as (2.11) may be due to

sampling errors. The question asked then is whether the equation is "significantly" unfulfilled. Further, redundant information (such as $\sigma_{12} = 0$ in our case) may be used, not to test the hypothesis, but to increase the precision of the estimate of the parameters.

21. Rather, *"significantly"* inconsistent, unless the sample is infinite. See previous footnote.

22. For the history and bibliography of the subject, see Olav Reiersøl and T. C. Koopmans, "The Identification of Structural Characteristics," *Annals of Mathematical Statistics*, Vol. 21, June 1950, pp. 165-181, esp. p. 167; T. C. Koopmans, "Identification Problems in Economic Model Construction," *Econometrics*, Vol. 17, No. 2, April 1949, pp. 125-144, esp. p. 126; Jerzey Neyman, "Existence of Consistent Estimates of the Directional Parameter in a Linear Structural Relation between Two Variables," *Annals of Mathematical Statistics*, V. 22, 1951, pp. 497-512.

23. This characterization of Z will simplify the exposition that follows presently, and also that of "policies" to be discussed in lecture III.

24. See also M. A. Girshick, "Model Construction in the Social Sciences--An Expository Discussion of Measurement and Prediction", *The Public Opinion Quarterly*, Vol. 14, No. 4, Winter 1950-51.

25. See footnote 26 below.

26. Suffice it to say that equation (3.1), stating that production (measured in dollars), y, is adjusted instantaneously to demand (measured in dollars), $b + c + \rho$, is merely an approximation of some equation that would state how this adjustment proceeds in time. For example, if one thinks that producers are stimulated by the excess of demand over supply one might try to replace (3.1) by the differential equation

$$(3.7) \quad dy/dt = \alpha\,(b + c + \rho - y)\,,$$

where t is time and α, a positive constant, is a behavior parameter measuring the speed of the producers' reaction to a unit discrepancy between demand and production. Using (3.2), (3.3), the equation (3.7) becomes

$$(3.8) \quad dy/dt = \alpha\,[\,y(\beta + \gamma - 1) + \rho - \gamma\tau + v_b + v_c\,];$$

if v_b and v_c were constant, (3.8) would imply that y grows exponentially ("explodes" through time if $\beta + \gamma - 1 > 0$, and declines exponentially ("fades out" towards the "equilibrium value" given in (3.4), if $\beta + \gamma - 1 < 0$. Because of random fluctuations of v_b and v_c, these trends will be distorted somewhat but it remains true that the inequality $\beta + \gamma - 1 > 0$ implies an "explosive" rise in income (measured in dollars) such as was historically observed only in times of a few exceptional hyper-inflations. At least when one has to decide between small upward or downward variations of ρ and τ, the behavior of consumers and businessmen can be assumed to be such as to preclude explosive hyperinflation, and hence to preclude that $\beta + \gamma > 1$, i.e., to preclude λ negative.

27. See also the author's two papers on "Statistical inference from non-experimental observations: an economic example" (in: *International Statistical Institute*, 25th Session, 1947. Volume III, Part A, pp. 289-301) and on "Economic measurements for policy and prediction" (in: *Studies in Econometric Method*, by Cowles Commission Research Staff, ed. by Wm. C. Hood and T. C. Koopmans, New York 1952. John Wiley & Son. Cowles Commission Monograph No. 14.)

5.

1. Only the first two of the three lectures are included in this volume.

2. Louis Guttman, "The Principal Components of Scale Analysis", Chapter 9 in Samuel A. Stouffer, ed., *Measurement and Prediction*, Vol. IV of Studies in Social Psychology in World War II, Princeton University Press, 1950.

3. Gilbert Shapiro, "Myrdal's Definitions of the 'South': A Methodological Note", *American Sociological Review*, 1948, 13: 619-621.

4. Of course, percentiles as usually defined are discrete, representing 100 *segments* on such a continuum; but we shall use the terminology of "percentiles" for convenience to designate a position that can vary continuously and not just discretely.

5. Two related types of diagrams which also yield the same results are the *scalogram*, with its parallelogram pattern (which serves as the basis for practical procedures), and the *bar chart*. Cf. *Measurement and Prediction*, Chapter 3.

6. We exclude from consideration the trivial cases of items with no variation, i.e., where a marginal is either 0% or 100%.

7. Louis Guttman, "The Cornell Technique for Scale and Intensity Analysis"; *Education and Psychological Measurement*, 1947, 7:247-279; also in Churchman, et al., *Measurement of Consumer Interest*, Univ. Pennsylvania Press, 1947, pp. 60-84. For a machine technique using IBM equipment, see Robert N. Ford, "A Rapid Scoring Procedure for Scaling Attitude Questions," *Public Opinion Quarterly*, 1950, 14:507-532. Since this lecture was given, newer techniques have been developed in Israel, based on the new concept of "images". A stenciled paper, *The Israel Alpha Technique for Scale Analysis*, is available upon request from the Israel Institute of Applied Social Research, Shell Building, Julian's Way, Jerusalem, Israel.

8. For the sake of brevity here, we are skipping mathematical details used in the actual formulas.

9. Louis Guttman, "The Quantification of a Class of Attributes," in P. Horst, et al., *The Prediction of Personal Adjustment,* Social Science Research Council, New York, 1941; pp. 319-348.

10. They are also known in mathematics and physics by various other names such as principal axes, latent vectors, eigenvectors, or eigenfunctions. I believe it was Professor Harold Hotelling who first advocated the terminology of "principal components" as being appropriate for psychological data.

11. This is for the case where all items are dichotomies. Higher order difference equations arise when more categories per item are used. But since items can always be dichotomized, this is sufficient for our purposes here.

12. Cf. *Measurement and Prediction,* ibid.; also "The Cornell Technique for Scale and Intensity Analysis", ibid.

13. Louis Guttman and Uriel G. Foa, "Social Contact and an Intergroup Attitude," *Public Opinion Quarterly,* 1951, 15:43-53.

14. Actually, the cutoff point on the general filter scale was determined from the pretest of 100 cases only by observing the tremendous jump in "No reply" on specific programs. The zero point from the intensity function could be determined only later from the total 2,000 cases of the final study, for 100 cases are too few for plotting the intensity function accurately. The two methods gave exactly the same zero point independently of each other.

15. One such is published in Uriel G. Foa, "Scale and Intensity Analysis in Opinion Research," *International Journal of Opinion and Attitude Research,* 1950, 4:192-208.

16. "The serendipity pattern refers to...an *unanticipated, anomalous and strategic datum* which becomes the occasion for developing a new theory or for extending an existing theory." Robert K. Merton, *Social Theory and Social Structure.* The Free Press, Glencoe, Illinois, 1949, p. 98.

17. Chapter 15 in *Measurement and Prediction,* ibid.

18. This statement and the one following it are not so true of crossing-points a, c, and e. We return to this in the next section on the fourth principal component.

19. Another possibility is that part of this type slightly dislikes remaining in uniform, but has decided to do so anyhow because it can do nothing better. For brevity, we do not pause to discuss this here, as it doesn't seem plausible that such men could be a majority in type d.

20. This portion is entirely revised from what was given orally in the lecture, on the basis of new data that became available when the writer

returned to Israel. At the time of the lecture, only a tentative example of job satisfaction in an office could be given, based on an inadequate number of cases. The present material is described here for the first time.

21. This is not to be confused with the "filter" scale described above in connection with the intensity function, although the two scales are closely related. The filter questions did not refer to the Voice of Israel nor to any other broadcasting service, but asked only about radio in general. The involvement scale now being described was asked of everybody--those with negative general listening habits as well as those with positive habits.

22. It does occur in "involution melancholia" in psychiatry, which may be a related usage; but there seems little danger of confusion of terms in any case.

23. Closure was not actually studied in this particular project.

24. Mathematicians will recognize this as saying that the derivatives of the nth component vanishes at the zeros of the $(n - 1)$st component.

25. Actually, perhaps more have been identified. If the law of identity holds between the bending points of one component and the crossing-points of the preceding one, then the *intensity of closure,* which has five bends in it when related to content--at points a, c, e in all cases, but then also at b and d under the hypothesis--could possibly be the sixth component; and intensity of involution could be the eighth. Perhaps then one could even think of closures of closures, involutions of closures, etc. If all this held, all higher components would be identified whose order n has numerical factors consisting only of 2, 3, and 4.

26. An additive constant is also involved, which we do not discuss here for brevity.

27. Problem for mathematicians: Given six (or eight) discernible percentile intervals as defined by the bending points of the first four components. What can be said about the universe parameters of the differential equation? If this information is adequate to estimate the universe parameters closely, then the equation might be solved to yield all higher order components than the fourth by purely numerically methods.

28. Uriel G. Foa, "Scale and Intensity Analysis in Opinion Research", *International Journal of Opinion and Attitude Research,* 1950, 4:192-208. Louis Guttman and Uriel G. Foa, "Social Contact and Intergroup Attitude", *Public Opinion Quarterly,* 1951, 15:43-53.

29. Samuel A. Stouffer and Jackson Toby, "Role Conflict and Personality", *American Journal of Sociology,* 1951, 16:395-406.

6.

1. "The Principal Components of Scalable Attitudes," in this volume.

2. Only the first two of the three lectures are included in this volume.

3. Were we to give a fourth lecture in this series, it could have been on *nodular* structures, which provides a general theory covering both qualitative data and quantitative data with curvilinear regressions (as well as linear regressions). Nodular theory is one kind of generalization of common-factor theory; it contains also Lazarsfeld's *latent structure* theory as a special case.

4. Louis Guttman, "A Reanalysis of Factor Analysis." (In preparation). This analysis is made possible by the new theory of images. The need for solving this problem has been clearly expressed by L. L. Thurstone, who devotes an entire chapter to what is known about it; see Chapter XIII in his *Multiple-Factor Analysis*, Univ. Chicago Press, 1947.

5. It was first announced in my review of Thurstone's *Multiple Factor Analysis*, in the *Journal of the American Statistical Association*, 1947, 42:651-656.

6. In scale analysis, where the items are dichotomous, there *is* a meaning to the ranking of items as well as of people. Dichotomous scale items can be ranked according to their marginals. For nondichotomous items, and in particular for continuous variables, there is no such immediate and direct meaning for a ranking.

7. L. L. and Thelma Gwinn Thurstone, *Factorial Studies of Intelligence*, Psychometric Monographs Number 2, Univ. Chicago Press, 1941.

8. These data are now being reanalyzed (subsequent to the oral lecture) in connection with a larger set of variables, and it appears that *several* different verbal simplexes exist, although substantially interrelated. The present example is left here as originally presented, since it suffices for its purpose here.

9. From Table 4, p. 90, L. L. Thurstone and Thelma Gwinn Thurstone, *Factorial Studies of Intelligence*, Univ. Chicago Press, 1941.

10. Cf. Stouffer, et al., *Measurement and Prediction*, Princeton Univ. Press, 1950, pp. 410-412.

11. Louis Guttman, "The Nodular Scale" (In preparation).

12. Louis Guttman *"The Israel Alpha Technique for Scale Analysis"* (Stenciled), The Israel Institute of Applied Social Research. Jerusalem, 1951.

13. From Table 18:2, p. 499, John Gray Peatman, *Descriptive and Sampling Statistics*, New York, 1947. The data are originally from C. C. Brigham, *A Study of Error*, College Entrance Examinations Board, New York, 1932, and were later analyzed also in John C.

Flanagan, *Factor Analysis in the Study of Personality*, Stanford Univ. Press, 1935.

14. After the original oral presentation of this lecture at Columbia University. The monograph is out of print. I am indebted to Mr. Jack Elinson and the Attitude Research Branch, Department of Defense, Washington, D.C. for providing me with photostats (with the permission of the publishers) of the material cited below from this work of Thurstone's.

15. From Table 2, pp. 110-112, L. L. Thurstone, *Primary Mental Abilities*, Psychometric Monographs Number 1, Univ. Chicago Press, 1938.

16. The monograph gave no description of the Arithmetical Reasoning test; but we tried it anyway just because of its title, in order to have more data for the table. It does seem to fit in rather well.

17. See previous lecture, "The Principal Components of Scalable Attitudes."

18. Regardless, addition has a special relationship to multiplication not possessed by subtraction, as a more precise analysis of this particular simplex shows in a subsequent part of this lecture.

19. Two other reported experiments of a different nature from maze learning are omitted from Table 7.

20. From M. I. Tomilin and C. P. Stone, "Intercorrelation of Measures of Learning Ability in the Albino Rat," *J. Comp. Psych.*, 1934, 17:73-88. Cited in Joseph R. Royce, "The Factorial Analysis of Animal Behavior," *Psychological Bulletin*, 1950, 47:235-259.

21. This can be seen from the determinantal formulas for multiple-correlation. Cf. Louis Guttman, "A Note on the Derivation of Formulae for Multiple and Partial Correlation," *Annals of Mathematical Statistics*, 1938, 9:305-308. To relate the present notation with the notation there, use the fact that $r^{jk} = R_{jk}/R$.

22. Cf. previous footnote.

23. Louis Guttman, "Enlargement Methods for Computing the Inverse Matrix," *Annals of Mathematical Statistics*, 1946, 17:336-343. The inverses of hypothetical tables 10 and 11 were computed by explicit formulas for the simplex, involving only the complexity loadings; cf. the section on principal components below.

24. From Peatman, *op. cit.*

25. Louis Guttman, "Two Empirical Studies of Weighting Techniques," in P. Horst, et. al., *The Prediction of Personal Adjustment*, Social Science Research Council, New York, 1941, esp. pp. 355-364.

26. This and the immediately following sections are primarily for those who wish to see the algebraic tie-up with previous factor theories. Other readers may wish to skip ahead to the section on the circumplex.

27. Actually, we need require that only two of the three laws hold; for if any
    two hold it is easily seen from (30) that the third must then also
    hold; except that (33) for j = k does not follow from (32) and
    (34), but is an additional assumption.

28. Louis Guttman, "The Theory of Image Analysis for Quantitative Variates,"
    (in preparation).

29. The derivations from here on follow the familiar lines of common-factor
    analysis; so the steps will be omitted and only the conclusions
    stated.

30. Students of common-factor theory are more accustomed to seeing (55) in
    the form $t_{ij} = a_j c_i + u_j e_{ij}$, where t_j, c, and e_j are all in standard
    form, with unit variances as well as zero means. In (55), the
    factor loadings are implicit, rather than explicit, being absorbed
    in the standard deviations of the respective variables.

31. A corollary of the theorem that the square of the multiple-correlation
    coefficient of a test on all the remaining tests in a battery cannot
    exceed the communality of that test. Cf. Louis Guttman, "Multiple
    Rectilinear Prediction and the Resolution Into Components,"
    Psychometrika, 1940, 5:75-99; esp. pp. 92-93.

32. Louis Guttman, *ibid*.

33. This section is largely for those familiar with matrix algebra and can be
    omitted by others who may wish to proceed to the next section on
    the circumplex.

34. Cf. equations (46) and (65), pages 344 and 347 respectively, of Louis
    Guttman, "The Principal Components of Scale Analysis," in
    Samuel A. Stouffer, et al., *Measurement and Prediction*,
    Princeton Univ. Press, 1950.

35. It is because items in a scale of dichotomies cannot have a normal
    multivariate distribution that they therefore can satisfy a differ-
    ence equation and have a law of oscillation.

36. Cf. Louis Guttman, "Relation of Scalogram Analysis to Other Tech-
    niques," in Samuel A. Stouffer, et al., *Measurement and Predic-
    tion*, Univ. Princeton Press, 1950; esp. p. 203.

37. Data from L. L. Thurstone, *Factorial Studies of Intelligence*, Psycho-
    metric Monographs 2, Univ. Chicago Press, 1941; Table 1,
    pp. 83-85.

38. Data from L. L. Thurstone, *Factorial Studies of Intelligence*, Psycho-
    metric Monographs 2, Univ. Chicago Press, 1941; Table 1,
    pp. 83-86.

39. Wechsler's test on Digit Span also fits in a manner similar to that in
    Table 21, but only for younger adults. For older adults,
    apparently the complexity of numerical memory does not keep up
    with that of other abilities.

40. Louis Leon Thurstone, *The Vectors of Mind,* Univ. Chicago Press, Chicago, 1935. Esp. Chapter VI, "Primary Traits".

41. After Louis Leon Thurstone, *The Vectors of Mind,* Univ. Chicago Press, Chicago, 1935; p. 151.

42. The same property we have already seen for the additive simplex as in formula (43) above.

43. For an excellent bibliography and summary of previous theories, see Dael Wolfle, *Factor Analysis to 1940,* Psychometric Monographs No. 3, Univ. Chicago Press, 1940.

44. From Table 4, pp. 115-116, L. L. Thurstone, Primary Mental Abilities, Psychometric Monographs Number 1, Univ. Chicago Press, 1938.

7.

1. See Samuel A. Stouffer et al., *Measurement and Prediction,* Vol. IV in Studies in Social Psychology in World War II (Princeton, N. J.: Princeton University Press, 1950), Chapters 10 and 11; Bert Green, Jr., "A General Solution for the Latent Class Model of Latent Structure Analysis," *Psychometrika* (1951), Vol. 16, Number 2; and P. F. Lazarsfeld et al., *The Use of Mathematical Models in the Measurement of Attitudes,* (Santa Monica, Calif.: The RAND Corporation, 1951).

2. Carl Hempel, *Concept Formation in the Empirical Sciences,* University of Chicago Press, 1952, p. 24 ff.

3. Max Weber, *The Theory of Social and Economic Organization,* (edited by Talcott Parsons. New York: Oxford University Press, 1947) p. 119, italics supplied.

4. W. James, *The Meaning of Truth,* p. 148, italics supplied.

5. *Critical Historical Essays,* Everyman's Library, Vol. 2, p. 17, italics supplied.

6. M. Sherif and H. Cantril, *The Psychology of Ego-Involvements,* (New York: John Wiley and Sons, 1947) passim.

7. D. Krech and R. Crutchfield, *Theory and Problems of Social Psychology,* (New York: McGraw-Hill Company, 1948) p. 48.

8. L. J. Henderson, *Pareto's General Sociology,* (Cambridge, Mass.: Harvard University Press, 1935) p. 64, italics supplied.

9. In Stouffer et al., *op. cit.,* p. 80, italics supplied.

10. *Ibid.,* pp. 83-84, italics supplied.

11. University of Chicago Press, 1939, pp. 19 ff.

12. When the questions deal with attitudes or opinions, the settings, the probabilities of answering positively, can be anywhere in the range 0 to 1.00. Not so with matters of fact, however. When we

ask an individual whether he has had certain experiences or whether he is characterized in a particular way, we expect him to give the same answer every time. That is, except for minor errors in his reports, we do not expect his answers to change at all. Thus, for questions of this kind, the probability mechanism is set very nearly for either 0 *or* 1.00.

13. Yule and Kendall, Introduction to the Theory of Statistics, Lippincott, 1940, Chapters 1 and 2.

14. See Yule and Kendall, *op. cit.*, Chapter 3.

15. When we talk here of "frequencies," we mean *"relative frequencies,"* the proportion observed in the total sample.

16. At this point we can add some further clarification to the principle of local independence (pp. 27 ff.). Strictly speaking it has to be introduced as an axiom into the latent structure model. But it has considerable intuitive strength. Suppose someone objects, along the lines of the following example. The joint probability that a man will answer two anti-Negro questions positively is greater on a day on which he feels especially aggressive toward Negroes. The *joint* probability on this day is greater than the product of the "average" probability for each question separately. Correctly this should be expressed differently. If a person is interviewed repeatedly, his replies to two such questions will be positively related. This, however, is due to the fact that he moves from one latent class to another according to the variation of his "underlying" aggressiveness toward Negroes. The positive relation between his manifest (repeated) responses is therefore the result of his shifting on the latent characteristic. The principle of local independence of repeated responses to two (or more) items presumes, however, the respondent's constancy regarding his latent class position. In this sense it is an axiomatic element, because it cannot strictly be tested in empirical terms.

17. The logic of this kind of "accounting" has been discussed by P. L. Kendall and P. F. Lazarsfeld in "Problems of Survey Analysis," in *Continuities in Social Research,* (ed. by R. K. Merton and P. F. Lazarsfeld; Glencoe, Ill.: The Free Press, 1950) pp. 147-167.

18. S. A. Stouffer et al., *Adjustment During Army Life,* Vol I in Studies in Social Psychology in World War II, (Princeton, N. J.: Princeton University Press, 1949).

19. The difference between the figure in Table 2 for the response pattern { + - + -} in Class 1, and that given previously, is that here we have carried the computations out more exactly.

20. A precise statistical test of the fit might be provided by some measure like Chi-square.

21. Although we shall not show it in this paper, position values for the latent classes need not be chosen arbitrarily. They can actually be

computed from the manifest data. This is one of the major
consequences of latent structure analysis.

22. Clyde Coombs has suggested the general idea of a dispersion index, but
not any concrete procedure for obtaining it. See his paper,
"Some Hypotheses for the Analysis of Qualitative Variables,"
Psychological Review, Vol. 55, No. 3.

23. *The Use of Mathematical Models in the Measurement of Attitudes,*
Part V, distributed by the RAND Corporation.

24. *Ibid.,* Part III.

25. A complete inventory of these cases will be found in a forthcoming
publication prepared for the RAND Corporation.

26. *Measurement and Prediction,* Princeton University Press, 1950,
pp. 410-12.

27. For a first publication, see S. A. Stouffer, "An Emipirical Study of
Technical Problems in Analysis of Role Obligations," in *Toward
a General Theory of Action* (edited by Talcott Parsons and Edward
Shils. Harvard University Press, 1951), pp. 497 ff.

28. *Measurement and Prediction op. cit.,* Chapters X and XI.

29. Stouffer, Borgotta, Hays, and Henry, "A Technique for Improving Cumulative Scales," *Public Opinion Quarterly,* V. 16, 1952, pp. 273-291.

30. Special thanks are due to Dr. George Brown, who supervised these
sampling experiments, and to Miss Jean Hall, who carried out
the work.

31. *Measurement of Attitudes* (Chicago, Ill.: University of Chicago Press,
1937) p. 56.

32. "The Application of Latent Structure Analysis to the Measurement of
Social Status," unpublished dissertation, Columbia University,
1951.

33. *Latent Structure Analysis and Its Relation to Factor Analysis,* Research
Bulletin RB-50-65, Educational Testing Service, Princeton, N.J.,
1950.

8.

1. I am indebted to a number of colleagues and others for helpful comments
on an earlier draft of this paper. Among these are Messrs. G. L.
Bach, Read Bain, W. W. Cooper, R. M. Cyert, H. Guetzkow,
P. Lazarsfeld and members of the University Seminar on Organization at Columbia University.

2. Since I have taken as my central theme the canons of strategy that have
guided my own work, I hope I may be pardoned for including a
disproportionate number of footnote citations to others of my own

publications where particular topics have been treated at greater
length. More adequate references to predecessors, contempo-
raries, and collaborators will be found in these other publications.

3. The economist who is still practising intellectual isolationism can begin
to reform himself by reading a book like George Katona,
Psychological Analysis of Economic Behavior (McGraw-Hill,
1951); the political scientist can try David B. Truman, *The
Governmental Process* (Knopf, 1951); the organization theorist,
Herbert A, Simon, Donald W. Smithburg, and Victor A. Thompson,
Public Administration (Knopf, 1950).

4. Further elaboration of this point will be found in the section below on
preference fields.

5. For an extended (verbal) discussion of this model, and a comparison with
the less satisfactory "means-ends" model employed by Parsons,
Tolman and others, see H. A. Simon, *Administrative Behavior*
(Macmillan, 1947), ch. 4. *Cf.* Paul A. Samuelson, *Foundations
of Economic Analysis* (Harvard U. Press, 1947), pp. 21-3, 97-8.

6. The method just illustrated is the method of comparative statics. See
Samuelson, *op. cit.*, pp. 7-20 for a more complete discussion.

7. This "canon of strategy" was first proposed by the author as a basic
principle for the guidance of research in administrative theory.
See *Administrative Behavior*, pp. 39-41, 240-4.

8. For a description of the Cournot model see R. G. D. Allen, *Mathematical
Analysis for Economists* (Macmillan, 1938), pp. 200-204; 345-
347. The Cournot model has an obvious affinity to sociological
models, like those of Mead and Cooley, which involve "taking the
role of the other." These models are discussed in Theodore M.
Newcomb, *Social Psychology* (Dryden Press, 1950), ch. 9.

9. J. von Neumann and O. Morgenstern, *The Theory of Games and Economic
Behavior*   (Princeton U. Press, 1944), pp. 8-15, 31-45. For a
nontechnical introduction to the theory of games, see John
McDonald, *Strategy in Poker, Business and War* (Norton, 1950),
particularly the Introduction and Part 2.

10. Von Neumann and Morgenstern, *op. cit.*, pp. 88-95.

11. The specific requirements with respect to stability have been discussed
in full by Samuelson, *op. cit.*, ch. 9, and do not need to be
reviewed here.

12. Norbert Wiener, *Cybernetics* (Wiley, 1948), particularly ch. 4. An
introduction to servomechanisms will be found in H. Lauer,
R. Lesnick, and L. E. Matson, *Servomechanism Fundamentals*
(McGraw-Hill, 1947), ch. 1. The idea of biological and human
feedback systems goes back to the physiologist Claude Bernard.
See Alfred J. Lotka, *Elements of Physical Biology* (Williams
and Wilkins, 1925), pp. 362-416.

13. These theories are discussed by Jacob Marschak elsewhere in this volume.

14. H. A. Simon, "On the Application of Servomechanism Theory in the Study of Production Control," *Econometrica,* Vol 20, 1952, pp. 247-268.

15. Jacob Marschak, "Role of Liquidity under Complete and Incomplete Information," Papers and Proceedings, *American Economic Review,* vol. 39, May, 1949, pp. 182-195; H. A. Simon, "A Formal Theory of the Employment Relationship," *Econometrica,* July 1951, vol. 19, pp. 293-305.

16. For an example of some recent work in this field, see Kenneth J. Arrow, *Social Choice and Individual Values* (Wiley, 1951), pp. 9-21.

17. The contrast between the optimizing man of the economists and the adaptive man of the psychologists is discussed in Simon, *Administrative Behavior,* chapter 4 (previously referred to), and chapter 5.

18. There are other less trivial situations that exhibit the characteristics of this model, as will be shown later, but this one is simple, and will serve to illustrate the point.

19. See William Archibald Dunning, *A History of Political Theories: From Rousseau to Spencer* (Macmillan, 1920), pp. 211-24, 395-402. As Carl Becker puts it: "Whereas the 18th century held that man can by taking thought add a cubit to his stature, the 19th century held that a cubit would be added to his stature whether he took thought or not." (Article on "Progress" in *Encyclopedia of the Social Sciences,* vol. 12, p. 498.)

20. See Gunner Myrdal, *An American Dilemma* (Harper, 1944), Appendix 3. While Myrdal does not speak explicitly of multiple equilibria this seems to an implicit element of his model. For a mathematical model, along these lines of revolutionary change see Nicolas Rashevsky, *Mathematical Biology of Social Behavior* (Chicago U. Press, 1951), chapter 13. I might add that I am greatly indebted to Professor Rashevsky's work, which he discusses elsewhere in this volume, for stimulating my thinking along the general lines of this and the following section.

21. For definitions of "formal" and "informal" see Simon, Smithburg, and Thompson, *op. cit.,* pp. 85-90.

22. *Ibid.,* pp. 492-8.

23. Norman R. F. Maier, *Psychology in Industry,* pp. 244-7.

24. *Ibid.,* pp. 57-70.

25. George Homans, *The Human Group* (Harcourt, Brace, 1950). A more detailed discussion of the formal model of Homans' system is presented in "A Formal Theory of Interaction in Social Groups," *American Sociological Review,* Vol. 17, 1952, p. 202-211.

26. Homans, *op. cit.*, p. 102.

27. *Ibid.*, p. 111.

28. *Ibid.*, p. 112.

29. *Ibid.*, p. 118.

30. *Ibid.*, p. 120.

31. See any standard textbook on differential equations, e.g., Lester R. Ford, *Differential Equations* (McGraw-Hill, 1933), ch. 8.

32. Homans, *op. cit.*, pp. 356-62, 450.

33. *Ibid.*, pp. 263-5.

34. *Ibid.*, ch. 13.

35. H. A. Simon, "A Comparison of Organization Theories" *Review of Economic Studies*, *20*, 19, p. 40-48. See also, Simon, Smithburg, and Thompson, *op. cit.*, pp. 498-503.

Index